W9-DIA-555

The Sexual Behaviour of Young People

Also by Michael Schofield

SOCIOLOGICAL ASPECTS OF HOMOSEXUALITY

THE CENTRAL COUNCIL
FOR HEALTH EDUCATION

STEERING COMMITTEE

*Dr J. D. Kershaw, MD, BS, DPH (Chairman)
*Miss C. Barton
Sir Herbert Broadley, KBE
*Dr A. J. Dalzell-Ward, MRCS, LRCP, DPH, FRSH
Frank Dawtry, MBE
*The Rev. G. R. Dunstan, MA, FSA
Dr C. M. Fleming, MA, EdB, PhD
*Dr T. C. N. Gibbens, MBE, MD, DPM
Professor D. V. Glass, BSc, PhD
Dr M. E. M. Herford, DSO, MBE, MC
*Professor H. T. Himmelweit, MA, PhD
*Miss D. M. Marshall
*Professor C. A. Moser, BSc
*Dr C. S. Nicol, MD, FRCP
*Dr H. C. Maurice Williams, OBE, MRCS, LRCP, DPH

Ex-officio Members of Committee
Sir W. Allen Daley, MD, LLD, FRCP (late President, CCHE)
Councillor J. A. Brown, CBE, JP (Council Member, CCHE)
G. S. Burden, BSc (Econ.) (late Chairman, CCHE)
A. S. Mays, OBE (Hon. Treasurer, CCHE)
Alderman Mrs. C. C. Scott, JP (Acting Chairman, CCHE)

Observers

Dr I. G. Davies, MD, FRCP, DPH (Ministry of Health)
Dr C. B. Huss, MB, BS, DPH (Department of Education and Science)

*Members of the Research Sub-Committee

ACKNOWLEDGEMENTS

This research was made possible by a generous grant from the Nuffield Foundation and it has been carried out under the auspices of the Central Council for Health Education.

In the early days of the research I talked to many people who were in the youth service or concerned with adolescent problems. There are notes on our files of 53 of these people who gave freely of their time. Mr A. Chisnall, Mr Maurice Lee, Mr J. G. H. Newfield, Mr and Mrs E. Page-Symonds, and Mr H. A. Smith were particularly helpful during the pilot stage of the research. As the research moved from area to area, much help was received from the Local Authorities, particularly from the staffs of the Education and Health Departments. I should like to thank all these people for their advice and assistance.

Dr A. J. Dalzell-Ward, Mr K. E. Watson and the staff of the CCHE made sure that the administrative side of the research ran smoothly. The seven interviewers especially recruited for this work were: Anne Bardsley, Conway Daly, John Dixon, Roger Farnworth, Naomi Honigsbaum, Laura Renouf and Gay Rice. The statistical consultant throughout the research was Miss Kathleen Gales. Most of the analysis was done by English Electric-Leo Computers Ltd., under the guidance of Mr D. J. Flower, Miss R. Kerfoot and Miss R. Hoad. The factor analysis was carried out by Dr A. Hendrickson on an IBM Computer. Miss V. Evelyn and Miss R. Lang provided the secretarial assistance; Miss Lang also gave considerable help with the analysis. Mr B. Ellis gave valuable assistance in the preparation of the manuscript and the diagrams. I am grateful to all these people for the work they did for this research.

I owe a special debt to the members of the Research Sub-Committee (listed on the previous page) who gave encouragement and guidance throughout the three years of the research. Finally I should like to add my particular thanks to my three collaborators who are named on the title page.

M.S.

FOREWORD

SIR HERBERT BROADLEY

This study into the sexual behaviour of young people had its origin in an after-dinner discussion at the Apothecaries' Hall, where the delegates who had been attending the meeting of the International Union against Venereal Diseases and the Treponematoses held in London in October 1959 had been entertained.

At the Conference papers were read on the incidence of promiscuity among a selected group of girls and young women, and interviews were reported with a number of male patients suffering from venereal disease. These and other papers led to a more general discussion regarding sexual intercourse among young people and the probability that this might be a cause of the admitted increase in venereal diseases, particularly gonorrhoea.

The statistics presented referred to a very limited number of cases and were drawn from specialised sources, such as clinics attended by those apprehensive of venereal disease or by girls concerned with undesired pregnancies. Some of us who attended the meeting considered that the impression created was not representative of the young people of today and felt that an impartial survey should be undertaken covering all types and classes of young people. This was ultimately made possible as the result of the enthusiastic support of Dr A. J. Dalzell-Ward, the Medical Director of the Central Council for Health Education, the wise guidance of Dr J. D. Kershaw who acted as Chairman of a specially created Steering Committee, the generosity of the Nuffield Foundation which in 1960 gave a grant for the purpose of establishing facts in an area where there are too many ill-founded judgements, and, of course, Mr M. Schofield who, with the help of a Research Sub-Committee, planned and carried out the research and prepared this report.

Considering the origin of the project as an attempt to determine how far the incidence of venereal disease might be due to increased teenage sexual intercourse it is reassuring to note the finding on page 253 of the report that 'These results suggest that promiscuity although it exists, is not a prominent feature of teenage sexual behaviour. Consequently the risks of venereal disease are not very great.'

Promiscuity is not the same as indulgence in sexual intercourse. It means sexual intercourse with several partners over a period of

time. The report shows how small is the number of those young
people indulging in promiscuity as thus defined. And it is promiscuity, not sexual intercourse limited to only two individuals, which
can be the means of spreading the disease.

The research has gone far beyond the conception of those who
originally proposed it and throws new light on many problems of
great importance to social workers concerned with young people.
On the main theme it is particularly significant to read on page 248,
'Our results have made it clear that premarital sexual relations are
a long way from being universal among teenagers as over two-thirds
of the boys and three-quarters of the girls in our sample have not
engaged in sexual intercourse.' Notwithstanding all the influences
to which the young people of today are exposed – greater independence; more money in their pockets and purses; the weakening of
family bonds and religious influences; the development of earlier
maturity, physically, emotionally and mentally; the impact of
modern books, television, periodicals – it is clearly wrong to regard
our young people as a bored, undisciplined, sex-obsessed generation.

It is impossible to say how the behaviour of today's younger
generation compares with that of the past. Unfortunately no survey
comparable with the present one has ever been undertaken before.
This one is, indeed, an historic document. We can therefore only
relate its findings to our individual recollections of perhaps nearly
half a century ago – now dimmed by time and probably unrepresentative of the youth of those days. A survey undertaken in the
'twenties might not have reached results widely different from those
of today.

Nevertheless the findings of this report do not justify complacency.
They raise many problems to which attention must be paid. The
sexual development of young people is a natural process, in the
course of which wise guidance is needed. It is remarkable how few
of those interviewed had learned 'the facts of life' from parents or
school teachers. What they had picked up from various sources was
often inadequate and frequently misleading. Widespread ignorance
was found to exist regarding venereal disease, its symptoms and
consequences. Far too little was known of, and less practised in, birth
control methods. The whole question of the method and character
of sex education must be reconsidered.

Sexual intercourse between young people before marriage exists
and will continue. Whether we disapprove or consider it a perfectly
natural and normal phenomenon must be for each of us a matter of
personal judgement. What is needed is not moral denunciation or
exhortation but the inculcation into members of the younger

generation of a greater sense of responsibility, a recognition that whatever their actions or their behaviour they must fully understand and accept the consequences involved. Only so will a sane social system continue to evolve to meet the new challenges of this exciting and stimulating age.

CONTENTS

Part III. The Difference between Sexually Experienced Teenagers and Others

Part IV. Summary and Discussion

Part V. Appendices

PART I
THE DESIGN OF THE RESEARCH

I INTRODUCTION

A. AIMS AND SCOPE

The object of the investigation was to obtain facts about the sexual attitudes and behaviour of young people aged fifteen to nineteen. In particular an attempt was made to measure the extent of sexual experience in this age group, and to identify some of the sociological and psychological factors associated with sexual experience.

Despite the welter of comment and opinion, there is a shortage of adequate knowledge about the sexual activities of young people. It was the object of this research to provide the basic information which is the essential first step before suitable educational measures can be developed.

While the research was in progress Professor G. M. Carstairs broadcast his series of Reith Lectures. The third lecture included the now famous passage (which has been widely quoted out of context) in which the relative importance of chastity and charity is questioned. This sparked off such a heated controversy that few people noticed in the same lecture his statement that 'if we turn to consider young people's sexual behaviour today, we encounter many vehement opinions, but little reliable data' (Carstairs, 1962). Dr Alex Comfort (1963), who has a rather more outspoken style, writes: 'In the absence of facts, poppycock of every kind flourishes in the public mind and much sheer moonshine in the medical textbooks.'

Like every other social research this one was limited by time and money. But a generous grant from the Nuffield Foundation made it possible to use techniques and methods which had been beyond the compass of previous investigations into sexual behaviour. Nevertheless our resources were not limitless, and it was necessary to put some restrictions on our objectives. Consequently it was decided that the scope of the research was to find out as much as possible about the sexual activities of teenagers within the following framework:

1. the information was obtained direct from the teenagers themselves;
2. the interviewers were especially recruited and trained for this work;
3. the research was based on a series of random samples;

4. the questions on sexual behaviour were preceded by a large number of questions on family background and leisure activities;
5. a sufficiently large sample was interviewed so as to be able to describe certain norms of sexual behaviour;
6. care was taken to exclude all moral injunctions or value judgements during the course of the interviews.

A large number of people connected with the youth service were consulted before the interviews began. The research team did not suffer from a shortage of advice from youth leaders and others concerned with the care of youth. The striking thing about the opinions of these youth workers is their complete lack of uniformity. It is possible to put this down to a failure in observation, but youth leaders are not slow to supply considerable detail. The real explanation seems to be that they are generalising from information acquired from a particular group.

Probation officers and others concerned with delinquents are liable to forget about the thousands of boys who never get into trouble. A social worker who spends most of her time interviewing teenagers in a VD clinic is tempted to generalise about the country's youth, although less than one in a thousand teenagers ever get venereal disease. The Research Director attended discussion groups with parents who were slow to impart information about their own children but became less inhibited when discussing the failings of other people's.

Although some useful advice was obtained from doctors, teachers probation officers and youth workers, much of the early period which was spent on a study of the background of the problem turned out to be a disappointment and produced only a small amount of reliable information. On the question of today's youth, it seems as if everyone has already taken up his position and formed his attitudes and the small amount of available factual data has not been weighty enough to persuade anyone to change his views.

For these reasons it was decided that the basic information to be used in this research should come from the young people themselves. There were obvious advantages in getting the facts direct from the teenagers, and some difficulties as well. The interviewers had to be sure that feelings of self esteem did not distort the replies. There was a natural inclination to tell the interviewer rather less than the truth on some occasions. There was also the temptation to tell the interviewer what the teenager felt he wanted to hear, rather than give real opinions when questioned about attitudes.

This meant that special techniques had to be evolved to persuade each teenager to tell the truth. It was impossible to use the ordinary market research methods and a small corps of interviewers had to go through an intensive course of training so that they might learn how to win the confidence of the young people in a short time. Their task was made easier because boys and girls of this age and of this generation tend to be more frank about sex than is the case with older people.

Previous researches in this country and elsewhere into youth problems have used subjects recruited from youth clubs, university students or other restricted groups. But this leaves important segments of the population unrepresented. For example, 75 per cent of this sample were not members of youth clubs. It was decided that this research must be based on a random sample, although it was known from the start that this was the most expensive sampling method. So far as we know this is the only research into sexual behaviour which has the advantage of being based on a sample of this kind. Even Kinsey (1948, 1953), who used very large numbers, did not use random sampling methods to find his subjects.

As one of the primary aims of this research was to determine the extent of sexual experience within the fifteen to nineteen age group, it was essential that the sample should be as representative as possible. Generalisations based on anything less representative than a random sample would be subject to the same type of criticisms which have been levelled at many other researches (Cochran, Mosteller and Tukey, 1954; Himelhoche and Fava, 1955). All the teenagers who lived in each of the seven areas where this research was carried out had an equal chance of being interviewed.

It was obvious that intimate questions on sex behaviour could not be asked until the interviewer had built up a large measure of *rapport*. In any case we wanted to cover many other areas besides sex behaviour so that we could build up a general picture of contemporary youth culture and thus identify the non-sexual factors which seemed to be associated with certain kinds of sex behaviour. This meant that we also asked a large number of questions on leisure activities and on social behaviour in general.[1]

Many of these sociological factors lend themselves to reasonably exact measurement (such as academic achievement, youth club membership, cinema attendance), but the fact that some of the answers to our questions were more difficult to quantify was not always a reason for excluding them. Thus some attempt was made to

1. Much of this material has had to be left out of the present report. It is hoped that some of the information on leisure activities will be incorporated with a later report on other parts of this research.

find out something about the extent of family discipline and the influence of the peer group. We also included questions to test the young people's knowledge of sexual matters and to estimate the extent of their sex education.

Our knowledge about the sexual norms of our society is very meagre and information about the sexual norms of the younger generation is almost non-existent. That is why it is not possible to make any comparisons between this generation of teenagers and previous ones because the information about past generations is missing. As a result of the 1,873 interviews carried out for this research on a representative sample of teenagers, it is now possible to make statements about the incidence of sexual behaviour in this age group. This will also mean that comparisons with future generations will be more meaningful.

At all times we tried to avoid any moral implications in the questions we asked. Our position was neutral. At no time did we attempt to change the teenagers' views or introduce any opinions of our own. It was not the role of this research to disseminate moral values nor did we assume a uniformity of moral standards in others. We hope the results of this research will assist those whose job is to help and advise young people, but we did not regard advice as part of our task. Our concern was to get the facts.

B. THE NEED FOR THIS RESEARCH

According to the BMA Report on Venereal Disease and Young People (1964): 'In spite of new drugs and improved methods of treatment, an increase in sexually transmitted diseases has taken place and this is the most marked among young people.' The Registrar General's *Statistical Reviews* show that the percentage of illegitimate births among girls under twenty-one has also increased in recent years.

The BMA Report and others argue that this can best be explained by an increase in the amount of promiscuous behaviour among young people. Neither this research nor any other can show whether there has been an increase or not because the historical information is not available. But an increase in our knowledge of sexual behaviour as it is today should put us in a better position to tackle VD and illegitimacy as social problems.

The public disquiet about teenage sexual behaviour has increased the demand for more sex education. But there is considerable disagreement about the best method of presenting this information, by whom and at what age. There is a need for the concept of sex education to be based on a realistic assessment of adolescent sexual experience.

A rough measurement of the extent of this public disquiet is given by the amount of newspaper coverage. During the early stages of the research a press-cutting agency was employed to send us all items which dealt with any aspect of teenage sexual behaviour. Over a period of four months (September 1961 to January 1962) 414 relevant cuttings were received. Of these, 55 per cent were critical of adolescent sexual activities, 15 per cent set out to defend these activities, and 30 per cent were neutral or expressed approval of some activities and disapproval of others.

It would be a mistake to make too much of these figures, for news coverage by the popular press can arouse and instigate as well as report public disquiet, and therefore a content analysis of press cuttings is measuring both cause and effect. However it is interesting to note that about half of those expressing concern were people who dealt with adolescents professionally. Even among these people there was no agreement as to the true state of affairs. A rational discussion of the teenage problem has always been hindered by lack of information.

Some people have suggested that there is nothing new about the teenage problem. The development of adolescent into adult has always created difficulties. But there are exceptional differences between this generation of adolescents and their predecessors, and these differences are discussed in detail in the next section of this chapter. Furthermore there seems to be a failure in the communication between parents and teenager. Parents have told our interviewers 'there's nothing she doesn't discuss with me', but within the next hour or so, our interviewers have learnt quite otherwise. Obviously there are some matters where communication between parent and adolescent can be very difficult and this is especially the case where problems of sex behaviour are concerned.

Our sample was in the middle of the so-called bulge. This sudden increase in the birth-rate was caused by the war; many young adults who would have had children during the war years were prevented from raising a family either because the husband was overseas, or else because they felt it was inadvisable to marry during the war. The result is that many of the children of the bulge have older parents than in previous generations. This difference in age between parent and child may account for some difficulties of communication.

At all events there are clear signs of alienation between the young people of today and the adult generations. There is much justification in the claim of some of these young people to be left alone to lead their own lives, but no one generation is completely independent from the others, and the successes and failures of these young men and women will affect us all.

If, as the Albemarle report (1960) suggests, 'adolescents are the litmus paper of a society', then for our sake as well as theirs, it is necessary that we gain more knowledge about the sexual behaviour and attitudes of young people.

C. THE TEENAGE POPULATION

The power and influence of the teenage population is far greater today than in the years before the last war. Although there are signs that the importance of this group is beginning to be exaggerated, not least among the teenagers themselves, it is still true that they have become a more salient section of the community.

Abrams (1961) has studied in detail the economic influence of this group, although it should be noted that his definition of teenager is much wider than ours, for he included everyone who is unmarried and under the age of twenty-five.

Although their total spending power is only 5 per cent of all consumer spending, they are the biggest purchasers of certain commodities. Thus they buy 42 per cent of all the records and record players that are sold, 37 per cent of all bicycles and motor-bicycles, 29 per cent of all cosmetics and toilet preparations, 28 per cent of all cinema admissions and 30 per cent of the money spent on other entertainments, 18 per cent of all recreational goods, 15 per cent of all cigarettes and tobacco, 15 per cent of all money spent on meals out and snacks, 13 per cent of all soft drinks, and 13 per cent of all the money spent on holidays. Their total spending is far higher than it used to be and tends to be concentrated on these commodities. 'Money at the disposal of Britain's average teenager is spent mainly on dress and on goods which form the nexus of teenage gregariousness outside the home' (Abrams, 1961).

People have become well aware of the increased spending power of the teenagers and the suggestion that 'they have too much money to throw about' is often used as an explanation for teenage misbehaviour. But their total spending power is not out of proportion to their numbers in the whole population. Their economic power has become noticeable because they spend their money on articles which are highly visible and audible, and because their spending tends to be concentrated on certain areas of the total market. They are also subjected to exploitation by many adults who have realised the commercial possibilities of the teenage market where a large part of the income is not committed to essential family expenditure like rents or mortgages, household goods, or children's food and clothes.

The visibility of this increased teenage economic power has led to its exaggeration. The teenage market is run by adults and all our social institutions are still dominated by older people. Youth has often been in revolt against the old-fashioned and outworn ideas of the older generations and has challenged the traditional and conventional. The main difference now is that the balance has changed. In the past the adults had all the economic power. Now through the mechanics of supply and demand, the teenager has more money to spend and so his ideas and desires are treated with more respect by the commercial world.

The demands of teenagers which were once ignored have now become important, and their activities are reported in the mass media. In some areas, popular music for example, their demands completely dominate the market and the newspapers and periodicals give much of their space to stories about the latest recording stars, the new teenage fashions and the latest teenage craze.

But the newspapers are still run by adults and still reflect the views of the adults who respond to the new economic power of the teenagers with a strange mixture of bewilderment, scorn and envy. So teenagers are news, but only certain kinds of teenagers – those who are in trouble, those who are defying convention, those who are good copy.

The frequent articles in the press and the radio and TV programmes tend to create a teenage mythology. Just as a boy learns how to behave towards his family, or his schoolmaster, so by a similar social learning process he learns the role of a teenager. The press reports have created this image of the typical teenager and the young people who do not measure up to this archetype begin to feel that they are missing something, or else something is missing in them.

It has been shown that teenagers are better fed than in the past. They are taller and heavier. They are the healthiest section of the community and except for a very high rate of motor-cycle accidents (Lee, 1963), they have a very low mortality rate.

It is now well known that children mature at an earlier age than in the past. According to Tanner (1962): 'The age at menarche has been getting earlier by some four months per decade in Western Europe over the period 1830–1960.' It follows therefore that 'a girl today may expect to menstruate on average some ten months earlier

than did her mother' (Tanner, 1961). Boys now complete their
growth on average at about seventeen years of age; this compares
with twenty-three years of age at the turn of the century. The
average girl reaches menarche aged about thirteen-and-a-half;
about a hundred years ago she reached it at about seventeen. This
lowering of the physical age of maturity must mean that today's
boys and girls are also sexually mature at an earlier age than their
parents and grandparents. So they will feel sexual desire and be
sexually at risk at an earlier age. Twenty years ago some activities
between thirteen-year-olds would have been regarded as mere
sexual play; today the same activities could have much more serious
consequences. Physical development is of considerable importance
in a study of sexual behaviour and we shall refer to this again
(chapter 13).

Not only have teenagers become more dominant, but also there
are more of them. There are almost a million more teenagers now
than there were ten years ago – an increase of 20 per cent. The
number of young people aged fifteen to nineteen is expected to
remain around three and a half million for the next ten years, then
the expansion will continue and according to the Registrar General's
Statistical Review there will be over four million teenagers in 1982.

Although the increase in the teenage population could have been
foreseen, unfortunately the expansion of facilities for young people
has not kept pace. Despite the warnings given in many reports
(Crowther, Newsom, Albemarle, Robbins, the King George V
Jubilee Trust), there is not enough room in the schools, colleges,
universities and apprenticeship schemes. Consequently for many
years to come there will be intense competition for the available
places and inevitably there are going to be some young people who
will be left disappointed and frustrated because the opportunities
have not expanded at a rate proportionate to the increase in population. In addition there are several areas where there is a shortage of
youth clubs and other recreational facilities.

One of the penalties of being young is that some youthful activities
will be labelled deviant behaviour if only because young people are
less inhibited than older generations and less inclined to be restricted
by convention or the sour looks of neighbours. Therefore there will
always be teenage problem groups and as the size of the teenage
population grows, it is to be expected that the size of the problem
groups will increase correspondingly.

In addition it is well known that in the more serious problem
areas, like juvenile delinquency and illegitimacy, the numbers are
increasing out of proportion to the increase in population, as shown

in table 1.1 which is based on figures from the Criminal Statistics and table 1.2 which is based on figures from the Registrar General's *Reviews* 1938–62.

Table 1.1. *The increase in the number of boys found guilty of indictable offences between the ages of 15–19 between 1938 and 1960 shown in numbers of persons per 100,000*

Age	Number per 100,000 found guilty in 1938	Number per 100,000 found guilty in 1960	Percentage increase
15	1,145	2,246	96
16	1,110	2,114	90
17	867	2,266	161
18	740	2,183	195
19	766	2,313	201

The young and unattached are the progenitors of change. They are more flexible in their attitudes and have no social status to safeguard. As long as they are unmarried the greater part of their income is uncommitted, and they will have power to pursue their particular ends without regard for adult society or its traditions.

Table 1.2 *Illegitimate births as a percentage of all live births under the age of twenty*

	1938	1940	1950	1960	1961	1962
All births 15–19	12,463	27,641	31,103	52,125	60,309	67,774
Illegitimate births 15–19	2,221	4,746	5,370	9,743	11,925	13,929
Percentage illegitimate births	17·8	17·1	17·2	18·6	19·8	20·5

Thus the values of adult society will be unintentionally challenged. This challenge will be in the non-acceptance of adult mores. This non-acceptance is clearly illustrated in the dancing, dress and hairstyles of teenagers; some people fear that it has extended to a rejection of adult standards in other things such as sexual relations. The challenge will have most significance when the unintended consequences of teenage behaviour force adult society to take action as in the case of unmarried mothers or juvenile delinquency. Inevitably the adult reaction will be restrictive and this will produce defiance in some of the young people.

Teenagers have become aware of their increased importance in the community. The commercial market panders to their demands and the mass media creates a teenage mythology. The most influential factors are their increased purchasing power and the younger age at the onset of puberty. These economic and physiological factors have so altered the situation that the sexual behaviour of teenagers is now more crucial than in the past. This presents a challenge which society has not yet been able to meet.

2 RESEARCH PLAN

A. OTHER RESEARCHES INTO SEX BEHAVIOUR

Very few of the researches into sexual behaviour have sampled directly from the general teenage population. Most of them have been content to ask older people to try to remember the early sexual experiences of their youth. The few that have dealt specifically with teenage sexual behaviour have always used captive or particular groups of the population, such as delinquents in prison (Merrill, 1918); psychiatric patients (Hamilton, 1929; Strakosch, 1934; Landis, *et al.*, 1940); hospital patients (Pearl, 1925; Dickinson and Beam, 1931); army conscripts (Hohman and Shaffner, 1947); and especially college students (Taylor, 1933; Peterson, 1938; Bromley and Britten, 1938; Finger, 1947; Ross, 1950; Burgess and Wallin, 1953; Ehrmann, 1959; Kirkendall, 1961). No research has used a random sample of the general population of teenagers and very little attempt has been made to evolve new techniques for studying this area of human relations. Only three studies had broad objects which covered the incidence of premarital sexual patterns, namely, Bromley and Britten (1938), Kinsey (1948, 1953), and Ehrmann (1959).

The report by Bromley and Britten was aimed 'to secure facts about the sexual habits of the younger generation, free from myth and legend; also to present these facts with detachment'. Their study covered 1,364 college men and women from 46 different colleges. They used college students because they wished to simplify their work. As journalists they required easy access to a large number of articulate young people who would be more receptive to this type of inquiry. They distributed 5,000 questionnaires and received 1,088 back; this represented a 20 per cent return. As 80 per cent had failed to answer their questions they did not attempt a complex statistical analysis.

Kinsey's two books are by far the most extensive and best known studies on human sexual behaviour. The broad purpose was 'to accumulate an objectively determined body of facts about sex which strictly avoids social or moral interpretation of the facts'. A total of 6,200 males and 5,800 females were interviewed. No statistically systematic method of selection was used, and it is difficult to ascertain from the first volume either the age or the educational level of the men interviewed. It is assumed that a very large proportion

13

were students, but it is not known how many teenagers at lower educational levels were interviewed. Seventy-five per cent of the women interviewed were college educated, whereas only 13 per cent of American women are college educated. In fact Kinsey and associates interviewed 297 non-college girls aged sixteen to twenty compared with the 920 non-college girls in our sample.

Kinsey did not use standardised questions; his interviewers simply had a checklist of questions to be asked at each interview; the different interviewers had a standard definition of the items but used different words to get the information. Once the subject had agreed to be interviewed Kinsey was relentless in his cross examination; and used methods of persuasion which would not have been advisable to use with our sample of adolescents. He takes considerable care to show in his study of the male that these unstandardised interview techniques did not produce significantly different results between the three male interviewers. Unfortunately he did not repeat these tests in his study of the female. Our own results make it clear that it is far more difficult to get this kind of information from girls and interviewing women about sex is more variable and uncertain than interviewing men; and Kinsey made it even more precarious by using men to interview women, whereas we found girls responded much more readily to female interviewers.

Nevertheless there is no doubt that the study by Kinsey, which is still being carried on by his associates, is by far the most important work of its kind. The usefulness of this work lies not only in the methods and results, but also in the frank critical assessment of their own work. These comments are very helpful to others undertaking similar studies and this research owes much to their pioneering work.

Ehrmann's study covered 1,157 male and female college students and its objective was 'to describe the aspects of dating behaviour in terms of the varying degrees of physical love-making intimacies'. During the exploratory interviews Ehrmann became aware of developmental stages, through which the vast majority of adolescents pass. His 'degrees of intimacy' were quite similar to the stages of sex which we used as a basic classification (in section G of chapter 3). He obtained his data by distributing a self-administered questionnaire among college students on a random basis. Later 100 of the sample were randomly selected for intensive interviewing to test the reliability of the questionnaire. The median age of the males was 21·3 years and the females 19·7 years, compared with our median age for both sexes of 17 years.

Many of the researches which were carried out over large segments of the population do not report age breakdowns, and therefore it is impossible to glean much information from them about the sex behaviour of young unmarried men and women. But the main disadvantage in all these researches is not the incompleteness of the analysis, but the imperfections in the method of collecting the data. The overwhelming majority of previous researches have used subjects who are available and easy to interview, but not necessarily representative of young people in general; and the value of the results, in spite of the statistical sophistication of some, must remain very limited. Table 2.1 is a list of researches carried out since 1915, giving their sample size and the source of their samples.

All the researches in table 2.1 are American except the last one which compared Danish students with others from two American universities, the study of 200 British soldiers admitted to hospital for neurotic or other illnesses by Slater and Woodside, and Chesser's inquiry into the sexual, marital and family relationships of English women. The information in Dr Chesser's inquiry was collected by approaching general practitioners and inviting them to distribute a self-administered questionnaire to their patients. Only 33 per cent of the questionnaires distributed were returned. About 490 of those who replied were single women over eighteen and under twenty-one. Although useful information was obtained from the inquiry, it was not a study of teenage sex behaviour and the sample was over-represented in the higher educational and income groups.

B. THE SAMPLE DESIGN

Strictly speaking the young people in our random samples were not volunteers in the first place. They received a visit from one of the research team and then they had to be persuaded to cooperate. This was not always an easy task. The activities of some doorstep salesmen who pretended to be doing a research, but use this only as a sales gimmick, have made many people wary of all social surveys.

The difficulty is that if a person refuses, another cannot be brought in as a substitute. It is therefore important to try to get the actual person drawn for the sample to agree to an interview and this can only be done by being prepared to fit in with the time and place most convenient to the young person concerned. This method of obtaining interviews is expensive and takes far longer than the usual methods used by market researchers. Much of the work done on sexual behaviour in America suffers from the failing that the researchers have used students as subjects because they were available

Table 2.1 *Researches on sex behaviour*

Author	Date	Source of sample	Size of sample Male	Female	Total
Exner	1915	College students	948	—	948
Merrill	1918	Juvenile delinquents	100	—	100
Achilles	1923	High school and college students	1,449	483	1,932
Peck and Wells	1923	College graduates	550	—	550
Pearl	1925	Hospital patients	257	—	257
Hughes	1926	Mill workers	1,029	—	1,029
Davis	1929	College alumnae	—	2,200	2,200
Hamilton	1929	Psychiatric patients	100	100	200
Dickenson and Beam	1931	Hospital patients	—	1,448	1,448
Taylor	1933	College students	40	—	40
Strakosch	1934	Psychiatric patients	—	700	700
Bromley and Britten	1938	College students	592	772	1,364
Terman	1938	College level	1,242	1,242	2,484
Peterson	1938	College students	419	—	419
Landis *et al.*	1940	Psychiatric patients	—	295	295
Landis and Bolles	1942	Psychiatric patients	—	100	100
Ramsey	1943	High school, boys' clubs and YMCA	291	—	291
Gardner	1944	College students	221	—	221
Finger	1947	College students	111	—	111
Hohman and Schaffner	1947	Army conscripts	4,600	—	4,600
Kinsey	1948⎱ 1953⎰	Volunteers all social classes	6,200	5,800	12,000
Ross	1950	College students	95	—	95
Slater and Woodside	1951	Hospital patients	200	—	200
Burgess and Wallin	1953	College and high school level	580	604	1,184
Landis and Landis	1953	College students	600	1,000	1,600
Chesser	1956	Patients of general practitioners	—	6,034	6,034
Kanin	1958	College level	—	190	190
Ehrmann	1959	College students	734	423	1,157
Knonhausen	1960	College students	200	—	200
Kirkendall	1961	College students	600	—	600
Christensen and Carpenter	1962	College students	456	302	758
Greene	1964	College students	76	538	614

and likely to volunteer. But it can be shown that student sexual behaviour is not typical of the behaviour of all young people. The boys and girls interviewed for this research are much more repre-sentative of the whole teenager population and this has enabled us to present our results with more confidence.

The first area to be sampled was designated London C. Here the sample was drawn from a list of all the National Health patients in the area. A full description of the method of sampling is given in section A of appendix 4. Unfortunately the Ministry of Health did not allow the Executive Councils in other areas to supply us with lists from which to draw our samples, and so other sampling methods had to be used.

The next two areas were South A and South B where samples were drawn from the school attendance lists. This is described in detail in section B of appendix 4. Although the lists were almost a year out of date they proved to be satisfactory for drawing the samples of teenagers. But it was found that school attendance records had not been kept up to date in the other areas that we wished to visit, so a third method of sampling was devised.

The remaining areas were visited in this order: North A, North B, London A, London B. In these four areas the sample was drawn from lists especially constructed for this research. A market research agency was employed to locate all the teenagers living in selected districts in each area. The sampling methods for each of these areas are described in sections C and D of appendix 4.

The first sample covered a wide area – a whole London borough – with a large sampling fraction; one in 41 of the teenagers in the area were interviewed. The second method covered a smaller area of only three wards, and the third method covered a still smaller area, but with a low sampling fraction – so low in London A that one in every three teenagers in the area were in the sample. The sampling fraction for each area and the estimated proportion of teenagers interviewed relative to the population of each area is given in sections A–D of appendix 4.

Despite the difference in sampling methods, the results from the seven areas are very similar, and where there is a difference, it is more reasonably explained by other factors than by the different methods of sampling. An evaluation of the three sampling methods is given in section E of appendix 4.

By the end of the research, 1,873 young people had been inter-viewed. (Other interviews of people in special groups, such as un-married mothers, girls in care and patients with venereal disease were also interviewed, but the results from these interviews are not included in this report.) All the married teenagers were excluded. The remaining 934 single boys and 939 single girls were classified into two age groups according to their year of birth. The older boys and the older girls had a modal age of eighteen and were not younger than seventeen, not older than nineteen at the time of the interview. The two younger groups had a modal age of sixteen, and an age range of fifteen to seventeen. The method used for forming the two age groups is described in sections A and B of appendix 4.

The basic information on the size of the sample and sub-samples is given in table 2.2. Between 249 and 290 were interviewed in each of the seven areas and no age/sex/area group is less than 60.

Table 2.2 *The sample shown by age, sex and area groups*

Age/Sex group	London A	London B	London C	South A	South B	North A	North B	Total
Younger boys	82	67	63	70	70	63	63	478
Older boys	65	62	61	64	72	65	67	456
Younger girls	74	68	60	70	72	64	67	475
Older girls	69	65	65	69	64	67	65	464
TOTAL	290	262	249	273	278	259	262	1873

Areas marked A were particular wards of a town which were selected because they were expected to produce a relatively large proportion of young people from middle-class homes. Areas marked B were expected to produce mostly working-class teenagers. London C was an area chosen because we hoped to find young people from all types of homes, but in the event most of them were the children of artisans (Registrar General's Class III). The numbers in each area are shown in table 2.3.

C. THE PROCEDURE

It cannot be assumed in any research that reliable information about sex behaviour can be easily obtained just for the asking. It does not require much skill or cost much money, first to make up a questionnaire on sex, and then to send it out to thousands of people in the hope that a few hundreds will reply. This has been done by newspapers, college magazines and agencies. The results are unlikely to be of much value. The number who do not answer the questions is often so large that they form a sizable proportion of the population under consideration; nor is this a method that is likely to elicit the truth on such a personal matter.

This research was as much concerned with the method of getting the information as with analysing, interpreting and reporting the results. For this reason we have a special chapter on validity and the research plan is described in detail in appendices 1–7. This section outlines the procedure that was adopted and refers those readers who require more details to the relevant sections of the appendices.

Table 2.3 *The distribution of social class analysed by A, B and C areas*

Social class	Boys				Girls			
	A areas, %	B areas, %	C areas, %	Total, %	A areas, %	B areas, %	C areas, %	Total, %
Middle class RG I and II	43	7	11	23	44	9	15	25
Artisan * RG III	42	62	62	54	42	63	59	54
Working class RG IV and V	15	31	27	23	14	28	26	21
TOTAL	100	100	100	100	100	100	100	100
No. (100%)	409	401	124	934	413	401	125	939

* Class III in the Registrar-General's classification is an amalgamation of skilled manual workers and non-manual workers. In this sample 362 boys came from the homes of skilled manual workers, 114 from the homes of non-manual workers; among the girls 380 from the homes of skilled manual workers and 95 from the homes of non-manual workers.

We realised that many people would be reluctant to cooperate once they knew the research was about sexual behaviour, and we felt others would prevaricate unless the whole exercise was made as easy and as pleasant as possible. We were allowed a long exploratory period to study the methodological problems, to seek advice from those concerned with youth work, and to try out different ideas and techniques.

Consequently it was with feelings of anticlimax that we came to the conclusion that the only satisfactory way of obtaining the data was by using good interviewers. Despite the progress and refinement of psychological tests, self-administered questionnaires and group

c

discussion techniques, we came to believe that valid information about sex behaviour could only be obtained during the course of a lengthy face to face interview (section A of appendix 1).

The questions were tried out in schools and youth clubs, and discussed with youth leaders and many others concerned with youth work, and groups of teenagers were invited to criticise and comment on the schedule of questions. Some of the questions did not reach their final form until they had been tried out on over 300 teenagers (section B of appendix 1).

Ten young graduates were used as the interviewers in this research. After some experiments it was found that the best results were obtained when men interviewed boys and women interviewed girls. The five male interviewers and five female interviewers were selected for their ability to get on with young people and they were all required to undergo an extensive course of training before they started interviewing (section A and B of appendix 6).

After the young person had been drawn for the sample (sections A–D of appendix 4), he (or she) was sent an introductory letter telling him about the research and asking for his cooperation (section B of appendix 5). The interviewer called at the teenager's home soon after he had received the letter and arranged with the boy and his parents a time and place for an interview. If he preferred to be interviewed at home the interviewer arranged to call back at a convenient time; sometimes it was possible to carry out the interview at the time of the first call. It was always stressed that privacy was essential if the interview was to be held at home. If he preferred to be interviewed away from home, the interviewer could arrange to meet him at a nearby office which had been hired especially for this research (section C of appendix 5).

If the teenager failed to keep the appointment the interviewer was required to call back to try to arrange another interview (section D of appendix 5). Sometimes this was not possible and of course there were some teenagers who would not agree to an interview in the first place. It was expected that there would be a high number of refusals and it was imperative that everything should be done to cut down this loss. In fact 328 would not agree to an interview and this represents a refusal rate of 14·9 per cent (section B of appendix 7).

The interviewers were instructed to continue to call on the teenager until it became clear that there was no chance of getting an interview (section D of appendix 5). Interviewers were not allowed to give up before six call-backs had been made. When it was decided that a particular case would have to be classified as a refusal, the interviewer wrote up a detailed history and the reason for refusing (section D of appendix 7), and the teenager was sent a letter and a form containing 16 questions about his background and leisure interests. About half those who refused an interview answered the questions on this form, so at least something is known about many of those who refused (section E of appendix 7).

At the start of each interview the main task was to make the teenager feel at ease, so the interviewer concentrated upon establishing *rapport*. The schedule was so designed that only simple information was sought in the early part of the interview; this was followed by questions on leisure which the teenager usually found interesting; only then were questions on sex behaviour introduced, and this started with questions on dating and kissing, and gradually came to the more personal and intimate questions (section B of appendix 2 and section C of appendix 6). The whole schedule consisted of 261 items of which 234 were direct questions (section C of appendix 2).

When all the questions had been asked the teenagers were given an attitude inventory. This consisted of 50 statements on controversial topics and they were asked to indicate whether they agreed or disagreed with these statements (sections A and B of appendix 3).

Before the interviewer handed in the record of the interview to the supervisor he was required to rate the teenager under ten headings (section D of appendix 2). The record was checked by a supervisor soon after the interview had been completed, so that questions of validity and correct coding could be discussed with the interviewer while the answers were still fresh in his mind (section D of appendix 5).

When all the material had been collected, the information from the interview records was put on to 13,111 punch cards (seven cards for each individual), fed into a computer and analysed. Many statistical tests were applied to the results (section A of chapter 8 and section C of appendix 3).

D. PRESENTATION

In general the percentages given in Part II of this report are based upon the four age/sex groups, i.e.

478 younger boys (aged 15–17)
456 older boys (aged 17–19)
475 younger girls (aged 15–17)
464 older girls (aged 17–19)

However 42 of the 261 items were revised and modified after the first 249 interviews in London C. This means that the percentages calculated for these 42 items will be based on the results obtained in six instead of seven areas, i.e.

415 younger boys (aged 15–17)
394 older boys (aged 17–19)
416 younger girls (aged 15–17)
399 older girls (aged 17–19)

For reasons explained in chapter 8 the percentages given in Part III (except chapter 12) are based on the older age groups. On other occasions the percentages will be based on smaller segments of the sample; for example, in chapter 4 there are percentages based upon only those girls who had experience of sexual intercourse, but these cases will be clearly identified when they occur in the relevant chapters.

The next five chapters (Part II) give the basic results of the investigation into sex behaviour and attitudes; this is followed by six chapters (Part III) on the association between sex behaviour and other factors; then the last chapters discuss the validity of the material and some questions of public concern.

PART II
THE EXTENT OF TEENAGE
SEXUAL ACTIVITIES AND ATTITUDES

3 INCIDENCE

A. DATING

The first date is an important event in the life of an adolescent. Until this moment the social life of a boy has probably been restricted to an all-male group whose interests revolve around football, cycling or some other hobby where the presence of girls is not welcome. Even those boys who have grown up in a mixed group will reach the stage when there is a desire to pair off from the group and go out with a particular girl. As well as this inner desire which is a reawakening of sexual interest as the boy reaches puberty, there is also an outside pressure on each boy to find a girl and take her out. But not all boys feel this desire or give way to this social pressure and in this group 107 (22 per cent) younger boys (aged 15–17) and 34 (7 per cent) older boys (aged 17–19) had never gone out with a girl (from table 3.1).

Adolescent girls are more likely to have been out on a date. Their earlier interests in family games, clothes and appearance lead naturally towards an interest in the opposite sex, and fantasies about boy friends are encouraged by comics, films and pop records before they ever go out with a boy. But the first date is still an important event, for it may be the first time the girl has been on her own with a boy, when she will experience her first physical contact as a reality rather than in fantasy. In this sample 43 (9 per cent) of the younger girls (aged 15–17) and 20 (4 per cent) of the older girls (aged 17–19) had never gone out with a boy (from table 3.2).

Of the younger boys who had never been out with a girl, only a third said they would like to, whereas half the younger girls who had not been dated said they would like to go out with a boy. So many boys, and a few girls also, do not want to start dating before the age of seventeen.

As well as the 204 (11 per cent) teenagers who had never been out with members of the opposite sex, there were many others who had very little experience of dating. Over half (52 per cent) the younger boys and a third (33 per cent) of the younger girls had not been out with more than four of the opposite sex. But from the age of seventeen onwards many more went out on dates, and nearly a half (49 per cent) of the older boys and well over a half (58 per cent) of the older girls had been out with ten or more different people.

Dating is a useful activity that enables boys and girls to get to know each other, and eventually to find a wife or husband. The girls start younger than the boys and one in five boys do not start dating before seventeen. Thereafter the boys begin to catch up with the girls, but it is still a more important activity for a teenage girl than it is for a boy. Beyond the age of seventeen dating for teenagers is usual but not universal.

B. KISSING

The first specifically sexual contact experienced by most teenagers is a kiss. But children have experience of non-sexual kissing from parents and other adults, and during party games. An attempt was made to leave these out of the reckoning and to limit our definition of kissing to an activity which has some slight element of sexual arousal. After experimenting during the pilot stage of the research, it was found that the most satisfactory wording was: 'When was the first time you kissed a girl/boy on your own – and liked it?' This took the situation out of the context of 'kiss in the ring' and suggested an occasion which might have led on to further activities of greater intimacy.

The amount of kissing for both sexes is very similar to the incidence of dating. This suggests that a boy and girl often experience their first serious kiss on their first date. In the two younger groups all those who have been out on dates had experienced their first kiss at the same age. This was also true of the older girls, and among the older boys just 1 per cent more had been out on a date without experiencing a kiss. Perhaps these figures do no more than reflect the custom of giving the girl a goodnight kiss after taking her home.

Deep kissing, sometimes known as french kissing, where the tongue of one partner enters the mouth of the other, is an activity with a much more specific sexual component in it. But it does not necessarily follow on from lip kissing and is shunned by some teenagers who take part in other forms of sexual activity. In fact over a third of our sample had never done this, and less than a half expressed any interest in deep kissing.

There are some signs that deep kissing is more acceptable to middle-class teenagers. Of the 91 middle-class older boys who had kissed a girl, 20 (22 per cent) had never tried deep kissing; but among the 85 working-class older boys who had kissed a girl, 31 (36 per cent) had not tried deep kissing. Of the 107 middle-class older girls who had been kissed, 15 (14 per cent) had not tried deep kissing; yet among the 76 working-class older girls who had been kissed, 21 (28 per cent) had not tried deep kissing.

More girls than boys had experienced this type of kissing; 72 per
cent of all the girls compared with 54 per cent of all the boys. But
many of the girls did not enjoy it. Only 10 per cent of the younger
girls and 14 per cent of the older girls said they liked it very much,
compared with 16 per cent of the younger boys and 27 per cent of
the older boys who said they enjoyed it. Teenage boys appear to be
less likely to have experienced deep kissing, but those that have tried
it are more likely than the girls to enjoy the experience.

C. PETTING

Kissing is a form of sexual contact accepted by most people even in
semi-public places, but most other kinds of love-making usually
take place in private. Furthermore they are subject to more restrictions, limitations and taboos, and can only take place when the
circumstances are expedient. Those forms of sexual contact which
fall short of sexual intercourse are often referred to as *petting*. This is
an American expression used to cover a wide variety of activities
from a simple caress to a situation closely resembling sexual intercourse. This is too wide a definition for this research as petting is
not an entity in itself but a generic term applied to various acts
which have many different social consequences. In this chapter it
will be clearer and more useful if we define and specify eight forms
of sexual behaviour that may precede intercourse. Dating, kissing
and deep kissing have already been mentioned. The other five
activities are described in the next four paragraphs.

Stimulating breasts over clothes. Boys were asked when they first felt a
girl's breasts, and girls were asked when they first allowed a boy to
do this. More than half the sample had experience of this activity.
In the younger age group the incidence among the girls (60 per
cent) was higher than it was among the boys (49 per cent); in the
older age groups the difference between the sexes had narrowed,
but it was still more common among the girls (79 per cent) than
among the boys (74 per cent).

Stimulating breasts under clothes. Not many (1 per cent) people refused
to answer questions once the interview had started, but it was at the
point when a question on this activity was asked that a refusal was
most likely. It seems to provide a strong dividing line between the
sexually sophisticated and the others. It is also at this point that the
incidence falls away by as much as 12 per cent or more in each of
the four groups. About one-third (36 per cent) of the younger boys
and about two-thirds (63 per cent) of the older boys had fondled
the breasts of a girl under her clothes. This is also the point where

as many boys as girls have the same experience, for 38 per cent of
the younger girls and 61 per cent of the older girls had allowed their
breasts to be fondled by a boy.

Genital stimulation. This is really two kinds of activity. The boys
were asked when they first touched a girl's sex organs, and then they
were asked when they first let a girl touch[1] their sex organs. The
girls were asked the same question but in reverse order. As expected
more boys had stimulated a girl's genitals than girls had stimulated
a boy's genitals. Among the boys 37 per cent had fondled a girl's
genitals (active genital stimulation), compared with 28 per cent
who had let a girl fondle their genitals (passive genital stimulation).
Among the girls 33 per cent had let a boy touch their genitals but
had reciprocated in only 20 per cent of the cases. It is at this stage
where the incidence among the younger age groups fall away, and
in this and the following activities the incidence is always twice as
great among the older boys and girls (from tables 3.1. and 3.2).
Over half the older boys had experience of active genital stimulation,
and nearly half the older girls had experience of passive genital
stimulation.

Genital apposition. This is the term used to describe the circumstances when the sex organs of the male are in close contact with
those of the female, but where penetration does not occur. It may
be a preliminary to full sexual intercourse, alternatively it may be a
substitute for intercourse. In this sample 14 per cent of the younger
boys and 38 per cent of the older boys had experienced genital
apposition; in other words slightly more than a quarter (26 per cent)
of the boys had experienced this activity. It was a rather less frequent activity for the girls: 13 per cent of the younger girls and
29 per cent of the older girls had experienced genital apposition; in
total about one-fifth (21 per cent) of all the girls. In most cases
where genital apposition is possible, the physical surroundings
would also allow sexual intercourse with full penetration, and yet
43 boys (17 per cent of those with experience of this activity) and
72 girls (28 per cent of those with experience of this activity) said
they would prefer genital apposition to sexual intercourse.

D. ALL SEXUAL ACTIVITIES

The remaining form of sexual activity considered in this report is
intercourse with full penetration. A few other activities, such as
oral–genital contacts, were mentioned very occasionally in the inter-

1. The word 'touch' was used in this context because in the vernacular 'touching
up' means genital stimulation.

view, but these are more likely to occur after intercourse has been experienced. American researches sometimes report extensive oral–genital contacts, but it was very rare among the teenagers in this sample.

The group who experienced intercourse in this sample of teenagers will be the subject of further detailed discussion. In this section only the straightforward incidence is reported and this is compared with the other activities.

In the group of 478 younger boys (aged 15–17) a total of 55 (11 per cent) said they had experienced sexual intercourse at least once. A total of 138 (30 per cent) of the 456 older boys (aged 17–19) reported at least one experience of sexual intercourse. The figures for the girls are much smaller. Out of 475 younger girls, 29 (6 per cent) said they had experienced sexual intercourse at least once. Among the older girls 73 (16 per cent) out of 464 reported at least one experience of sexual intercourse. Thus 20 per cent of all the boys in the sample had experienced sexual intercourse and 12 per cent of all the girls.

Tables 3.1 and 3.2 bring together the incidence for the nine forms of heterosexual activity described in this and the previous sections. Figure 3.1 shows the same information graphically with the age groups added together.

The difference in development between the boys and girls in our sample is shown clearly in figure 3.1. In the first three activities more

Table 3.1 *Percentage of boys who have participated in an activity at least once; by age groups*

Activity	Younger (15–17), %	Older (17–19), %	Total (15–19), %
Dating	78	93	85
Kissing	78	90	85
Deep kissing	43	67	54
Breast stimulation over clothes	49	74	62
Breast stimulation under clothes	36	63	49
Active genital stimulation	24	51	37
Passive genital stimulation	16	39	28
Genital apposition	14	38	26
Sexual intercourse	11	30	20
Sample no. (100%)	478	456	934

girls than boys are involved. Thereafter the boys catch up with the girls and the gap gradually widens until there is a difference of 8 per cent.

The incidence of deep kissing is higher among girls than the incidence of breast stimulation, whereas for boys the opposite is the case. It seems that girls are more likely to permit this intimate type

Table 3.2 *Percentage of girls who have participated in an activity at least once; by age groups*

Activity	Younger (15–17), %	Older (17–19), %	Total (15–19), %
Dating	91	96	93
Kissing	91	96	93
Deep kissing	64	81	72
Breast stimulation over clothes	60	79	69
Breast stimulation under clothes	38	61	49
Active genital stimulation	12	29	20
Passive genital stimulation	22	44	33
Genital apposition	13	29	21
Sexual intercourse	6	16	12
Sample no. (100%)	475	464	939

of kissing, though most of them do not like it; they are less likely to allow their breasts to be fondled. Kissing represents romance and is acceptable, but touching the breasts is thought of as a sexual act and therefore is less easily accepted.

There is very little difference between the number of girls who have fondled a boy's genitals, and the number who have experienced genital apposition. The former activity could take place in several situations where genital apposition would not be possible, as is shown by the incidence of active genital stimulation by the boys. But it is clear that very few girls are prepared to reciprocate in these situations, and even those girls who will permit genital apposition may not agree to fondle the boy's penis. This again demonstrates that most girls prefer a passive role and do not want to initiate a sexual activity. A girl who is prepared to touch a boy's sex organs will probably agree to genital apposition, but this does not necessarily mean that she is on the threshold of sexual intercourse.

Figure 3/1
The incidence of eight activities shown in percentages for boys and girls

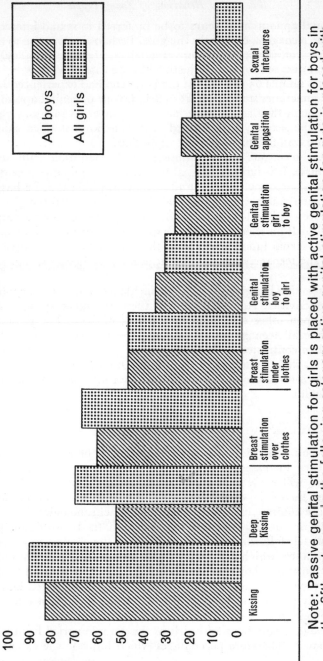

Note: Passive genital stimulation for girls is placed with active genital stimulation for boys in the fifth category. In the following category active genital stimulation for girls is placed with passive genital stimulation for boys. In general girls take the passive role in most sexual activities; thus when the activities are put in this order, the overall pattern of sexual development for both sexes is followed.

Genital apposition appears to be preferred to sexual intercourse by some teenagers, especially the girls. Perhaps it gives rise to a less troubled conscience, or removes anxiety about pregnancy and venereal disease (not wholly justified in the case of VD).

In this sample 65 per cent of the boys who had experienced intercourse sometimes stopped short of it in favour of genital apposition, even though they could have had intercourse. As many as 73 per cent of the sexually experienced girls sometimes stopped short of intercourse in favour of genital apposition.

A few teenagers may confuse genital apposition with sexual intercourse. It is just possible, although we have no direct evidence for this, that a boy may be under the impression that he has had sexual intercourse when he has not in fact penetrated the girl. It is still more possible that a boy who has experienced genital apposition will tell his friends (and perhaps our interviewers) that he has had full sexual intercourse. Thus there seem to be some situations where the teenagers had genital apposition in lieu of sexual intercourse.

This section has given the simple incidence figures for the various sexual activities. An evaluation of these rudimentary figures depends upon other standards and points of view. For those who denigrate all teenage sexual activity, the figures may seem high. But when contrasted with the recurring outcry about teenage immorality, these figures may seem low. Our task in the rest of this chapter is to examine these figures so that they become more meaningful.

E. ACCUMULATIVE INCIDENCE

It will be no surprise to anyone to find that the amount of sexual experience increases as the teenagers get older. Although later chapters will show that many other factors must be taken into account, there is no doubt that one of the most important influences upon the adolescent's sexual experience is chronological age. This is partly due to rapid changes in physical maturity during the years immediately following puberty, and also to the changes in the social circumstances which are closely tied to age at this time. Thus at the age of fourteen a boy may be discouraged by parents from taking a girl out even if he wanted to; but by the age of nineteen he is expected by adults and his own friends to be showing an interest in the opposite sex.

The ages of the boys and girls in this sample varied from fifteen to nineteen. Therefore percentages which indicate the extent of a particular activity are misleading because adolescents of fifteen who have not participated in a particular activity may well experience that activity before they reach the age of nineteen. This discrepancy is allowed for by dividing the sample into older and younger groups. But in this section a more detailed analysis by age will be carried out so that an estimate can be made of the number of adolescents who will have experienced a specific activity by a particular age.

Table 3.3 *Accumulative incidence of seven sexual activities among boys showing percentage with experience at each age*

Activity	Age							
	Under 12	12	13	14	15	16	17	18
Kissing	3·2	8·9	23·0	47·7	70	82	90	92
Deep kissing	—	0·6	3·0	15·0	27	46	61	70
Breast stimulation over clothes	1·1	2·0	6·0	17·0	36	55	71	80
Breast stimulation under clothes	0·5	1·1	3·5	11·5	25	43	60	69
Active genital stimulation	0·4	1·1	2·1	6·7	16	30	45	56
Passive genital stimulation	0·2	0·9	1·6	4·4	10	22	37	44
Sexual intercourse	0·2	0·5	0·9	2·3	6	14	26	34

This can be done by using the concept of *accumulative incidence* as devised by Kinsey (1948). This is defined as the percentage of all the people in the sample who have experienced an activity by a given age. This concept as used by Kinsey has been criticised because it relied upon accurate recall of adults about their early sexual experiences, and because it is assumed that there would be no variation in outside environmental circumstances between the generations (Cochran, Mosteller and Tukey, 1953). But neither of these criticisms are really applicable in this research. The teenagers are being asked to remember events which happened only a few years ago, and in some cases just a few months or weeks ago. Also as the age range of this sample only covers a span of five years, there is no question of a variation in conditions between generations.

The accumulative incidence of seven sexual activities is given for boys in table 3.3, and for girls in table 3.4. From these tables it can be seen (for example) that 15 per cent of all boys will have experienced deep kissing by the age of fourteen, whereas nearly 17 per cent of all girls will have had this experience by the same age.

Figures 3.2 and 3.3 are graphs derived from tables 3.3. and 3.4, plus the accumulative incidence for dating (for which we obtained incidence figures for five of the eight age levels shown). By taking any point between the years one can estimate the number of boys or girls who are expected to be experienced in a particular activity.

Table 3.4 *Accumulative incidence of seven sexual activities among girls showing percentage with experience at each age*

Activity	Age							
	Under 12	12	13	14	15	16	17	18
Kissing	2·1	6·5	25·0	54·0	80	94	95	96
Deep kissing	—	—	3·6	16·6	40	62	75	83
Breast stimulation over clothes	0·2	0·6	3·2	15·0	38	58	74	80
Breast stimulation under clothes	—	—	0·8	7·2	19	36	51	62
Active genital stimulation	—	—	0·1	0·9	4	11	19	31
Passive genital stimulation	—	—	0·1	2·2	10	21	33	46
Sexual intercourse	—	—	0·1	0·4	2	5	10	17

The graphs show that kissing and dating are learnt at about the same time by both boys and girls; deep kissing and breast stimulation over clothes seem to go together for the girls, but the boys experience deep kissing at a later age.

The ascent of the lines indicates that between fifteen and seventeen the teenagers are learning fast; at fifteen less than a fifth of the boys have touched the genitals of a girl, but by seventeen nearly half have done this; at fifteen less than a fifth of the girls have experienced breast stimulation under clothes, but at seventeen over half have experienced this. If one were to make the assumption that the lines on these graphs would continue at the same angles, then by the age of twenty about half the boys and a third of the girls will have experienced sexual intercourse.

Despite the few unhappy cases reported in the newspapers, tables 3.3 and 3.4 show that less than 1 per cent of the boys or girls

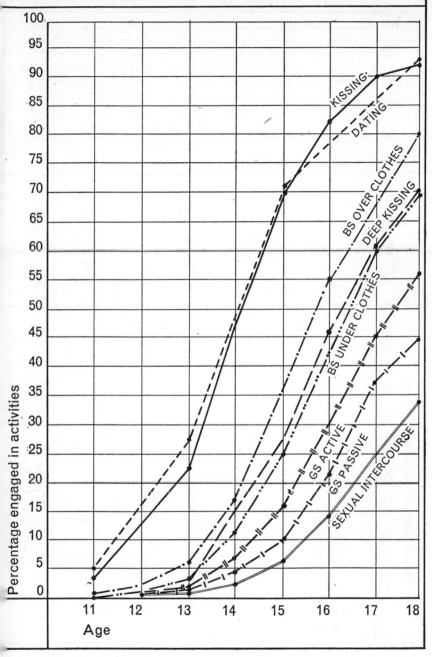

Figure 3/2
Accumulative incidence curves of eight activities for boys

KISSING

DATING

BS OVER CLOTHES

DEEP KISSING

BS UNDER CLOTHES

GS ACTIVE

GS PASSIVE

SEXUAL INTERCOURSE

Percentage engaged in activities

Age

D

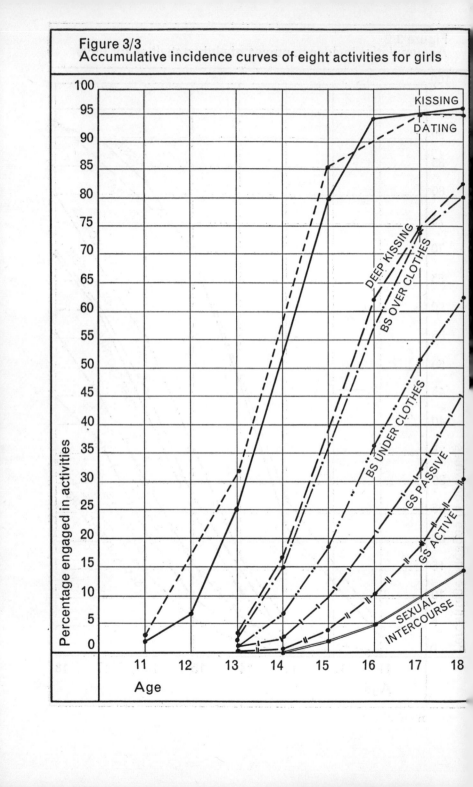

Figure 3/3
Accumulative incidence curves of eight activities for girls

have experienced sexual intercourse before the age of fourteen. But two out of 100 fourteen-year-old schoolboys will be sexually experienced and so will one in about 200 schoolgirls of the same age if the results in our sample are typical. By the age of sixteen 14 per cent of the boys and 5 per cent of the girls will have had sexual intercourse. By eighteen a third of the boys and about one in six of the girls will have experienced heterosexual relations at least once.

F. SEXUAL DEVELOPMENT

In the previous sections the incidence figures have been given in terms of the total number in the whole sample who have experienced a particular activity. Thus the incidence of any one of these activities includes all those who have also proceeded to activities at the next level. In this section we are interested in the number who have reached a particular level of activity without going on to the next level.

The path of sexual development from no contact with the opposite sex up to sexual intercourse depended in part upon the way in which the questions in the interview were interconnected. When it had been established during the interview that a particular activity had not occurred, then it had to be assumed that no further activity had followed. This procedure had to be adopted so that those adolescents with little or no experience of sexual activities should not be upset or disturbed by the questions. Although it is conceivable that a person may have taken part in one of the later activities without experiencing an earlier one (e.g. genital apposition without breast stimulation), in practice the assumption that these activities are sequential is a workable arrangement, and it is doubtful if any information has been lost for this reason.

This procedure means that by simply subtracting the number of more experienced people at each level of activity, we can see how many remain at each step of sexual development. Tables 3.5 and 3.6 show how many of the adolescents have stopped at each level of activity.

From table 3.5 it can be seen that almost a quarter of the boys have got as far as kissing but no farther. The numbers at the succeeding levels are smaller and there is not much difference between the younger and older boys. The implication is that once a boy has fondled a girl's breasts over her clothes, he is unlikely to remain at any of the following levels for very long.

For younger girls the transition is at a later level and is less well defined. The majority (62 per cent) will allow kissing or breast

Table 3.5 *The number of boys at each level of sexual activity*

Activity	Younger (15–17), %	Older (17–19), %	All (15–19), %
No contact with girls	22	8	15
Kissing only	29	18	23
Breast stimulation over clothes	13	11	13
Breast stimulation under clothes	12	12	12
Genital stimulation	10	13	11
Genital apposition	3	8	6
Sexual intercourse	11	30	20
TOTAL	100	100	100
No. (100%)	478	456	934

Table 3.6 *The number of girls at each level of sexual activity*

Activity	Younger (15–17), %	Older (17–19), %	All (15–19), %
No contact with boys	9	4	7
Kissing only	31	17	24
Breast stimulation over clothes	22	18	20
Breast stimulation under clothes	16	17	16
Genital stimulation	9	15	12
Genital apposition	7	13	9
Sexual intercourse	6	16	12
TOTAL	100	100	100
No. (100%)	475	464	939

stimulation over clothes; another 16 per cent have allowed breast stimulation under clothes; beyond this the numbers at each level are small. But the older girls are equally distributed among all six levels. This suggests that agreement from a girl to participate at a particular level of activity does not indicate that she can easily be persuaded to move on to the following levels.

Figure 3.4 shows the level of each activity as a column of sexual development. Each shaded portion shows the extent of a particular level of activity, and the distance up the column shows the number who have not gone beyond that level. Thus it can be seen that 76 per cent of the younger boys have got as far as breast stimulation under clothes compared with 78 per cent of the younger girls.

This figure shows considerable overlap between boys and girls at all levels of activity except for genital apposition where the overlap is small. It will have been noted that in both age groups the boys have had more sexual intercourse than the girls. But more girls have experienced genital apposition. When these two activities are added together the totals in the younger groups are almost the same, as figure 3.4 clearly illustrates. Among the younger boys 14 per cent have experienced sexual intercourse and/or genital apposition; among the girls the sum of these two activities is 13 per cent. This suggests a possible obscurity in the minds of the younger teenagers between these two activities. It may indicate a conscious desire by the boys to exaggerate genital apposition into sexual intercourse, or a tendency among the girls to disclaim full penetration during the sexual act.

In the older age groups 30 per cent of the boys have had sexual intercourse compared with 16 per cent of the girls. But this gap is reduced when genital apposition is added; then it is found that 38 per cent of the older boys have experienced sexual intercourse and/or genital apposition, compared with 29 per cent of the older girls. We can only speculate whether the boys are exaggerating the number of their sexual adventures or the girls are minimising their experiences. There may well be a little of both influences in these results. But this difference between boys and girls has been found in all studies of sexual behaviour and is not necessarily a reason to suspect the validity of the material.

G. FIVE STAGES OF SEX

The previous sections of this chapter have given in detail the incidence of the various levels of sexual activity. These figures show that sex experience at this age level tends to follow a progression from no contact with the opposite sex, to dating and kissing, then through various degrees of physical intimacies, up to full sexual intercourse. At any one of these levels the specific sexual activity may be an end in itself, or it may be the stepping-stone to the next level of activity.

A consideration of these results now enables us to view this progression as five major stages of sex experience. Obviously the first

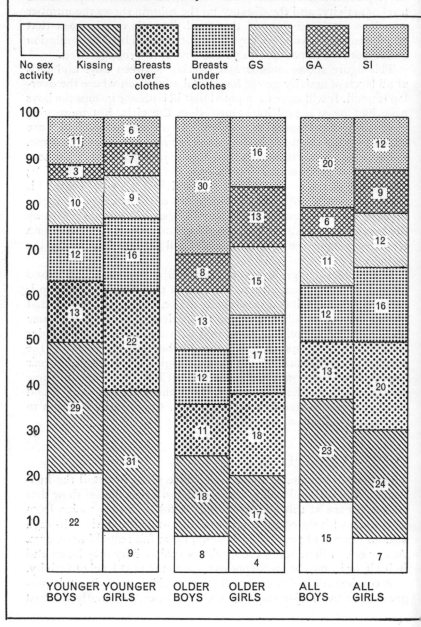

Figure 3/4
Diagram showing the percentage of boys and girls who have reached each level of activity

Legend: No sex activity | Kissing | Breasts over clothes | Breasts under clothes | GS | GA | SI

stage must be that situation where the adolescent does not go out with others of the opposite sex.

The next two stages are an attempt to make a more meaningful division of the phenomenon often described as petting. One type of petting results in sexual arousal only. This will include kissing, deep kissing and the fondling of the girl's breasts over her clothes. These activities are differentiated from the other type of petting because no undressing takes place and kissing is the central activity. The other type of petting involves some disarrangement of clothing and close physical intimacy that is not usually acceptable in public. Thus this includes fondling the breasts under clothes, stimulating of the sex organs and genital apposition. These activities are more likely to lead to orgasm and often happen in the circumstances and surroundings in which sexual intercourse itself could take place.

The fourth and fifth stages are made up of those who have experienced intercourse. The fourth stage refers to those people who have had this experience with one person only; and the teenager reaches the fifth stage when he has sexual intercourse with more than one person. Thus we have a five-point scale as follows:

I. *Little or no contact with the opposite sex:* may have been out on a date but has never kissed.

II. *Limited experience of sexual activities:* has experience of kissing as defined in this research and may have experience of breast stimulation over clothes, but has never experienced this under clothes.

III. *Sexual intimacies which fall short of intercourse:* has experience of breast stimulation under clothes and may have experienced genital stimulation or genital apposition, but has no experience of sexual intercourse.

IV. *Sexual intercourse with only one partner.*

V. *Sexual intercourse with more than one partner.*

These five stages of sex experience are used throughout this report. In this chapter these stages are examined by age, area, social class and education; then the figures are weighted so that the intentional middle-class bias in our sample can be eliminated.

Table 3.7 shows the age of the boys who fall into each of these five stages of sex experience. This table shows that this is the critical age period; for most boys the extent of their sex experience will increase considerably during the span of these five years. If this sample is typical, then about 45 of the 135 fifteen-year-old boys will have had sexual intercourse in the next four years (not including the six fifteen-year-old boys who have already had this experience).

One-third of the youngest boys are in stage I, but only 7 per cent of the oldest boys are at this stage. Conversely 3 per cent of the youngest boys are at stage V, but one-third (33 per cent) of the oldest boys are at this stage.

Table 3.7 *Sexual experience of 934 boys analysed by age*

Sex experience	Age					
	15, %	16, %	17, %	18, %	19, %	Total, %
I	33	22	9	8	7	16
II	49	40	37	24	23	35
III	13	29	29	37	33	29
IV	1	2	5	9	4	5
V	3	6	20	23	33	15
TOTAL	100	100	100	100	100	100
No. (100%)	135	250	217	235	97	934

Table 3.8 *Sexual experience of 939 girls analysed by age*

Sex experience	Age					
	15, %	16, %	17, %	18, %	19, %	Total, %
I	16	9	4	6	2	7
II	56	54	48	39	35	46
III	23	30	37	42	40	35
IV	4	5	8	9	10	7
V	2	2	3	3	13	5
TOTAL	100	100	100	100	100	100
No. (100%)	140	237	237	233	92	939

The same information for girls is given on table 3.8. Only a few girls are at stage I. Even among the fifteen-year-olds there are only 16 per cent and the number drops rapidly beyond that age until only 2 per cent of the oldest girls are at stage I. Most of the girls aged fifteen, sixteen and seventeen are in stage II, and the majority of eighteen- and nineteen-year-olds have reached stage III, although even at these ages over a third of the sample remain in stage II. As noted in section D the number of girls with sexual experience is much lower than the boys, but it tends to increase with age in the same way. Only 2 per cent of the fifteen-year-olds are in stage V, whereas 13 per cent of the nineteen-year-olds have had intercourse with more than one person. These are also momentous years for girls and, like the boys, this is the age when they are learning new sexual experiences, and so moving from one end of the scale towards the other. About half the 100 fifteen-year-old girls at stages I and II will have moved on to stage III or higher before they are twenty. But for the girls, and not for the boys, there is a barrier between stages III and IV, and a large number remain at stage III.

Table 3.9 shows the percentage at each stage of sex experience for younger and older boys and girls in the seven areas visited by the research team. The average number seen in each area was 468 and the average size of each age/sex group was 67, so these percentages are based on fairly small figures. The table suggests that the boys in London are more sexually active than elsewhere; but the difference between the London girls and the others is not so marked. In the three B areas more teenagers are in stages IV and V than in the A areas; on the other hand there are more teenagers from the A areas in stage III. London C seemed to have provided an unusually large number of stage II older girls; this was the first area visited and it is possible that the inexperienced interviewers missed several girls who should have been in stage III or higher. Apart from these differences there is a remarkable similarity in the figures of the seven areas.

The stages of sex experience in three social classes are shown in figure 3.5. These social classes are based on the Registrar-General's table of five occupational classifications which depend upon the occupation of the fathers of the teenagers. Those in RG classes I and II are the children of professional men, managers and supervisors; those in RG class III are the children of non-manual workers and skilled manual workers; those in RG classes IV and V are the children of semi-skilled and unskilled manual workers.

Figure 3.5 shows that there were more middle-class girls in stage III. Among the younger girls there were a few more working-class girls in stages IV and V, but in the older group there is practically no difference in the number of girls who have experienced sexual intercourse. Among the boys there are signs that the working class

Table 3.9 *Stages of sexual experience analysed by area for the four age/sex groups*

Younger boys

Stage of sex	Areas							
	London A, %	London B, %	London C, %	South A, %	South B, %	North A, %	North B, %	All areas, %
I	21	15	19	33	27	29	11	22
II	37	37	35	41	43	41	54	41
III	27	28	27	21	21	25	22	25
IV	2	3	2	0	1	2	5	2
V	13	16	16	4	6	3	6	9
TOTAL	100	100	100	100	100	100	100	100
No. (100%)	82	67	63	70	70	63	63	478

Older boys

Stage of sex	Areas							
	London A, %	London B, %	London C, %	South A, %	South B, %	North A, %	North B, %	All areas, %
I	15	3	11	5	7	11	7	9
II	18	19	18	36	43	37	22	28
III	34	23	34	36	29	35	42	33
IV	2	8	8	6	8	5	13	7
V	31	47	26	17	13	12	16	23
TOTAL	100	100	100	100	100	100	100	100
No. (100%)	65	62	61	64	72	65	67	456

Table 3.9 (cont.) *Stages of sexual experience analysed by area for the four age/sex groups*

Younger girls

Stage of sex	Areas							
	London A, %	London B, %	London C, %	South A, %	South B, %	North A, %	North B, %	All areas, %
I	9	6	15	21	7	8	5	10
II	41	59	63	46	54	56	64	54
III	45	29	19	31	28	28	26	30
IV	1	6	3	1	8	5	4	4
V	4	0	0	1	3	3	1	2
TOTAL	100	100	100	100	100	100	100	100
No. (100%)	74	68	60	70	72	64	67	475

Older girls

Stage of sex	Areas							
	London A, %	London B, %	London C, %	South A, %	South B, %	North A, %	North B, %	All areas, %
I	6	2	5	9	3	4	2	4
II	28	35	70	29	39	32	48	40
III	49	35	15	51	41	53	34	40
IV	12	19	8	7	13	7	8	11
V	6	9	2	4	5	4	8	5
TOTAL	100	100	100	100	100	100	100	100
No. (100%)	69	65	65	69	64	67	65	464

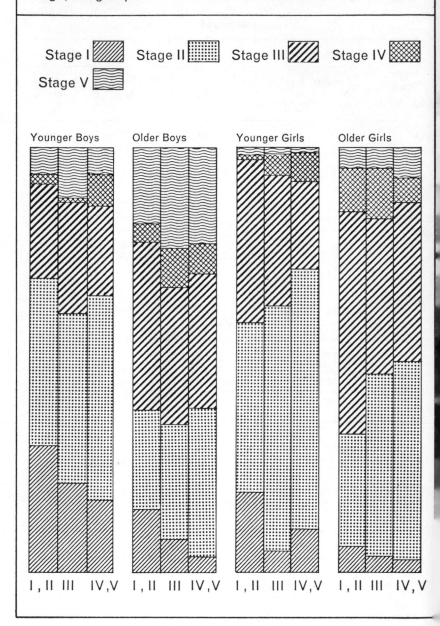

Figure 3/5
Stages of sex experience analysed by social class for four age/sex groups

Stage I ▨   Stage II ▦   Stage III ▨   Stage IV ▩
Stage V ▤

Younger Boys   Older Boys   Younger Girls   Older Girls

I , II III   IV,V   I , II III   IV,V   I , II III   IV,V   I , II III   IV,V are more likely to have intercourse before the others and there were more middle-class younger boys in stage I. There are more middle-class older boys in stage III and more working-class boys in stages IV and V. The association between social class and sexual experience is considered in more detail in chapter 8.

The influence of education is shown in table 3.10 where the stages of sex experience are related to the various types of school attended by the teenagers. Among the younger boys the percentages at each stage hardly varied from school to school with the exception of

Table 3.10 *Stages of sex experience analysed by school last attended for four age/sex groups*

Younger boys

Stage of sex	Secondary modern*	Compre-hensive	Grammar	Private	Technical	Total
I	18	20	35	23	19	22
II	45	39	34	35	43	41
III	23	30	26	29	29	25
IV	3	0	2	3	0	2
V	11	11	2	10	10	9
TOTAL	100	100	100	100	100	100
No. (100%)	276	54	96	31	21	478

Older boys

Stage of sex	Secondary modern*	Compre-hensive	Grammar	Private	Technical	Total
I	5	8	10	24	13	9
II	31	21	29	20	19	28
III	29	39	41	34	31	33
IV	8	11	8	2	6	7
V	27	21	12	20	31	23
TOTAL	100	100	100	100	100	100
No. (100%)	251	38	110	41	16	456

* Includes all-age schools.

Table 3.10 (contd.) *Stages of sex experience analysed by school last attended for four age/sex groups*

Younger girls

Stage of sex	Secondary modern*	Compre-hensive	Grammar	Private	Technical	Total
I	7	17	14	17	0	10
II	61	51	45	37	63	54
III	25	24	36	46	38	30
IV	5	5	3	0	0	4
V	2	2	3	0	0	2
TOTAL	100	100	100	100	100	100
No. (100%)	277	41	114	35	8	475

Older girls

Stage of sex	Secondary modern*	Compre-hensive	Grammar	Private	Technical	Total
I	3	0	9	6	0	4
II	48	41	27	26	36	40
III	32	35	55	52	45	40
IV	11	15	6	12	18	11
V	6	9	3	4	0	5
TOTAL	100	100	100	100	100	100
No. (100%)	268	34	101	50	11	464

* Includes all-age schools.

grammar school boys who had far less experience than the others. The percentage of sexually experienced boys at independent or private schools is only 1 per cent less than for the secondary modern and all-age schools; most of the latter group had started work at the time they were interviewed, whereas nearly all the younger boys were still attending their private schools when they were interviewed by our research workers.

Among the older boys the difference between schools is more pronounced. The boys who went to secondary modern or comprehensive schools had the most sexual experience, and the grammar and private schoolboys had the least. It is surprising to find that 24 per cent of the older boys educated at private schools were still at stage I, as middle-class boys reach physical maturity earlier than working-class boys (Tanner, 1962). This suggests that social pressures are stronger than physical growth. But this generalisation should not be emphasised too much because 34 per cent of the private school boys are at stage III and 22 per cent have experienced sexual intercourse.

The number of sexually experienced younger girls is small when distributed over a table of this size and so conclusions cannot be drawn from the numbers in stages IV and V. But there does seem to be some indication that secondary modern and comprehensive girls pass more quickly from stage II to stage IV or V than grammar or private school girls of this age who seem more likely to remain at stage III for a longer period.

The older girls follow the same pattern. Like the younger girls the ex-secondary modern and ex-comprehensive girls are high at stage II and stage IV, whereas the grammar and private school girls are high at stage III. This suggests that the better-educated girls are prepared to allow more sexual intimacies as long as these stop short of sexual intercourse.

The figures for technical school girls and boys of both age groups are given in table 3.10 and figure 3.6, but the numbers are too small to be used as an indication of possible trends. A comparison of the other four types of schools suggests that boys at grammar and private schools start their sexual experience later, perhaps because they have less free time and less money to take girls out. This also applied to the grammar school girls but not, surprisingly, to the private school girls.

H. WEIGHTED INCIDENCE FIGURES

In order to get adequate numbers of middle-class teenagers in our sample, three of the seven areas were chosen particularly because we expected to find a large proportion of middle-class girls and boys in them. As the middle-class adolescents were over-represented in our sample, the incidence figures given in this chapter may not be exactly like those one would expect to find in a sample which was strictly representative of the whole teenage population.

In this section we shall attempt to redress the balance by removing the middle-class bias that we deliberately introduced. This can be done by comparing one of the basic characteristics in our sample

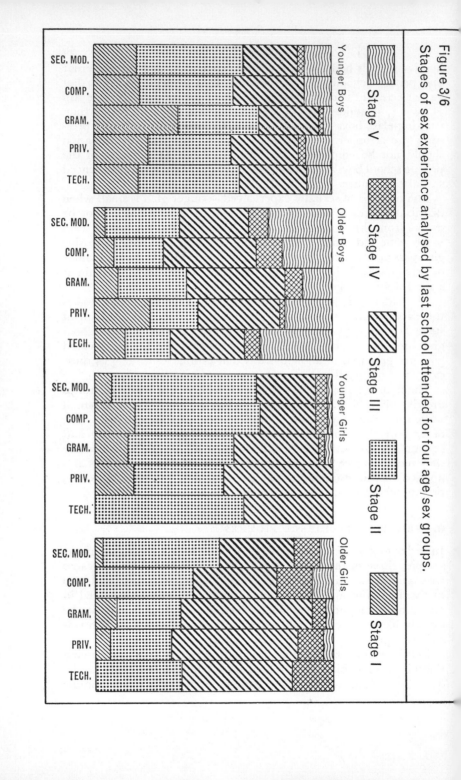

Figure 3/6
Stages of sex experience analysed by last school attended for four age/sex groups.

Stage V

Stage IV

Stage III

Stage II

Stage I

Younger Boys
SEC. MOD.
COMP.
GRAM.
PRIV.
TECH.

Older Boys
SEC. MOD.
COMP.
GRAM.
PRIV.
TECH.

Younger Girls
SEC. MOD.
COMP.
GRAM.
PRIV.
TECH.

Older Girls
SEC. MOD.
COMP.
GRAM.
PRIV.
TECH.

with the same characteristics in the total population as given in tables of national statistics. Then the incidence figures obtained in our research can be 'weighted' so that the characteristic has the same distribution in our sample as it has in the total population.

Ideally the characteristic to be used would be social class as classified by the Registrar-General. Unfortunately the national figures of the distribution of social class are not available even four years after the last Census. However there is another characteristic which has been shown to be highly associated with social class (Douglas, 1964) and this is the type of secondary school attended. The distribution of fourteen-year-old children attending various types of secondary schools is published each year by the Ministry of Education. Tables 3.11 and 3.12 give the percentages for the whole population, and then the percentages in our sample. The third columns of these tables show the weighting ratio (W) which should be applied to each person in our sample according to the type of school attended; this statistical exercise will change the proportions of social class in our sample, and so make it more like the total teenage population.

Table 3.11 *Type of school attended in the national population* compared with type of school attended in this research and the calculated ratio (W) for older boys and girls*

| Type of school | Older boys | | | Older girls | | |
	National, %	Sample, %	W	National, %	Sample, %	W
All-age and secondary modern	66	55	1·20	67	58	1·15
Grammar and direct grant	19	24	0·79	20	22	0·91
Technical	5	4	1·25	3	2	1·50
Comprehensive	3	8	0·38	3	7	0·43
Private	7	9	0·78	7	11	0·64
TOTAL	100	100	—	100	100	—
No. (100%)	346,875	456	—	331,693	464	—

* From the *Educational Record* of 1959, i.e. when eighteen-year-old boys in 1963 were fourteen.

E

Table 3.12 *Type of school attended in the national population* compared with type of school attended in this research and the calculated ratio (W) for younger boys and girls*

Type of school	Younger boys			Younger girls		
	National, %	Sample, %	W	National, %	Sample, %	W
All-age and secondary modern	67	58	1·15	67	59	1·14
Grammar and direct grant	19	20	0·95	20	24	0·83
Technical	4	4	1·0	2	2	1·0
Comprehensive	4	12	0·33	4	8	0·50
Private	6	6	1·0	7	7	1·0
TOTAL	100	100	—	100	100	—
No. (100%)	378,752	478	—	365,075	475	—

* From the *Statistics of Education* 1961, i.e. when sixteen-year-old boys in 1963 were fourteen.

Table 3.13 *The difference (D) between the sample results (S) and weighted results (W) for stages of sex experience in four age/sex groups*

Stages of sex	Boys						Girls					
	Younger			Older			Younger			Older		
	S, %	W, %	D	S, %	W, %	D	S, %	W, %	D	S, %	W, %	D
I	22	22	0	9	8	+1	10	9	+1	4	4	0
II	41	42	−1	28	29	−1	54	55	−1	40	42	−2
III	25	24	+1	33	32	+1	30	30	0	40	38	+2
IV	2	2	0	7	7	0	4	4	0	11	11	0
V	9	9	0	23	24	−1	2	2	0	5	5	0

Tables 3.11 and 3.12 show that we had more than the average number of boys at comprehensive, grammar and private schools, and less than the average at all-age, secondary modern and technical schools. The comprehensive and grammar school girls were over-represented in our sample, and the all-age and secondary modern girls were under-represented.

The difference between the percentages found in each stage of sex experience and the weighted percentages are shown in table 3.13. This shows that our complicated weighting procedure has made very little difference to the results. In only two cases do the sample percentages vary by more than 1 per cent, and in the other cases it has had practically no effect at all. Therefore we feel justified in concluding that the results we obtained in our sample would not have been much different if we had been able to obtain a much larger sample from a much wider area. We believe our results provide a good indication of the sexual behaviour of all teenagers in this country.

4 EARLY EXPERIENCES

A. THE FIRST CONTACTS

Less than 5 per cent of the teenagers had been out on their first date before they were twelve, but by the age of thirteen a quarter of the boys and almost a third of the girls had already had their first date. Before they reached sixteen, over 70 per cent of the boys and over 85 per cent of the girls had experienced dating. Therefore most teenagers make their first serious contact with the opposite sex between twelve and thirteen.

The first date was usually a visit to the cinema. Just over half (51 per cent) of the adolescents went to the cinema; the next popular place, but a long way behind, was outdoors – altogether 15 per cent went for a walk or met their first date outdoors. People also went to a dance (6 per cent) or a party (4 per cent) on their first date. About 3 per cent went to a club and 2 per cent stayed at home; the rest (19 per cent) did something else, or could not remember, or had never been out on a date.

Though a few have been kissed but have not been out on a date, and still fewer have dated but not kissed, by and large the two activities seem to start at the same age. Less than 3 per cent can remember kissing before the age of twelve. Almost a quarter (23 per cent boys, 25 per cent girls) had their first kiss before they were fourteen. By sixteen 70 per cent of the boys and 80 per cent of the girls had experienced a kiss as defined in this research. As in dating the boys were slower than the girls to start this activity.

It seems possible that the first time a teenager experiences a kiss with any kind of sexual component in it is at the end of the first date when, in some social circles, the goodnight kiss is obligatory. In this sample 20 per cent said they had their first kiss on the doorstep, 18 per cent in the cinema, 17 per cent outdoors and 10 per cent at parties. Neither school nor youth clubs are likely places, as some people have feared; in the whole sample only 2 per cent had their first kiss at school, and 1 per cent at a youth club.

The similarity of the figures has shown that kissing and dating is likely to occur at the same age, perhaps on the same day. This association was further explored when the teenagers were asked if they usually kissed a girl (boy) the first time they went out with her (him). Nearly 40 per cent said they did; a quarter (22 per cent boys, 27 per cent girls) replied fairly definitely, sometimes indignantly, that they did not; one in ten (12 per cent boys, 8 per cent girls) implied that it depended on the circumstances, and 5 per cent of the boys said they did if they got the chance. So for over half the teenagers a kiss on the first date with a new friend is a possibility, and for most of these it is a probability.

Deep kissing is a much less common activity and both boys and girls start this much later. Less than 16 per cent had experienced this before the age of fifteen (compared with 51 per cent who had kissed). The girls were quicker to learn this activity; by the age of eighteen 77 per cent of the older girls had experienced deep kissing compared with 61 per cent of the older boys.

Breast stimulation over clothes is an activity that the boys learnt before deep kissing; 6 per cent had done this before the age of fourteen, whereas only 3 per cent had experienced deep kissing. There is no difference between the two activities as far as the girls are concerned; 3 per cent had experienced breast stimulation over clothes before the age of fourteen, compared with the 4 per cent who had experienced deep kissing. Over a third (36 per cent) of the fifteen-year-old boys claimed to have fondled a girl's breasts over her clothes, and more than a third (38 per cent) of the fifteen-year-old girls admitted that this had been done to them. Thenceforward the girls and boys continue to have their first experience of breast stimulation at about the same age.

This section has shown that these stage II activities tend to be learnt earlier by the girls than the boys. Over a quarter of the boys and a third of the girls will have experienced kissing, deep kissing and breast stimulation over clothes before they are sixteen. Nearly half the boys and over half the girls will have participated in all these stage II activities before the age of seventeen.

B. EARLY INCEPTIVE BEHAVIOUR

At this point it is convenient to introduce the term *inceptive* to cover all the behaviour previously described as being at the third stage of sex experience, namely, breast stimulation under clothes, active and passive genital stimulation and genital apposition.

As expected these inceptive activities tend to start later as they require privacy and involve a certain amount of undressing. Less than 4 per cent of the boys and under 1 per cent of the girls had started breast stimulation under clothes before they were fourteen; 12 per cent of the boys and 8 per cent of the girls had started by fifteen. The girls continued to be behind the boys and at seventeen 60 per cent of the boys and 51 per cent of the girls had experienced it.

No girl admitted genital stimulation before the age of thirteen; 2 per cent of the boys had experienced both active and passive forms of this activity by fourteen. Thereafter there is a big sex difference with boys first learning the active part and girls first experiencing the passive part. In fact over three-quarters of the girls had never touched the genitals of a boy. It is clear that many of the girls who allow a boy to touch their genitals do not reciprocate.

Table 4.1 shows the location where three of these activities took place on the first occasion. As noted earlier the first kiss is most likely to be on the doorstep, outdoors or at the cinema. But the locations of the other two activities are more important because this inceptive behaviour leads to a greater intensity of sexual arousal, and is likely to take place in the kind of circumstance where intercourse also could take place.

Table 4.1 *The location of the first experience of three levels of activity for boys and girls*

Location	Kissing		Breast stimulation *		Genital stimulation †	
	Boys, %	Girls, %	Boys, %	Girls, %	Boys, %	Girls, %
Own home	2	5	3	9	3	7
Partner's home	4	3	15	9	14	7
Outdoors	19	17	10	8	7	5
Doorstep	15	26	1	2	1	1
Party	9	11	6	6	2	4
Cinema	19	17	4	5	1	1
Club	1	1	1	—	—	—
School	2	2	1	1	—	—
Car	—	—	1	5	1	4
Other or DK	12	9	7	4	4	3
N/A	17	8	51	51	67	68
TOTAL	100	100	100	100	100	100
No. (100%)	934	939	810‡	814‡	810‡	814‡

* These figures are for breast stimulation *under* clothes.

† This refers to *active* genital stimulation for the boys, and *passive* genital stimulation for the girls.

‡ These questions were asked in a different form in London C and so replies from this area have been excluded.

Breast stimulation under clothes is most likely to happen for the first time at the girl's home – according to the boys, and is equally likely to take place at the boy's or their own home – according to the girls. It also seems to have happened outdoors fairly frequently, and at parties less frequently. It very rarely happened at a youth club or at school.

The boys again report that the first genital stimulation happened in the home of their partners; the girls seem more reluctant to admit this and say it happened in either of the homes. It also took place outdoors sometimes, and very occasionally at parties. Hardly ever on the doorstep, at the cinema, at a youth club or at school. The girls report more activity in cars for both breast stimulation and passive genital stimulation. In fact only 10 per cent of the boys had the use of a car and more than a third of these were not in stage III–V. This suggests that some of the girls who experienced these activities in cars were going out with boys older than themselves, and in some cases with adults.

An overall look at the location of all these activities shows that the cinema, the doorstep and other places outside have been the first location for kissing, but the more serious inceptive activities took place outdoors sometimes but most often in a private home; even those listed in the category *party* have nearly always taken place at one of the teenager's homes. So places supervised by other adults, like school, club or cinema, figure low in the list, but the place where the parent is in charge is high on the list. It must be assumed that this sexual experimentation does not go on with the parents in the room, but it is clear that they cannot evade some of the responsibility.

C. HOMOSEXUALITY

Kinsey (1948), Westwood (1960) and others have shown that homosexuality is far from rare among young males, and so we could expect to find evidence of homosexual activities in this sample. But a research designed to get information about the homosexual histories of teenage boys would require a rather different approach than the one used in this survey which was designed primarily to find out about heterosexual experience.

Despite the widespread readiness of teenage boys to talk about most sexual matters, questions about homosexual activities often cause embarrassment, particularly if the boy is still involved in some way. Consequently we decided not to press these questions. We wanted to avoid the situation where one boy told other boys in our sample that they would be persuaded to talk about homosexuality if they agreed to an interview; this might put up the rate of refusals which would prejudice our chances of collecting representative information about heterosexual experiences.

About a fifth (21 per cent) of all the boys said they knew of homosexual activities among their school friends, and 5 per cent admitted they took part themselves. These figures are probably under-estimates. Westwood (1960) found that sexual play between boys aged thirteen to fifteen was usually a form of curiosity, and was not recognised or acknowledged as homosexuality by the boys themselves. After a phase of experimentation there was usually a latent period even for the boys who would eventually become adult homosexuals. Between sixteen and nineteen those with homosexual tendencies went through a period of shame and guilt combined with a strong determination to combat these inclinations. Only at a later age, usually in the early twenties, can the homosexual begin to accept himself and find his way to the homosexual coteries.

Therefore it can be seen that boys aged fifteen to nineteen will not readily answer questions about homosexuality, and information about these activities is more easily obtained by asking older people to look back to the time when they were teenagers.

Just under 2 per cent of the boys admitted to homosexual experience with adults, although 35 per cent said that at least one man had made sexual advances to them. In the attitude inventory 47 per cent of the boys agreed that homosexuals should be severely punished and 35 per cent disagreed with this statement. So many of the men who were alleged to have made sexual advances to these boys risked being severely repulsed. But it is not unknown for manifestations of friendship towards a boy to be mistaken for signs of homosexuality (Schofield, 1965).

Among the boys who had homosexual experiences with other boys there is little difference between the social classes. Homosexuality was slightly more prevalent at segregated schools, and much more prevalent at boarding schools. Among the boys 23 per cent said they knew of homosexual activities which had occurred at their segregated school (4 per cent admitted taking part themselves), compared with 17 per cent who said homosexual activities occurred at their coeducational school (5 per cent admitted taking part). At the boarding schools 44 per cent said homosexual activities between the boys were not unknown (28 per cent admitted taking part), whereas at the day schools 18 per cent said homosexual activities went on between the boys (only 3 per cent admitted taking part).

A similar trend was found in the girls' schools although the figures are smaller; homosexual activities occurred in 13 per cent of the segregated schools, 10 per cent of the coeducational schools; it was also reported in 39 per cent of the boarding schools and 11 per cent of the day schools. Kinsey (1953) found less homosexuality among the females he interviewed. We found 12 per cent who said there were homoesexual activities at school and 2 per cent who admitted taking part.

Slightly less than 1 per cent of the girls admitted homosexual activities with an adult, and 9 per cent said that a woman had made sexual advances to them. If these figures are credible, then it seems as if about one in ten girls to whom homosexual advances are made is likely to succumb, and about one in seven boys to whom homosexual advances are made may submit. But for the reasons given at the start of this section, and also because some of these percentages are based on small totals, it would be a mistake to attach much importance to any of these figures about homosexual activities.

D. THE FIRST EXPERIENCE OF SEXUAL INTERCOURSE

Very few (0·9 per cent) boys have sexual intercourse before the age of fourteen and even fewer (0·1 per cent) girls have this experience. Even before fifteen the figure is still less than 3 per cent for boys and less than 1 per cent for girls. Although some young teenagers appear to be sexually precocious and although the newspapers occasionally report cases where the age of a mother is fourteen and the putative father is the same age, our figures indicate that very early experience of sexual intercourse is rare. Among fifteen-year-olds 6 per cent of the boys and over 2 per cent of the girls had already had their first experience of sexual intercourse.

Tables 4.2 and 4.3 show the age of the partner compared with the age of the teenager at the time of his first experience of sexual intercourse. From the tables it can be calculated that 56 per cent of the sexually experienced boys had intercourse with a girl of about the same age, 31 per cent with older girls and 12 per cent with younger girls. Among the experienced girls, 33 per cent had intercourse with a boy of about the same age, 66 per cent with someone who was older and 1 per cent with a younger boy.

Girls who first had intercourse before they were seventeen almost always had an older partner; of the 19 per cent who started at fifteen, all but 3 per cent were with older people; of the 26 per cent who started at sixteen, all but 3 per cent were with older partners. The fourteen-year-old boys always started with older girls; the

Table 4.2[1] *The age of the partner compared with the age of 193 boys at the first experience of sexual intercourse (in percentages)*

Partner's age	Own age at first exp.				Total, %
	−14	15	16	17/18	
−15	9	11	5	0	25
16	1	6	17	7	31
17	0	2	6	14	22
18+	1	1	4	14	20
Adult	1	0	0	1	2
TOTAL, %	12	20	32	36	100

Table 4.3[1] *The age of the partner compared with the age of 102 girls at the first experience of sexual intercourse (in percentages)*

Partner's age	Own age at first exp.			Total, %
	−15	16	17/18	
−15	3	—	—	3
16	2	3	1	7
17	2	3	5	10
18+	11	10	22	42
Adult	1	10	27	38
TOTAL, %	19	26	55	100

fifteen-year-old boys were as likely to start with older girls as with those of the same age (9 per cent out of 20 per cent were with older, 11 per cent with the same age); the sixteen-year-old boys were more likely to start with girls of the same age (17 per cent of the 32 per cent were about the same age, 10 per cent older and 5 per cent younger).

Therefore a third of the boys and two-thirds of the girls are introduced to sexual intercourse by an older partner. In general the girls start later, but their partners are still older than they are. Further-

1. In tables 4.2 and 4.3 the dotted line encloses the percentage whose first experience of sexual intercourse was with someone of the same age.

more the number of male adults who have introduced girls to sexual intercourse is quite large (38 per cent of all those with this experience); the number of female adults who have introduced boys to intercourse is very small (2 per cent) – the proselytising older woman in search of virgin boys is either a myth, or very unsuccessful.

The teenagers were asked if they thought it was also the first time for their partner. Only 29 per cent of the boys and 21 per cent of the girls thought it was the first experience of sexual intercourse for both of them. Altogether 64 per cent of the boys thought their first girl was already experienced, and 70 per cent of the girls thought their first boy had previous experience of sexual intercourse; 7 per cent of the boys and 9 per cent of the girls were uncertain or unable to answer this question. Allowing for the fact that an experienced boy might be tempted to tell the girl that this was also the first time for him, and an experienced girl would be unlikely to volunteer the information that she was not a virgin, these results show a remarkably high number of cases where the partner was more experienced at the time of the teenager's first experience of intercourse.

Several other questions were asked about the first experience of sexual intercourse. For example, nearly all the girls (82 per cent) maintained that the boy on this first occasion was a steady; 16 per cent described the first partner as an acquaintance and only 3 per cent said the boy was a pick-up, i.e. someone they had met on the same day as intercourse took place. The figures for the boys are more equally spread over these three categories, probably because their idea of a 'steady' is quite different from the definition the girls would give. In fact 45 per cent of the boys described their first partner as a steady, 34 per cent as an acquaintance and 16 per cent as a pick up; only one boy (0·5 per cent) had his first experience with a prostitute; nine (4 per cent) others were unable to give a specific answer to this question. Although the girls may have been over-defensive when answering this question, even allowing for this, it seems likely that the first experience of intercourse for boys as well as girls was usually with a friend, and often with someone they knew very well.

Everyone who had experienced sexual intercourse was asked where they had met their first partner. The answers were various. Among the experienced boys, 18 per cent said they met the girl outdoors, 11 per cent at a dance, 10 per cent at a party, 8 per cent at school, 8 per cent at a club, 7 per cent at a cinema and 9 per cent said they had grown up together; the others (29 per cent) mentioned other places or else could not remember when they had met their first partner. Among the experienced girls 14 per cent had met the boy outdoors, 14 per cent at a dance, 11 per cent at a party, 6 per cent at a club, 5 per cent at a cinema and 7 per cent said they had grown up together; the others (43 per cent) mentioned other places or could not remember. Not much is to be learnt from these figures. Boys occasionally go out in groups to look for girls, and this seems to be the way they often met their first sexual partner, but it seems clear that there is no particular place where teenagers can expect to find sexual partners, and in the vast majority of cases they met their future sexual partners during the ordinary intercommunication among young people.

When one comes to look at the location where the first experience took place, the figures are more revealing. In most cases it seems to have happened in the home of the partner; among the boys the first experience was in the girl's home in 50 per cent of the occasions, and among the girls the first experience was in the boy's home in 43 per cent of the occasions; in addition to this a further 12 per cent of the girls had their first experience in digs or a flat occupied by the boy. This is in accordance with the finding that the first sexual partner is often older and, for both sexes, the initiation is more likely to take place in the home of the more experienced partner.

Occasionally it took place in the home of the girl or boy experiencing intercourse for the first time; 13 per cent of the boys and 15 per cent of the girls had their first experience in their own home. So in about two-thirds of the cases the first experience of sexual intercourse took place in the parental home of one or other of the partners concerned. The other places where the boys and girls had their first experience are shown in table 4.4.

No other place occurs as often as the parental homes of the teenagers; even in those cases where the first experience was at a party, this was usually at the home of one of the teenagers (but usually when his parents were out or away). The first experience which was outside was more likely to be in an urban park or the rural countryside for a boy, and more likely to be in a car for the girl; this reflects the much larger number of girls whose first experience was with an adult who was more likely than the teenagers to have a car.

Those who were sixteen or younger at the time of their first experience were more likely to be at a party or outdoors, whereas those whose first experience was at a home were usually older; 44 per cent of those at a party and 40 per cent of those outdoors were sixteen or younger, compared with 28 per cent at their partner's home and 24 per cent at their own home.

This suggests that the first sexual intercourse for the younger ones is more likely to be unpremeditated; for these people this first experience was less likely to take place in the comfort and privacy of their homes, but in a park, or a car, or during the uninhibited atmosphere of a party. This accords with a later question when the teenagers were asked if their first experience was 'planned beforehand or did it just seem to follow naturally from what you were doing?' Only 14 per cent of the boys and 15 per cent of the girls said it was planned, compared with 84 per cent of the boys and 82 per cent of the girls who said it was unpremeditated – 2 per cent of the boys and 3 per cent of the girls were uncertain.

Table 4.4 *The location of the first experience of sexual intercourse*

Location	Boys, %	Girls, %
Partner's home	50	43
Own home	13	15
Flat, digs	—	12
Party	7	9
Park, rural	10	3
Car	3	7
Other, NK	17	11
TOTAL	100	100
No. (100%)	193	102

The point was pursued still farther when the experienced teenagers were asked: 'Have you any idea why it happened?' This would be a difficult question for anyone to answer, especially as the interviewers were forbidden to prompt at this moment or help the teenagers to find the appropriate words. Naturally many of the replies were vague and inarticulate, but it was a good question in that it forced the teenager to look back, and their verbatim replies can be classified fairly easily into six main categories.

Their replies reveal the big difference in attitude between the two sexes. The boys were most likely to reply that they were impelled by sexual desire (46 per cent) whereas the girls were more likely to say they were in love (42 per cent). This would confirm the suspicions of those who see the male as essentially a predatory animal whereas the female is amative and romantic. However, despite the difference in the two outlooks, both are intrinsically based on the sexual appetite, and indeed 16 per cent of the girls gave this as the reason (table 4.5).

A large number of boys (25 per cent) and quite a few girls (13 per cent) were driven towards their first experience for reasons that can best be summed up by the word *curiosity*. Admonitory articles in the press and hand-wringing by important people have given some adolescents the impression that the average teenager is sexually experienced, and some of these boys and girls must have wondered why they were exceptional and whether they were missing something.

Table 4.5 *The reason for the first experience of sexual intercourse*

Reason given	Boys, %	Girls, %
Sexual appetite	46	16
In love	10	42
Curiosity	25	13
Drunk	3	9
Others	4	8
DK and NK	12	12
TOTAL	100	100
No. (100%)	193	102

A few boys (3 per cent) and more girls (9 per cent) said they were under the influence of drink at the time when they first had sexual intercourse. Two girls said they had their first experience because they were bored. No one gave drugs as a reason and indeed the drugs usually associated with teenagers (marihuana and drinamyl) are more likely to decrease sexual desire (Finestone, 1957).

Although it has been shown that for both boys and girls the partner is often older and more experienced at the time of first intercourse, yet there is little evidence that the teenagers were pushed into this against their will. Not surprisingly more girls (34 per cent) than boys (5 per cent) said they were persuaded to participate, but only one girl said she was forced into it. None of the girls were paid for their first experience and most (65 per cent) of the girls and nearly all the boys (95 per cent) stated that they were quite willing.

But this first experience was not always an unqualified success and did not always result in sexual gratification. Less than half the boys (48 per cent) and less than a third of the girls (30 per cent) said they liked it when they were asked for their reactions to this first experience of sexual intercourse. On the other hand 7 per cent of the boys and 7 per cent of the girls said they actively disliked it, while 14 per cent of the boys and another 7 per cent of the girls said they were disappointed. These and the other answers to the question ('What were your reactions?') are classified in table 4.6.

Table 4.6 *The reactions to the first experience of sexual intercourse*

Reaction	Boys, %	Girls, %
Liked	48	30
Disliked	7	7
Ashamed	10	25
Afraid	5	15
Disappointed	14	7
Unworried	2	9
No reaction	14	7
TOTAL	100	100
No. (100%)	193	102

The boys were more likely to express their feelings in terms of pleasure and enjoyment, or the lack of it. The girls were more inclined to describe their later reactions after the sexual excitement was over. It is interesting to see that among the girls more were ashamed (25 per cent) than afraid (15 per cent) and even among the boys 10 per cent felt ashamed. Leaving aside those who did not express a strong opinion either way, it still leaves over a third of the boys (36 per cent) for whom the first experience of sexual intercourse was not a success – that is, nearly half of all those boys who expressed an opinion. The equivalent figures for girls show that 54 per cent – that is, two-thirds of all those who expressed an opinion – were disenchanted with their first experience. These are unexpectedly high figures, especially for the boys who might have been reluctant to admit to the interviewer that they did not immediately take to sexual intercourse like a duck to water.

More specifically the teenagers were asked if they came to a climax during their first experience of sexual intercourse. Not everyone understood the word *climax* and in some cases it might have been inappropriate to go into detailed explanations, but the interviewers managed to make themselves understood in all but 14 (5 per cent) cases.

Not surprisingly the boys were much more likely than the girls to have an orgasm. Indeed it is possible that boys often reach a climax too soon at the first experience of sexual intercourse. Of the 193 experienced boys, 81 per cent said they reached a climax, 17 per cent said they did not and 2 per cent were uncertain. Only 28 per cent of the 102 experienced girls reached a climax, while 62 per cent said they did not and 10 per cent were either unsure or did not understand the question. It seems probable that complete sexual satisfaction for both boy and girl is not a likely outcome of the first premarital sexual experience.

Table 4.7 *The number of teenagers and their partners who experienced an orgasm during their first sexual intercourse*

Orgasm experienced	Boys, %	Boys' partners, %	Girls, %	Girls' partners, %
Yes	81	48	28	75
No	17	31	62	12
DK or NK	2	21	10	13
TOTAL	100	100	100	100
No. (100%)	193	193	102	102

When they were asked if their partners had come to a climax, it is not surprising that some (21 per cent) of the boys did not know; even 13 per cent of the girls were uncertain. Table 4.7 gives the replies for the two questions on orgasm at the time of the first experience of sexual intercourse. This shows that 75 per cent of the girls knew that their partners had reached a climax and 31 per cent of the boys were aware that their partner had not. It seems likely, however, that some of the boys have been over-confident in their claim that their first girl reached a climax; on the other hand it has been noted that the boy's first sexual intercourse has usually been with an experienced girl.

As so many of them did not enjoy their first sexual intercourse, one is prompted to ask why they should continue to repeat the experience if it was not a success the first time. A few of them (6 per cent boys, 11 per cent girls) did not try again, and there was an interval of over six months for another 7 per cent of the boys and 6 per cent of the girls before they had their second experience. Moreover 7 per cent of the boys and 30 per cent of the girls said they were not interested when they were asked: 'How did you feel about having sex another time?'

But the disillusioned ones were in a minority. Most of them, girls as well as boys, were ready to try again; 73 per cent of the boys and 51 per cent of the girls said they wanted to repeat the experience after their first sexual intercourse, and within a month 54 per cent of the boys and 61 per cent of the girls had experienced sexual intercourse more than once; 7 per cent of the boys and 2 per cent of the girls had their second experience within twenty-four hours of the first. More girls (34 per cent) than boys (26 per cent) had sexual intercourse again within a week of their first experience (table 4.8). The girls may start later than the boys, and be more reluctant at first, but these figures and the next chapter on frequencies show that once they have crossed this barrier, they are not more inhibited than the boys.

Table 4.8 *The interval between the first and second experience of sexual intercourse*

Interval	Boys, %	Girls, %
One day	7	2
Up to a week	19	32
Up to 2 weeks	12	13
2–4 weeks	16	14
1–6 months	32	19
Longer	7	6
No more sex	6	11
DK or NK	1	3
TOTAL	100	100
No. (100%)	193	102

The teenagers were asked if they had intercourse with their first partner on more than one occasion. Table 4.9 shows that over half the boys (54 per cent) and three-quarters of the girls (76 per cent) repeated the experience with the same person. The relationship continued for some time in many cases, for 20 per cent of the boys

F

and 44 per cent of the girls had sexual intercourse with their first partners on more than five occasions. The boys, who in general were more likely to enjoy the first experience than the girls, were also more likely to move on to fresh fields and new conquests. Although the girls often felt unhappy about the first experience, they were prepared to try again with the same boy, sometimes for a considerable period. It is clear that, in some circumstances at least, the first sexual intercourse did not weaken or strain the relationship between the girl and the boy, and it may even have deepened and strengthened their association.

Table 4.9 *The number of boys and girls who repeated their first experience of sexual intercourse with the same partner*

Second and subsequent partners	Boys, %	Girls, %
Same partner, over 5 times	20	44
Same partner, up to 5 times	34	32
Second partner different	46	24
TOTAL	100	100
No. (100%)	131*	91*

* Excludes the 12 boys and 11 girls who have had only one experience of sexual intercourse.

This first experience of sexual intercourse was sometimes a fortuitous adventure. It took place, sometimes in their own homes, more likely in their partners' who were often older and usually more experienced. Nearly all of them, however, agreed that they were willing participants to the initiation, although the introduction, when it came, was unexpected for many of the younger ones. This first experience was not often a great success, but most of them went on to their second experience after a fairly short interval, often with the same person.

E. EARLY STARTERS

Is the adolescent who starts dating or kissing at an early age more likely to have premarital intercourse? Some connection between physical maturity and sexual behaviour is to be expected; for example, some teenagers develop physically much later than others and these boys and girls would tend to be older before they experienced sexual arousal. Although the physical facts do not, in themselves, mean that premarital intercourse is necessarily associated with early physical development, the following paragraphs of this section will make clear that early sexual behaviour and premarital intercourse are linked in some way.

Dating. Boys who started dating before the age of fourteen were more likely to have had experience of sexual intercourse. Girls who started dating before the age of fourteen were also more likely to be sexually experienced. In both cases those who started dating early are significantly different from the others ($p = 0.001$).[1] Boys who started kissing before the age of fourteen were more likely to have had premarital intercourse ($p = 0.001$), and this also applies to the girls ($p = 0.001$).

Breast stimulation. Boys who started breast stimulation under clothes before the age of sixteen were more likely to be sexually experienced, and so were girls who permitted this ($p = 0.001$).

Genital stimulation. Boys who had active genital stimulation and girls who had passive genital stimulation before the age of seventeen were more likely to have had premarital intercourse ($p = 0.001$).

For the purposes of this research, a boy who has had sexual intercourse at fifteen or earlier is said to be an 'early starter'. Only 2.3 per cent of the girls have had sexual intercourse by the age of fifteen, so for our definition of an early starter among the girls, we will advance the qualifying age by one year; therefore we define an early starter as a girl who has had sexual intercourse at sixteen or younger. In the whole sample 6.4 per cent of the boys and 5.4 per cent of the girls are early starters according to this definition. Taking into account only those who have had sexual intercourse, 33 per cent of the boys and 47 per cent of the girls are early starters. It can be shown that boys and girls who start intercourse early will also start other sexual activities at an early age. For example, among the boys:

Fifty-six per cent of the early starters had their first date at thirteen or younger compared with 31 per cent of the other boys with experience of sexual intercourse.

Fifty-two per cent of the early starters had their first kiss at thirteen or younger compared with 25 per cent of the other boys with sexual experience.

Ninety-three per cent of the early starters had experienced

1. For an explanation of these values of *p*, see section A of chapter 8.

breast stimulation at fifteen or younger compared with 41 per cent of the other boys with experience of sexual intercourse.

Forty-four per cent of the early starters had experienced active genital stimulation at fourteen or younger compared with 11 per cent of the other boys with experience of sexual intercourse.

Among the girls the same tendency is apparent. Those who have early experience of sexual intercourse are much more likely to start inceptive behaviour at an early age. For example:

Fifty-two per cent of the early starters dated at thirteen or younger compared with 40 per cent of the other girls with experience of sexual intercourse.

Forty-one per cent of the early starters had their first kiss at thirteen or younger compared with 28 per cent of the others with experience of sexual intercourse.

Fifty-five per cent of the early starters had experienced breast stimulation at fifteen or younger compared with 26 per cent of other girls with experience of sexual intercourse.

Forty-eight per cent of the early starters had experienced passive genital stimulation at fifteen or younger compared with 12 per cent of other girls with experience of sexual intercourse.

Thus we can say with some assurance that those who start minor sexual activities at an early age are more likely to have sexual intercourse before marriage. Furthermore those who have started premarital intercourse at an early age are more likely to have started other sexual activities earlier than their peers; and this is true not only of inceptive behaviour, but also of socially acceptable behaviour like dating and kissing.

F. CHARACTERISTICS OF THE EARLY STARTERS

This last section will attempt to see if there are any other differences between those who have sexual intercourse at an early age and the other experienced teenagers. We will use the same definition of early starters as before (i.e. boys whose first experience of sexual intercourse is at fifteen or younger; girls whose first experience of sexual intercourse is at sixteen or younger). It is important to remember that these comparisons are with the other sexually experienced teenagers – not with all the boys and girls in the sample. (The sexually experienced are compared with the others in Part III, chapters 8–12.)

We found that 4 per cent of the early starters and 11 per cent of the other experienced boys were still at school. Apart from these, 69 per cent of the early starters left school at the age of fifteen compared with 58 per cent of the other experienced boys. Therefore the early starters were more likely to leave school at the statutory minimum age; indeed the age of fifteen seems to be the critical age for these early starters as most of them have their first experience of intercourse during their last year at school or soon after leaving school.

The early starters were also more likely to come from working-class homes; 85 per cent compared with 77 per cent of the other experienced boys. Although there was little difference in religious affiliation, fewer early starters came from religious homes; 14 per cent of the early starters came from homes where one or both of the parents went to church compared with 22 per cent of the other experienced boys. The early starters were also more promiscuous; 86 per cent of them had more than one partner, compared with 73 per cent of the other experienced boys.

The early starters among the girls reflect the results found among the boys. For example, 70 per cent of the early starters left school at fifteen compared with 54 per cent of the girls who had sexual experience at seventeen or later; 89 per cent compared with 72 per cent came from working-class homes; 11 per cent compared with 16 per cent came from religious homes; and 45 per cent of the early starters compared with 28 per cent of the others had more than one sexual partner.

The first experience was less likely to be in a home (his own or his partner's), and more likely to be outside. This suggests that the first experience of sexual intercourse is more likely to be on the spur of the moment for early starters. When the boys were asked to suggest a reason why this first intercourse happened, a quarter of the early starters found it difficult to give any reason at all. This seems to reinforce the suggestion that this first experience was improvisatory. The most frequent reasons given by the early starters were sexual desire and curiosity, and these are also the reasons most often given by the boys who started later. But only 4 per cent of the early starters gave love as the reason whereas 14 per cent of the other boys gave this reason. Among the girls love was given as the reason by 30 per cent of the early starters compared with 48 per cent of the others. All the girls were less interested in sex and more interested in love than the boys, but the girls who were early starters were not so romantic as the others.

We found that only a few enjoyed their first experience of sexual intercourse, but the early starters, among both boys and girls, more often said they had enjoyed it. It seems as if age and maturity do not guarantee the success of the first experience.

Not unexpectedly the early starters were more likely to have people older than themselves as their first sexual partners. Among the boys the partners of the early starters were older in 39 per cent of the cases compared with 18 per cent of the others; among the girls 84 per cent of the early starters had older partners compared with 50 per cent of the others.

When the boys were asked to describe their first partners, it was found that 23 per cent of the early starters had a fiancée or a steady as their first partner, compared with 50 per cent of the others. In 44 per cent of the cases the partner of the early starters was classified as an acquaintance, compared with 27 per cent of the others. The partner was a pick-up for 27 per cent of the early starters compared with 15 per cent of the others. It was impossible to classify the answers of 6 per cent of the early starters or 8 per cent of the others. So the partners of the early starters are likely to be girls they have not known for long, usually about the same age or a bit older.

All the experienced girls were likely to claim that their first partner was a fiancé or a steady, but the early starters were less likely to make this claim. In fact 68 per cent of the partners of the early starters were steadies compared with 88 per cent among the others. While 23 per cent were acquaintances of the early starters compared with 12 per cent of the others; none of the others said their first partner was a pick-up, but one (2 per cent) of the early starters admitted this, and another 7 per cent did not answer the question in a way that permitted classification. So the girls who are early starters are less likely than the others to have their first sexual experience with a regular boy friend, and are more likely to have a casual acquaintance as their first partner, and it is usually someone older than they are.

This chapter has shown that dating and kissing usually starts between the age of thirteen and fifteen; the boy is most likely to take the girl to the cinema on this first date, and most adolescents of that age assume that a kiss is an integral part of the date. Deep kissing is a much less common activity and seems to start at about the same time as breast stimulation over clothes. All these are activities that the girls learn before the boys; by the age of seventeen nearly half the boys and over half the girls will have experience of these activities.

Inceptive behaviour consists of more intimate, less socially acceptable activities which require privacy. Now the boys are no longer lagging behind the girls, but tend to learn these activities at the same time as the girls, and sometimes earlier. The dominance of the boy in the sexual situation is more apparent, and he now plays the active part while the girl is passive. Among boys of fifteen, less than one in five (17 per cent) have reached the inceptive stage; among boys of seventeen over half (54 per cent) are at this stage, and at nineteen the majority (70 per cent) have inceptive experience (from table 3.7). The percentages among the girls is higher among the younger ones, lower among the older; 29 per cent of the fifteen-year-olds had reached the inceptive stage, 48 per cent of the seventeen-year-olds, and 63 per cent of the girls who were nineteen were at stage III or beyond (from table 3.8).

Very early experience of sexual intercourse is relatively rare. Some teenage girls are introduced to sexual intercourse by adults; this hardly ever happens to boys, but their first partners were often older and usually more experienced. So the first experience was usually an indoctrination by someone else for boys as well as girls.

The first experience of sexual intercourse usually took place in a parental home, often with someone they had known for a long time. Although rarely planned beforehand, there is very little sign of force or excessive persuasion. The boys were impelled by sexual desire, but most girls gave love as the reason; a few decided to try it because they were under the impression that most teenagers had premarital intercourse. Alcohol was hardly ever an influencing factor.

The majority did not get much enjoyment from their first experience; shame and fear were a common reaction among the girls, and disappointment was a common reaction among the boys. Boys nearly always reached a climax, but only a quarter of the girls did. Nevertheless most of them repeated the experience before long, often with the same person, and in some cases the association continued for a long time.

Finally it has been found that those who start dating, kissing and inceptive behaviour at an early age are also more likely to have early sexual intercourse, and there are a number of differences between these early starters and others who have later sexual experience.

5 FREQUENCY

A. THE INTENSITY OF DATING

The extent of teenage sexual experience can be measured in several ways. In the previous chapter we were concerned with those who started their sexual experiences at an age earlier than the average. In chapter 3 we reported on the incidence – the number of people who had experienced a particular activity. In this chapter we shall concentrate upon frequency – the extent to which a particular activity is practised. In particular we shall consider the frequency of four activities – dating, two forms of inceptive behaviour and sexual intercourse.

The first date a boy or girl arranges may be looked upon as the first serious socio-sexual activity and the more mature development of the activity is when the boy and girl decide to go steady, or become engaged. In between the extremes dating is recognised as a convenient social arrangement that gives a boy or girl a chance to know each other in the light of their different sexual outlooks.

In our sample girls began their dating at the mean age of 13·8 years, and boys began at the mean age of 14 years. Girls are also ahead in the number of dates they have, and in the number of enduring relationships. Table 5.1 shows the dating behaviour of the teenagers at three levels of intensity. For example, it shows that 7 per cent of the younger boys have been out with a girl once or twice, but have not been out with any girl three or more times; 12 per cent have taken a girl out at least three times, but not more than six; and 58 per cent of the younger boys have taken at least one girl out more than six times.

These levels of dating activity indicate that most teenagers go through an experimental period where they have a series of very short relationships before they start to date the same person with any regularity; the younger boys and girls want to try out several different types of partners, whereas the older ones are passing through this period and in time they come to prefer a longer association. Thus 78 per cent of the older boys have been out with the same girl more than six times compared with only 58 per cent of the younger boys; and 25 per cent of the younger girls have not been out with anyone more than six times, but this applies to only 8 per cent of the older girls.

As well as the difference between older and younger age groups,

Table 5.1 *Three levels of dating among boys and girls analysed by two age groups*

Maximum number of times partners were dated	Younger boys, %	Older boys, %	Younger girls, %	Older girls, %
None	22	7	9	4
1–2	8	6	3	2
3–6	12	9	13	2
7+	58	78	75	92
TOTAL	100	100	100	100
No. (100%)	478	456	475	464

there is a difference between boys and girls, for the latter seem to have many more enduring relationships; twice as many boys as girls have experienced only very short dating relationships, whereas 784 (83 per cent) girls have experienced long term relationships compared with 625 (68 per cent) boys. The difference between the sexes is shown even more clearly in table 5.2 where only the longer

Table 5.2 *The number of partners who have been dated more than six times analysed by four age/sex groups*

Number of partners taken out more than six times	Younger boys, %	Older boys, %	Younger girls, %	Older girls, %
1	41	23	25	14
2	19	25	22	15
3	12	17	13	20
4	6	9	11	7
5	9	5	6	10
6–10	9	13	13	19
10+	4	8	10	15
TOTAL	100	100	100	100
No. (100%)	274	351	359	425

relationships are considered (i.e. those who have taken out the same person more than six times).

This table is illustrated by figure 5.1 which is drawn as a cumulative frequency curve. This is made by simply accumulating the percentages from the bottom of the table. For example, 4 per cent of the younger boys have been out with more than ten partners, 22 per cent (4 + 9 + 9 per cent) have been out with five or more partners, and of course by definition all (100 per cent) have been out with at least one partner. These cumulative frequency figures will be used throughout this chapter as they reveal a similar pattern and illustrate a common trend in all the frequency distributions under discussion. In every case the figure is cumulated downwards so that the right-hand side illustrates the highest frequencies. Thus any point on one of these curves shows the percentage of teenagers *at or above* a certain level of frequency.

Figure 5.1 confirms that girls are more likely than boys to have a series of enduring relationships. Even the younger girls have more long relationships than the older boys, and the older girls are far ahead of the other three groups. For example, 44 per cent of the older girls have had at least five enduring relationships, whereas only 29 per cent of the younger girls, 26 per cent of the older boys and 22 per cent of the younger boys have had as many enduring relationships. This suggests that a girl seeks a longer, possibly more mature, relationship in her dating behaviour, while a boy prefers to be more diverse and less committed.

B. FREQUENCY OF GENITAL STIMULATION

In section D of chapter 3 it was reported that 37 per cent of the boys and 33 per cent of the girls had experience of either active or passive genital stimulation. But a few of these people have had this experience only once in their lives, while others engaged in this activity many times in the last year with several different people. Therefore besides knowing the incidence, it is useful to have information on the frequency, and this is best shown by the number of times the activity occurs over a specific period, and by the number of different people with whom it occurs. This information gives some indication of the depth of the experience, and the overall extent of inceptive behaviour among teenagers.

Only a few of those who have experience of genital stimulation take part in this activity very often. Figure 5.2 is a graph drawn from the accumulated percentages (constructed by the same method as was used in figure 5.1). It shows the percentages only for those

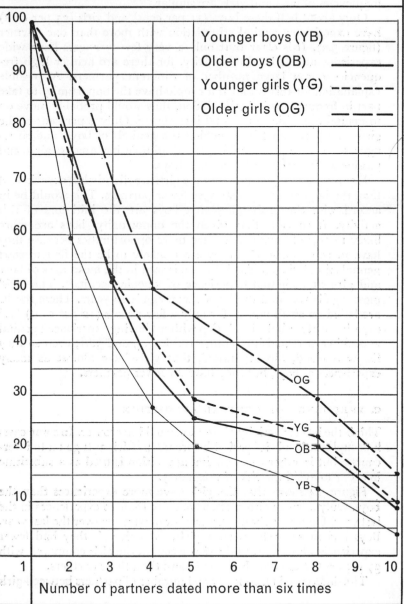

Figure 5/1
Cumulative frequency curve (cumulated downwards) showing the distribution of boys and girls in two age groups who have dated their partners more than six times by the number of partners they have dated

Younger boys (YB) ———
Older boys (OB) ——————
Younger girls (YG) — — — —
Older girls (OG) — — — —

Number of partners dated more than six times

who have reached this level of activity and not gone beyond it; i.e. 11 per cent of the boys and 12 per cent of the girls. Most of these teenagers had less than ten experiences in the last year, and the frequencies of boys and girls are similar.

Only about half these boys (51 per cent) and girls (35 per cent) have experienced genital stimulation with more than one partner (figure 5.3). It is clear that only a very few teenagers have wide experience at this level of activity, for there are neither high frequencies nor a large number of different partners. A possible explanation for this is that if a couple have the opportunity to take part in frequent genital stimulation, they would probably move on to genital apposition or sexual intercourse. Only 4 per cent of the girls have responded by touching the genitals of boys, and so no figures are given for active genital stimulation among girls and passive genital stimulation among boys.

Figures 5.2 and 5.3 show that the girls are slightly less experienced than the boys and they also have fewer partners. This would be in accord with the probability that boys are the initiators of this activity. It suggests that given the opportunity, boys are more likely to act; although girls have more opportunities because they have more dates, in fact they are unlikely to be the first to start genital stimulation. This difference is seen in the mean ages of boys and girls at their first experience of touching genitals. The girls' mean age is 16.6 and the boys' mean age is 16 years. These results are based on small figures for only a few people (12 per cent) had experience of genital stimulation without having experienced genital apposition or sexual intercourse (tables 3.5 and 3.6); even so they follow a trend, already noted, that girls have almost as many experiences as boys, but they have far fewer partners.

C. FREQUENCY OF GENITAL APPOSITION

This is the level of activity closest to sexual intercourse. In some cases it occupies only a brief period before the participants go on to intercourse, but in other cases genital apposition is used as a substitute in order to avoid the risk of pregnancy.

Figure 5.4 shows that the girls have more experiences than the boys. Only a few of either sex have more than 20 experiences in the last year. Figure 5.5 shows the number of partners over the last year. Boys had more partners than girls, even though they had fewer experiences altogether. Only 18 per cent of the girls compared with 37 per cent of the boys have had more than three partners.

The difference in frequency and number of partners between girls

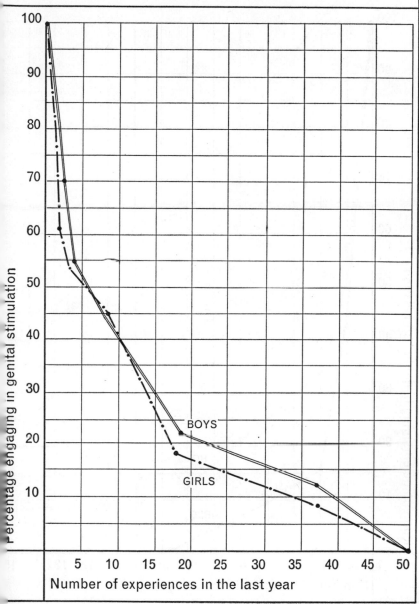

Figure 5/2
Cumulative frequency curve (cumulated downwards) showing the distribution of 88 boys and 81 girls with experience of genital stimulation by the number of occurrences in the last year

Percentage engaging in genital stimulation

BOYS

GIRLS

Number of experiences in the last year

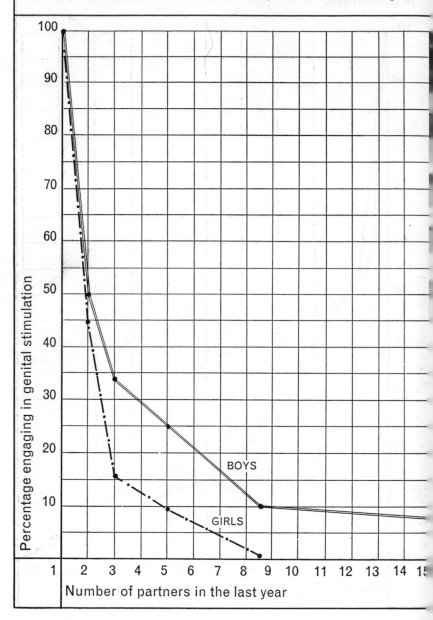

Figure 5/3
Cumulated frequency curve (cumulated downwards) showing the distribution of 88 boys and 81 girls with experience of genital stimulation by the number of partners in the last year

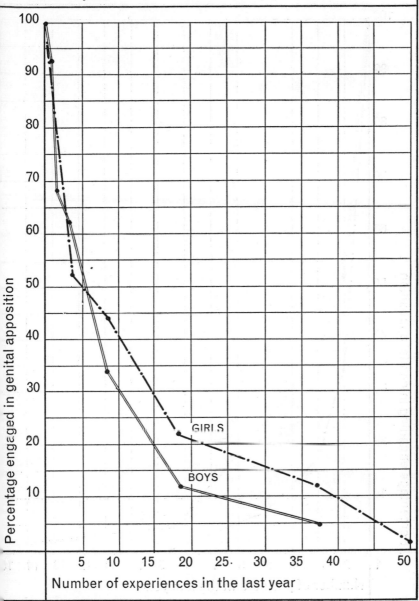

Figure 5/4
Cumulative frequency curve (cumulated downwards) showing
the distribution of 38 boys and 73 girls with experience of
genital apposition by the number of occurrences
in the last year

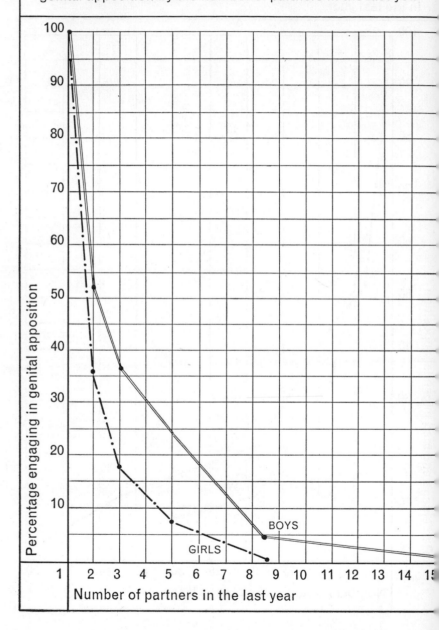

Figure 5/5
Cumulative frequency curve (cumulated downwards) showing
the distribution of 38 boys and 73 girls with experience of
genital apposition by the number of partners in the last year

and boys shows that girls tend to have more experiences with fewer partners, whereas the boys do not have genital apposition so often, but have more partners. The figures on incidence (chapter 3) may have given the impression that the boys are far more sexually active than the girls, but when the frequency figures are considered, they suggest that the total sexual outlet of girls is similar to that of boys.

D. TYPES OF PARTNERS DURING INCEPTIVE ACTIVITIES

All the teenagers who had taken part in genital stimulation or genital apposition, but had not gone on to sexual intercourse, were asked about their partners. Figure 5.6 shows the type of partner for genital stimulation, classified into five categories, and figure 5.7 gives the same information for genital apposition. In both figures the percentages add up to more than a hundred because some of the teenagers described several partners of different types.

In figure 5.6 the replies of the boys and girls are fairly similar, but the small differences amplify the conclusions drawn from figure 5.3 which showed that the boys had more partners and therefore tended towards a more casual type of relationship than the girls. These differences become more pronounced when we examine the type of relationship that existed between partners who had genital apposition in figure 5.7. Boys are more likely to have casual partners and this is consistent with the differences to be found in the number of partners in figure 5.5.

If we assume that no girl or boy has stated that they had genital apposition with a steady as well as a fiancé(e), then we can add the two longer types of relationships together. This would indicate that 60 per cent of the boys were intimate at this level compared with 84 per cent of the girls who permitted genital apposition with steady type relationships. There is a strong hint here of a fundamental difference of approach to sexual activities between girls and boys.

E. SEXUAL INTERCOURSE FREQUENCIES

At each level of sexual activity so far considered in this chapter, it has been noted that the girls tend to seek a more permanent relationship. This tendency is even more pronounced at the level of sexual intercourse. In actual incidence the boys are almost twice as active as the girls (chapter 3), but in figure 5.8, which shows how many times they had intercourse in the last year, the girls are more active than the boys. For example, 30 per cent of the boys were having intercourse about seventeen times in the last year, whereas

G

Figure 5/6
Types of partners of boys and girls with experience of genital stimulation

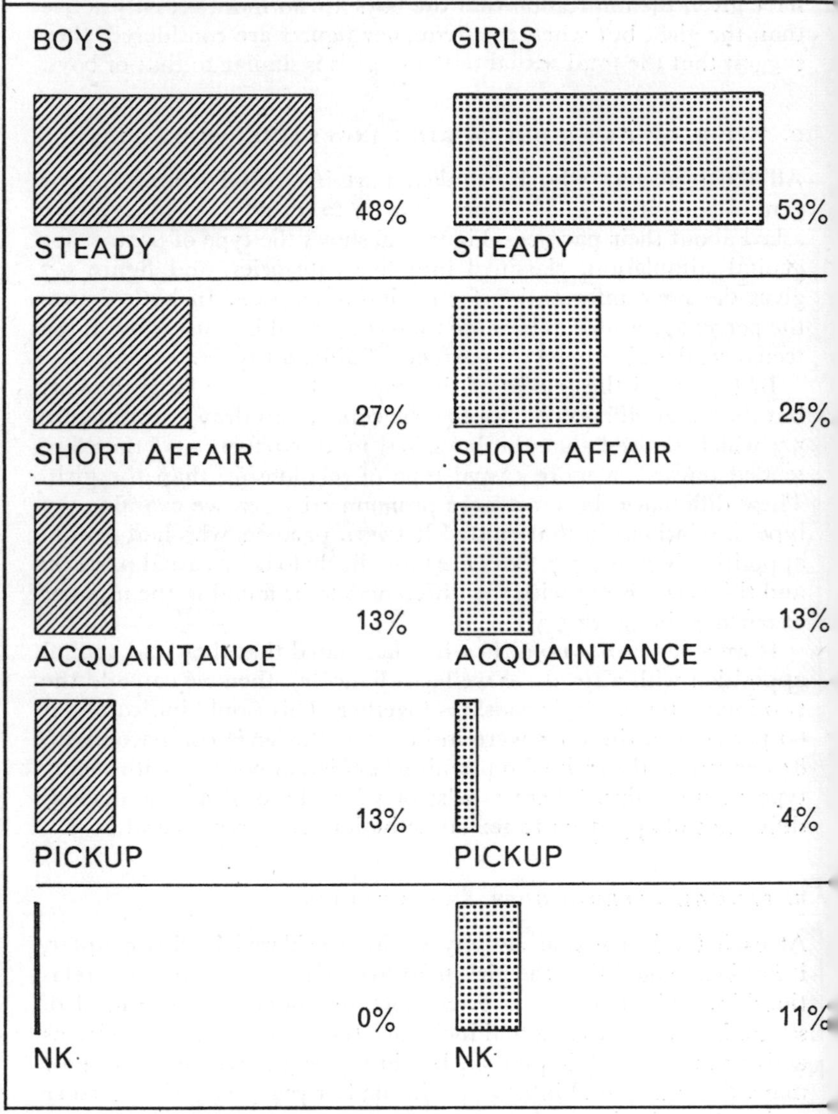

BOYS

STEADY 48%

SHORT AFFAIR 27%

ACQUAINTANCE 13%

PICKUP 13%

NK 0%

GIRLS

STEADY 53%

SHORT AFFAIR 25%

ACQUAINTANCE 13%

PICKUP 4%

NK 11%

Note: Interviewers recorded all the partners mention

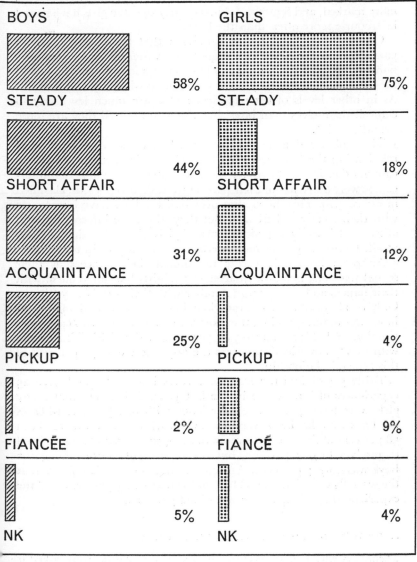

Figure 5/7
Types of partners of boys and girls with experience of genital apposition

BOYS
GIRLS

STEADY 58%
STEADY 75%

SHORT AFFAIR 44%
SHORT AFFAIR 18%

ACQUAINTANCE 31%
ACQUAINTANCE 12%

PICKUP 25%
PICKUP 4%

FIANCÉE 2%
FIANCÉ 9%

NK 5%
NK 4%

the percentages add up to more than a hundred.

30 per cent of the girls were having intercourse about forty times in the last year. Although about half of all the experienced teenagers have less than ten experiences in a year, as the frequencies of the other half get higher, the difference between boys and girls becomes more marked, and figure 5.8 shows clearly that the girls have sexual intercourse more often than the boys.

On the other hand figure 5.9 shows that the boys have more partners than the girls. This suggests that there is an inverse relationship between the number of partners these teenagers have and the number of times they have intercourse with any one partner. As in other levels of sex experience girls are much less likely to commit themselves than boys, but when committed they are more sexually active.

These observations are reinforced when we look at the type of relationship the boys and girls had with their partners. As in the case of other levels of activity those with experience of sexual intercourse were asked about their partners and their replies are classified in figure 5.10. This shows that over half the boys have intercourse with their steady girl friends. But they also have intercourse with others, particularly acquaintances and girls whom they do not know at all. Hardly any have had intercourse with a prostitute.

Although boys only rarely mentioned their fiancées as their sexual partners, nearly a quarter of the girls had intercourse with their fiancés and a very large number with their steady boy friends. Only two boys and one girl mentioned both a steady and a fiancé(e) in answer to this question, therefore we can add these two categories together and this shows that 86 per cent of the girls' liaisons were with steady boy friends whereas the boys show only 56 per cent of this type of relationship.

Table 5.3 divides the frequency rates into under and over 25 experiences of intercourse in the last year. This shows that many girls were having extensive experience with one partner, whereas the boys were having fewer experiences with more partners. Thus 58 per cent of the girls with more than 25 experiences had restricted themselves to one partner, but the equivalent figure among the boys was only 4 per cent. An approximate calculation shows that the sexually experienced girl had an average of 2·3 partners, and the experienced boy had an average of 6·2 partners.

F. REACTIONS TO SEXUAL INTERCOURSE

Teenagers who had experiences of sexual intercourse were asked if they enjoyed it and if they usually had a climax during intercourse.

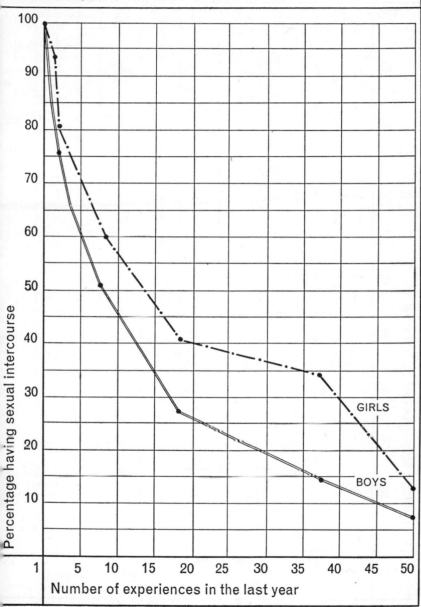

Figure 5/8
Cumulative frequency curve (cumulated downwards) showing the distribution of 193 boys and 102 girls with experience of sexual intercourse by the number of occurrences in the last year

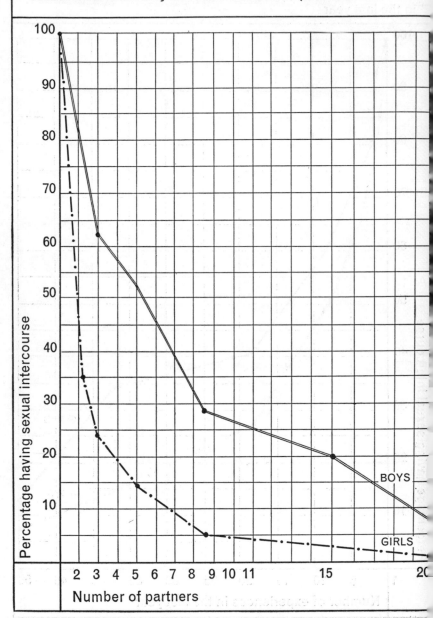

Figure 5/9
Cumulative frequency curve (cumulated downwards) showing the distribution of 193 boys and 102 girls with experience of sexual intercourse by the total number of partners

Percentage having sexual intercourse

Number of partners

BOYS

GIRLS

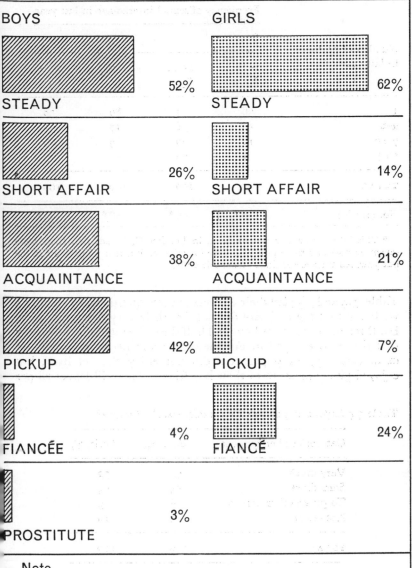

Figure 5/10
The type of partner classified into five categories of boys and girls with experience of sexual intercourse

BOYS   GIRLS

STEADY   52%   STEADY   62%

SHORT AFFAIR   26%   SHORT AFFAIR   14%

ACQUAINTANCE   38%   ACQUAINTANCE   21%

PICKUP   42%   PICKUP   7%

FIANCÉE   4%   FIANCÉ   24%

PROSTITUTE   3%

Note
Interviewers recorded all the partners mentioned, so the percentages add up to more than a hundred

Table 5.3 *The number of partners in the last year by the number of experiences of sexual intercourse*

Number of partners in last year	Frequency of sexual intercourse in last year			
	Boys		Girls	
	1–25, %	25+, %	1–25, %	25+, %
1	36	4	80	58
2–6	53	36	17	33
7–20	10	30	3	6
20+	1	30	—	3
TOTAL	100	100	100	100
No. (100%)	120*	23*	58*	33*

* This information was not obtained in London C; in addition there were seventeen boys and three girls who were experienced but had no partners in the last year. All these are excluded from this table.

Tables 5.4 and 5.5 give their answers to these questions. In chapter 4 we found that the majority did not like their very first experience, but three-quarters of the boys and half the girls stated unequivocally that they now enjoyed it. For the girls it was necessary to add an extra category, for 9 per cent did not enjoy the act itself, but enjoyed giving pleasure to their boy friend. This still leaves 28 per

Table 5.4 *Response to question: Do you enjoy sexual intercourse?*

Categories of enjoyment	Boys, %	Girls, %
Very much	72	52
Sometimes	23	23
To please other person	—	9
Not really	5	16
TOTAL	100	100
No. (100%)	193	102

cent of the boys and 39 per cent of the girls who did not always enjoy it, and some of these did not appear to enjoy it at all.

Table 5.5. shows that sexual intercourse among experienced teenagers is not always a success. Even among the boys only about half invariably have an orgasm, and over a quarter of the girls hardly ever or never reach a climax.

Table 5.5 *Response to question: Do you usually have a climax?*

Frequency of orgasm	Boys, %	Girls, %
Always	54	14
Usually	34	54
Hardly ever	4	3
Never	8	25
Don't understand	—	4
TOTAL	100	100
No. (100%)	193	102

Adults who criticise teenage morality always seem to assume that sexual intercourse is irresistible unless some form of restraint is put in the way. These figures show that other factors may be at work. Group pressures or a desire to be thought of as experienced and worldly may persuade some teenagers to take part in sexual intercourse although they do not really enjoy it; there may be strong pressures upon a boy to prove his masculinity, and upon a girl from the fear that she will lose the boy if she does not agree to intercourse. One can imagine a situation where neither the boy nor the girl really wants it, but both of them feel impelled to participate.

G. BOYS COMPARED WITH GIRLS

Two types of frequency have been examined:

1. The number of experiences over a measured period.
2. The number of partners.

This has revealed differences between girls and boys. Girls are much more likely than boys to sustain a relationship at each level of sex activity. In their dating behaviour girls begin at an earlier age than the boys, they have more boy friends and their relationships last longer. At the more advanced levels of intimacy the boys have more partners than the girls, but the girls are sexually more active. Girls prefer a more permanent type of relationship in their sexual behaviour. Boys seem to want the opposite; they prefer diversity and so have more casual partners. It might be said that the girls adopt a more rational approach considering the risk of pregnancy or venereal disease, but a more likely explanation is the emotional difference between boys and girls. The boy seeks adventure while the girl looks for security.

There is a hint, however, of a small pocket of less cautious girls who engage in more casual relationships. If we add the steady and fiancé categories in figure 5.10, they amount to 86 per cent of all the girls who have had sexual intercourse; this means that the remaining 14 per cent have only had intercourse with casual partners. Indeed 5 per cent of all the older girls (about a third of all those with experience) have had more than one partner, and a few of them have had a large number of partners.

The most important fact to emerge from this chapter is that the experienced girls are just as sexually active as the experienced boys, but there is a direct association between the type of relationship a girl has achieved and the degree of intimacy she will permit. Ehrmann (1959) also found that the sexually most active girls were those who were going steady. But this is not necessarily the case for boys, who have more partners and shorter less binding relationships. In this research it has been shown (chapter 3) that more boys have sexual intercourse, but this chapter reveals that those girls who do have sex, tend to have it more often than the boys.

6 KNOWLEDGE ABOUT SEXUAL MATTERS

A. CONCEPTION

All the teenagers were asked how old they were when they first found out about 'the facts of life'. After testing several other phrases, it was found that a knowledge of conception was best described in this way. The answers to this question are summarised in table 6.1 and figure 6.1. The mean age at which a boy learnt about the facts of life was 12·5 years and for a girl it was 12·2 years. Four boys said they did not understand conception and another eleven boys and two girls could not remember when they first found out about this. Apart from this, about a quarter of the boys and a third of the girls said they knew about the facts of life at the age of eleven or earlier. By thirteen two-thirds of the boys and three-quarters of the girls knew about conception. Whether or not their information was accurate is not relevant in this context; the important point is that most adolescents have heard at least one version of how babies are born soon after entering secondary school, if not before.

Table 6.1 *The age at which 934 boys and 939 girls first found out about the facts of life*

Age	Boys, %	Girls, %
Under 10	6	7
10–11	19	26
12–13	42	43
14–15	28	22
16–17	3	2
DK and never	2	0
TOTAL	100	100
No. (100%)	934	939

The source of this knowledge is shown in table 6.2. Most boys and girls learn about conception from their friends, usually through jokes. Table 6.2 shows that 62 per cent of the boys and 44 per cent of the girls learnt about the facts of life from school friends. In over

Figure 6/1
The age at which 934 boys and 939 girls first found out about the facts of life

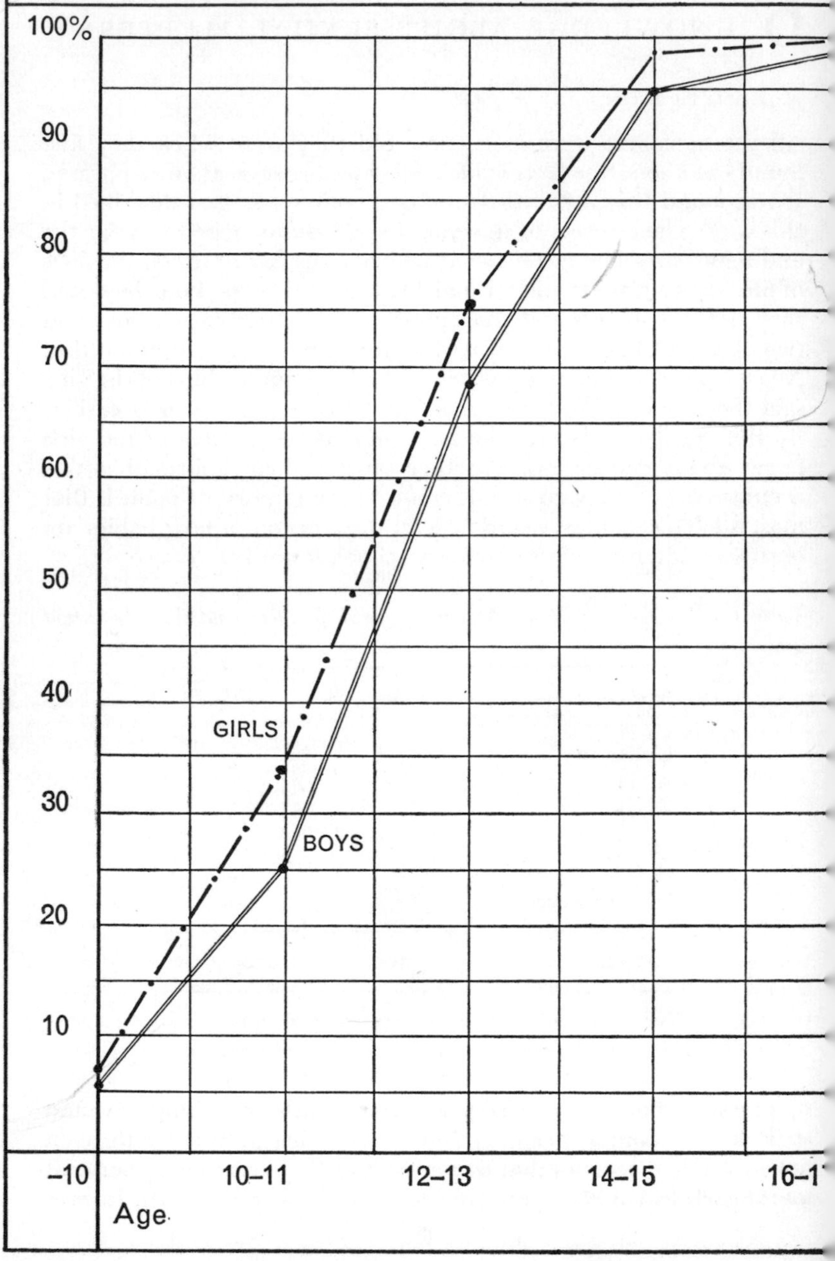

a quarter (27 per cent) of the cases the girls obtained this information from their mothers, but boys rarely learnt this from their
mothers. Fathers seem to have no role at all at this stage of their
daughters' education and sons do not fare much better. Only 7 per
cent of the boys learnt about conception from their fathers and the
same number obtained this information from books. Girls are still
less likely to learn from books and it appears that the many thousands of books published on this subject for adolescents (Dalzell-
Ward, 1960) are read after they have heard about conception from
other sources, if they are read at all. Teachers appear to fulfil a
more important role for both sexes and are the second most frequent
source for boys. Figure 6.2 summarises the sources of first sex knowledge and shows the relative proportions of the sources.

Table 6.2 *The source of knowledge about conception among 934 boys and 939 girls*

Source of knowledge	Boys, %	Girls, %
Mother	4	27
Father	7	1
Teacher	12	18
Sibling	1	2
Clergyman	1	0
Work mates	2	1
Other adults	2	1
Friends	62	44
Books	7	3
Other and N/A	3	2
TOTAL	101	99
No. (100%)	934	939

Figure 6.3 combines the source of the information with the age
when they first learnt about the facts of life. Those who learn from
friends or from parents tend to get the information early, while
those who learn from teachers are more likely to get the information
at fourteen or later.

The influence of the parents decreases. Those who feel that it is
up to the parents to give sex instruction should note that there seems
to be a maximum age when parents will do this. If the parents have
not instructed the child by twelve or thirteen, it becomes more and
more unlikely that they will ever do so.

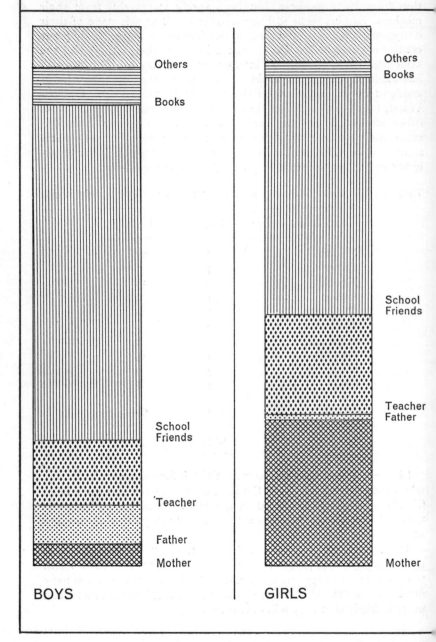

Figure 6/2
Source of knowledge about the facts of life

BOYS

Others
Books
School
Friends
Teacher
Father
Mother

GIRLS

Others
Books
School
Friends
Teacher
Father
Mother

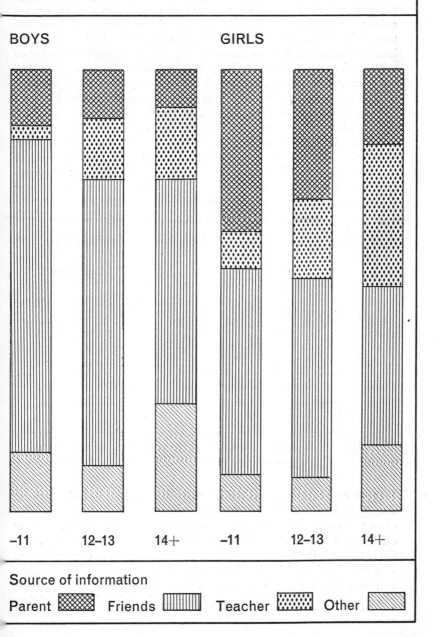

Figure 6/3
The source of knowledge about conception analysed by the age of finding out

BOYS   GIRLS

-11   12-13   14+   -11   12-13   14+

Source of information

Parent ▨▨▨   Friends ▦▦▦   Teacher ▩▩▩   Other ▥▥▥

As other studies (Spinley, 1953; Newson, 1963) have shown, there are differences in upbringing between the social classes. Table 6.3 separates age of early sex knowledge into three social classes using the Registrar-General's classifications. The differences between the mean ages when boys and girls receive their first knowledge of conception vary considerably. Only a small minority of middle-class girls were first informed as late as fourteen years old, whereas over a quarter of the girls in other classes were fourteen when they first found out. Among the boys the differences between the classes is not so pronounced, but they also tended to learn earlier when they were in classes I and II. Children from clerical and skilled manual homes (class III) do not show such a large difference between the sexes, and much the same may be said of children from working-class homes (classes IV and V); approximately one-twelfth of the class I and II adolescents are late learners compared with a third of those in classes IV and V.

Table 6.3 *Age obtained information about conception analysed by social class*

Age	Classes I & II		Class III		Classes IV & V	
	Boys %	Girls %	Boys %	Girls %	Boys %	Girls %
Up to 11	30	44	24	28	24	31
12–13	47	47	41	44	39	36
14+	22	8	34	28	35	32
Never/DK	1	1	1	0	2	1
TOTAL	100	100	100	100	100	100
No. (100%)	218	237	497	501	219	201
Mean Age	12·3	11·9	12·7	12·5	12·7	12·5

Some commentators have suggested that sex is talked about more simply and naturally in working-class homes, and it is the middle-class parents who are reluctant to discuss sexual matters with their children. We found that the middle-class children were more likely to learn the facts of life earlier than the working-class children. The middle-class girls were in advance of the boys of their own class and well in advance of either sex in the other classes.

This class difference between girls may be related to age of first menarche, as Tanner (1962) has shown that middle-class girls tend to reach puberty before working-class girls. It is possible that some middle-class mothers feel that it is necessary to warn their daughters before their first menstruation and this in turn leads to an explanation of conception. It is possible, of course, that working-class mothers are equally anxious to forewarn their daughters, but find it more difficult to put this into words. Bernstein's (1961) work on the use of language has shown that there are wide social class differences in the way parents are able to make use of abstract terms and generic notions in order to instruct their children. It also seems to be true that middle-class parents are more affected by the new ideas in health education (Schofield, 1964) and are more likely to be aware of the importance of sex education. This is suggested by figure 6.4 which shows the source of knowledge analysed by social class. The middle-class mother is much more likely to have talked to her daughter about the facts of life; indeed middle-class girls are the only group who are more likely to have heard about conception from parents than from friends.

The middle-class boys and girls are more likely to learn from their parents. In class III the role of the parent as a sex educator diminishes compared with the parents of classes I and II. Still fewer boys and girls in classes IV and V learn from their parents.

The role of the school teacher becomes more important for working-class girls, but not the boys; nearly a quarter of the working-class girls heard about conception from a teacher. By far the most important source among working-class boys is their friends; about two-thirds of the boys learn the facts of life from people of their own age.

B. PARENTAL ADVICE ABOUT SEX

Besides being initiators of sex knowledge parents can also play a continuing role as sex educators. Everyone was asked if their parents ever gave them any advice about sex. In fact 67 per cent of the boys and 29 per cent of the girls replied that they had never had any advice about sex from their parents. It is possible that some of these adolescents were advised by their parents, but they did not listen, or perhaps found the advice so unacceptable that they dismissed it from their minds. Even so it is remarkable that over two-thirds of the boys and a quarter of the girls felt that neither of their parents had helped them to deal with the problem of sex.

The remaining 33 per cent of the boys and 71 per cent of the girls were questioned about the kind of advice they received from their

H

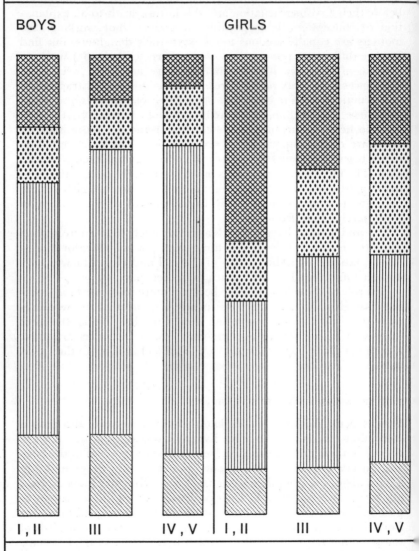

Figure 6/4
The source of knowledge about conception analysed by social class

BOYS   GIRLS

| I , II | III | IV , V | I , II | III | IV , V |

Source of information

Parent   Friends   Teacher   Other

parents and their answers were classified into five categories. These were operationally defined in the following way:

Biological – where reproduction was explained without reference to human physiology.

Physiological – where the differences between the male and√ female were explained without a discussion of sexual intercourse.

Technical – where reproduction was explained with a description of sexual intercourse.

Moral – where any reference to sex was accompanied by a parent or teacher saying some behaviour was right or wrong.

Other – for advice or information which did not fit easily into one or other of the above categories.

Table 6.4 shows the results of this classification. In some cases a boy or girl received advice that covered more than one of the categories so the percentages in table 6.4 add up to more than a hundred.

Table 6.4 *Advice about sex given by parents of 934 boys and 939 girls*

Type of advice	Boys, %	Girls, %
Biological	6	9
Physiological	10	34
Technical	13	12
Moral	12	53
Other	4	1
None	67	29

The number who received technical information was about the same for both sexes – 13 per cent of all the boys in the total sample and 12 per cent of the girls. But 53 per cent of the girls received moral advice compared with 12 per cent of the boys. It is difficult to escape the conclusion that although the girls received far more advice than the boys, it was vague and unspecific in most cases.

Most of the parents who gave moral advice did not give technical advice as well, but parents who gave technical advice also gave moral advice to their daughters in many cases, but less often to their sons. These categories give some indication of the kind of advice, but the quality and extent of the advice also varied considerably; to take two examples of this kind of advice, one parent merely told her daughter, 'no one wants soiled goods', while another mother instructed her daughter on the use of contraceptives.

C. SEX EDUCATION AT SCHOOL

When the teenagers were asked if they had ever received any sex education at school, over half (53 per cent) of the boys replied in the negative. Schools seem to be more concerned with giving sex education to girls than to boys. Altogether 86 per cent of the girls compared with 47 per cent of the boys had received some kind of formal sex education while they were at school.

Figure 6.5 shows the amount of sex education in three types of schools. The figures for technical and comprehensive schools are very similar to those shown for secondary modern and grammar. The girls more often received sex education than the boys in all types of schools except for private schools where many more boys received some sex education. Boys who attend grammar schools are no more likely to be given sex education than other boys receiving state education. The amount of sex education given to girls does not seem to vary among the different types of schools.

Although the amount of sex education is similar in all state schools, the type of education is more varied. The type of sex education has been classified into categories using the five definitions that were used in the previous section on parental advice. Figure 6.6 shows the kind of sex education given in the schools compared with the sort of instruction received from parents; the percentages have been calculated after excluding those who did not receive sex education or parental advice. The schools place more emphasis on biological information; the home on moral exhortation.

Table 6.5 shows the different categories of sex education in secondary modern, grammar and private schools; unlike figure 6.6 the percentages in this table take into account those who have not received sex education of any kind. This shows that one in three private school boys received technical information, but state-educated boys rarely received anything more than biological and physiological instruction. There was less difference between the schools as far as the girls were concerned; most of them received biological and physiological instruction, but few of them received technical information.

The figures in these categories cannot always convey the quality of the instruction. One girl reported that 'a teacher tried once; he started on about frogs, but after he had said about three lines on tadpoles and the fellows all laughed, he packed it in'. Another girl

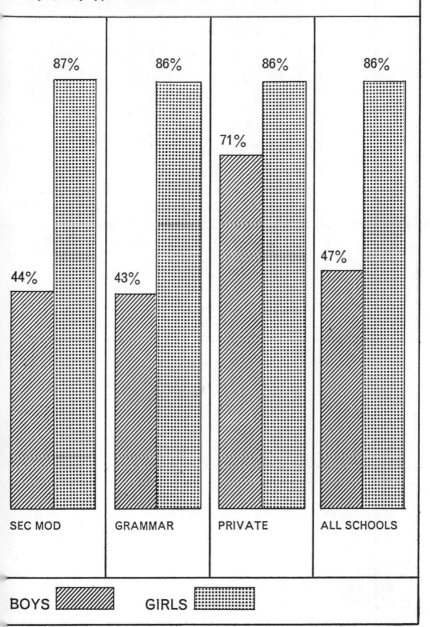

Figure 6/5
The number of boys and girls who received sex education
analysed by type of school

87%   86%   86%   86%

71%

44%   43%   47%

SEC MOD   GRAMMAR   PRIVATE   ALL SCHOOLS

BOYS   GIRLS

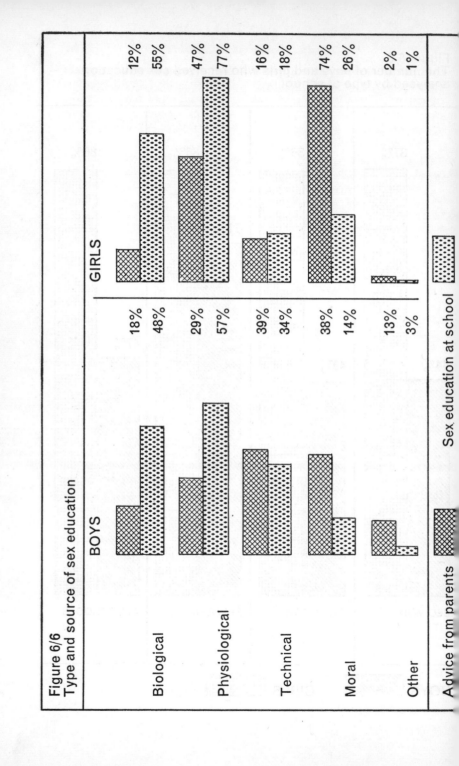

Figure 6/6
Type and source of sex education

BOYS   GIRLS

Biological   18%   48%   12%   55%

Physiological   29%   57%   47%   77%

Technical   39%   34%   16%   18%

Moral   38%   14%   74%   26%

Other   13%   3%   2%   1%

Advice from parents   Sex education at school

told our interviewer that there was only one lesson 'with a young mistress where we asked questions like was it right to have it before marriage'. There must be some doubt as to whether such situations can be classified at all as sex education. Doubtless there were other occasions when the instruction was clear, sensible and well planned.

Table 6.5 *Categories of sex education in three types of school**

Categories of sex education	Secondary modern		Grammar		Private	
	Boys, %	Girls, %	Boys, %	Girls, %	Boys, %	Girls, %
Biological	17	36	28	60	28	75
Physiological	22	73	18	59	42	45
Technical	15	15	7	15	34	13
Moral	5	22	5	24	12	16
None	56	13	57	14	29	14
No. (100%)	527	545	206	215	72	85

* These percentages add up to more than one hundred because some people received more than one kind of sex education.

D. BIRTH CONTROL

Everyone in the sample was asked if they knew anything about the sort of precautions people took to avoid pregnancy. Most of the teenagers (84 per cent boys, 82 per cent girls) claimed to have some knowledge of birth control. All those who made this claim were questioned further. Those without experience of sexual intercourse were asked what birth-control methods they knew about, and the sexually experienced were asked what methods of birth control they had used.

Table 6.6 gives the percentages for non-experienced boys and girls who knew something about birth control. All methods of birth control that were mentioned by the interviewee were recorded so the total of the percentages will add up to more than 100 per cent. The anomalies in table 6.6 are the high percentage for 'other', and the low percentage for 'withdrawal' in the case of the boys. At this time the contraceptive pill was receiving a lot of publicity and many teenagers gave this reply when faced with this question. These replies were put into the 'other' category because it was not a contraceptive method available to the teenagers. The reason why so few boys did not appear to know about withdrawal is probably because this form of birth control was too obvious to mention, and no prompting was allowed on this question. In many cases the teenagers were not aware of the precise technical term of a method they were attempting to describe – the sheath, for example, was nearly always known by a commercial brand name. All these influences may have caused some distortion of the figures, but the results in table 6.6 show without much doubt that the teenagers' understanding of birth control was often sketchy, even among those who claimed to have some knowledge of the subject.

Table 6.6 *The replies of 590 boys and 671 girls all without experience of sexual intercourse, on types of precautions they know about*

	Boys, %	Girls, %
Sheath	94	87
Diaphragm	18	36
Chemical	5	12
Douche	1	1
Withdrawal	4	7
Safe period	9	23
Other	44	45

Note: Interviewers recorded all the methods mentioned, so the percentages add up to more than a hundred.

All the teenagers with experience of sexual intercourse were asked if they always took precautions. Table 6.7 gives their replies. Less than half (43 per cent) the boys always used some form of birth control; about two-thirds (68 per cent) had used contraceptives more than once or twice; and a quarter (25 per cent) of the boys having sexual intercourse had never used any kind of birth-control method.

Not unexpectedly far fewer girls used any birth-control methods. A fifth (20 per cent) said they always did, but it was not always clear whether this referred to precautions taken by the girl herself, or by her boy friend. Well over half (61 per cent) said they never took precautions and if this is added to those who occasionally used birth-control methods, it is found that eight out of ten girls having sexual intercourse were at risk.

Many girls feel that birth control is the man's business, so all the experienced girls were asked if they insisted that their sexual partners took precautions. About a third (35 per cent) always insisted, but nearly half (45 per cent) did not insist. The other girls had insisted sometimes (15 per cent), or once or twice (5 per cent). Although the girls must bear nearly all the consequences of an unwanted pregnancy, the majority neither took precautions themselves, nor insisted upon their partners using any contraceptive method.

Table 6.7 *The extent that experienced boys and girls used birth-control methods*

Extent used	Boys, %	Girls, %
Always	43	20
Sometimes	25	13
Once or twice	5	3
Never	25	61
Don't know	2	3
TOTAL	100	100
No. (100%)	193	102

The teenagers who used birth-control methods were then asked what kind of precautions they used. Table 6.8 shows the responses in the same manner as table 6.6, but whereas the latter table shows the extent of knowledge, table 6.8 describes the birth-control methods actually used. Some teenagers had used more than one method so the percentages add up to more than a hundred.

Table 6.8 *Birth-control methods used by 140 experienced boys and 54 experienced girls shown as percentages excluding those who do not use contraceptives*

	Boys, %	Girls, %
Sheath	84	78
Diaphragm	8	14
Chemical	7	9
Douche	0	0
Withdrawal	24	40
Safe period	6	19
Other	7	9

These percentages refer only to boys who used some form of birth control and girls who used contraceptives or required their partners to use them. The replies of these 54 girls make it clear that all but a very few depended upon the man to take the precautions; 78 per cent mentioned the sheath and 40 per cent mentioned withdrawal, but only 14 per cent had used diaphragms and 9 per cent had used chemical methods.

Table 6.8 also shows that overwhelmingly the boys depend upon the sheath. Many more girls than boys depend upon withdrawal. This may be because these boys also thought it was too obvious a method even to mention to the interviewer; it was always difficult to get accurate answers on this category because teenagers are not always familiar with the word 'withdrawal' and many do not consider it to be a form of birth control. Very few boys relied upon the girl to provide any method of birth control. This table summarises all the methods that have been used by three-quarters of the experienced boys. But this does not mean that these boys took precautions on every occasion; as shown in table 6.7, many of them did not use contraceptives consistently.

It is often assumed that one of the strongest deterrents to permissive behaviour is the fear of pregnancy, and many people allege that young people are now more permissive precisely because contraceptives are easier to obtain. The sexually experienced girls were asked if they were ever afraid that they might become pregnant, and the experienced boys were asked if they feared that their girl friends might become pregnant. This possibility had never been considered by 8 per cent of the boys and 12 per cent of the girls. A further 41 per cent of the boys and 18 per cent of the girls said that the possibility of pregnancy had not worried them. But this is a real fear for 51 per cent of the experienced boys and 70 per cent of the experienced girls.

It is not of course surprising that a far larger number of girls fear the consequences of pregnancy, for they are the ones who have to deal with the problem and have to face the embarrassment and difficulties of conception before marriage, an illegitimate birth, or an abortion. Not only does the girl have to endure the physical strain, but also the social hostility towards unmarried mothers or illegal abortion is directed against the girl rather than the putative father. Only in the case of a forced marriage does the father share some of the consequences of an unwanted pregnancy.

Although only a very few boys were putative fathers and still fewer girls had been pregnant, an attempt was made to get the reactions of the teenagers to this situation. Altogether 165 younger boys and 274 older boys were asked what they would do if their girl friend was going to have a baby; this represents 35 per cent of the total sample of younger boys and 60 per cent of the older boys; the more inexperienced boys were not asked this question because the possibility was too hypothetical to produce useful answers. The replies of those who were asked the question are given in table 6.9.

Table 6.9 *The replies of 165 younger boys and 274 older boys to the question: What would you do if your girl friend was going to have a baby?*

	Younger boys, %	Older boys, %
Don't know/it couldn't happen	41	39
Offer to marry the girl	24	35
Tell parents	22	18
Try to arrange abortion	4	4
Offer to help financially	4	1
Take no action	2	3
Deny responsibility	2	0
Advise her to have it adopted	1	0
TOTAL	100	100
No. (100%)	165	274

There is little difference between the two age groups. In many cases (41 per cent of the younger and 39 per cent of the older boys) the possibility had not been entertained, and many others (22 per cent and 18 per cent) said they would go to their parents for advice. However, a quarter (24 per cent) of the younger boys and a third (35 per cent) of the older boys said they would offer to marry the pregnant girl. This shows a willingness to shoulder some of the responsibility. Unfortunately it is by no means certain that the shotgun marriage is always the right solution to this problem.

The old-fashioned attitude towards the fallen woman and the putative father provided for only two possible solutions – honourable and dishonourable. Under this dichotomy the boys come out quite well, for about half (46 per cent and 53 per cent) offered to marry the girl or at least talk to their parents about it, while only about one in ten (13 per cent and 8 per cent) suggested any of the 'dishonourable' solutions such as denial of responsibility, offer of financial help, attempts to arrange abortion or adoption, or inaction. But probably the most notable result from this table is that 41 per cent of the younger boys and 39 per cent of the older boys had no clear idea what they would do in these circumstances.

When the girls were asked what they would do if they found they were going to have a baby, only a very few (8 per cent and 4 per cent) were unable to answer the question. Pregnancy is a much more relevant contingency to a girl than to a boy.

As with the boys, some of the girls were thought to be too inexperienced to give meaningful replies to this question, but table 6.10 gives the replies of the 158 younger girls and the 241 older girls who were asked this question.

Table 6.10 *The replies of 158 younger girls and 241 older girls to the question: What would you do if you were going to have a baby?*

	Younger girls, %	Older girls, %
Tell parents	42	35
Try to marry the father	16	24
Make arrangements to keep it	16	20
Try to have it adopted	8	9
Get rid of it	8	6
Other	3	2
Don't know/couldn't happen	7	4
TOTAL	100	100
No. (100%)	158	241

By far the largest number (42 per cent and 35 per cent) would take the problem of their pregnancy to their parents. This represents almost 37 per cent of the girls who were asked this question, even so some people may find it surprising that more girls did not first think of their parents when faced with this problem. Over a third (32 per cent and 44 per cent) indicated that they would like to keep the child, either by marrying the father (16 per cent and 24 per cent), or by making other arrangements (16 per cent and 20 per cent). Less than one in ten (8 per cent and 9 per cent) would want the baby to be adopted, and still fewer (8 per cent and 6 per cent) would try to get rid of it. In view of the reported number of abortions, this last figure may be an under-estimate, and indeed it must be expected that the replies to this hypothetical question might be quite different from the dismayed action a girl would take in reality if she discovered she was pregnant. Nevertheless these figures do show that abortion and adoption are not a solution for many girls.

The results in this section suggest that the girls have a very real fear of pregnancy and yet they do almost nothing to take precautions. In the whole sample 82 per cent said they knew something about the sort of precautions people take to avoid pregnancy, and yet only three (less than 0·5 per cent) girls had ever bought a contraceptive and nearly all the experienced girls left it to the boy to decide what form of birth control he would use, if any.

The consequences of making their partner pregnant was not such a dominant fear for the boys. Less than half the sexually experienced boys always used a contraceptive, although 84 per cent replied that they knew about the sort of precautions people took to avoid pregnancies.

Of the 190 boys who had ever owned a contraceptive, 139 had experienced sexual intercourse; the other 51 either felt the need to be prepared or, more likely, were carrying around a sheath as a kind of status symbol. Table 6.11 shows where they got these contraceptives. Most (40 per cent) bought them from chemists and others (18 per cent) from barbers; 32 of the boys who obtained their contraceptives from chemists or barbers were in the younger age group and so were aged fifteen to seventeen. No one in the sample got their contraceptives from a slot machine. A very few obtained them from surgical stores (4 per cent) or agents (5 per cent). But a large

Table 6.11 *Places where 190 boys obtained contraceptives*

Outlet	Boys, %
Chemist	40
Barber	18
Agents	5
Surgical goods shop	4
Friends	33
TOTAL	100
No. (100%)	190

number (33 per cent) obtained them from friends and individual cases suggest that sometimes a sheath is sold and resold many times between schoolboys.

The occasional newspaper report about the discovery of a number of contraceptives as a result of a search of the pockets or lockers of schoolboys by a zealous master is not usually of much significance. Some people would feel more concerned by the fact that 54 of the 193 sexually experienced boys (i.e. 28 per cent) have never owned a contraceptive.

Table 6.12 *The reasons given by sexually experienced boys and girls for not using contraceptives*

	Boys, %	Girls, %
Don't have any	32	23
Don't like them	21	25
Don't care	29	12
Not necessary	6	12
Don't know about them	5	7
Religious reasons	1	6
Don't know/Other	6	15
TOTAL	100	100
No. (100%)	110	68

It has been noted that 57 per cent of the sexually experienced boys did not always use a contraceptive, and 65 per cent of the experienced girls did not always insist that their boy friend use one. These teenagers were asked if they had any particular reason for not using contraceptives. Table 6.12 gives their answers. A few (6 per cent) boys and a larger number (15 per cent) of the girls found it impossible to answer this question; many of the girls implied that it was up to the man to take this decision. The other answers required wide categories to accommodate them, for this kind of question is bound to produce some answers that are rationalisations, and some which are vague or inarticulate. Some of the teenagers who were answering this question had only limited experience of sexual intercourse and it is therefore not altogether surprising that they did not have contraceptives at the isolated moments when intercourse occurred.

But the other categories reveal fairly strong attitudes among the teenagers. A fifth (21 per cent) of the boys and a quarter (25 per cent) of the girls did not like the idea of using any contraceptive method; it is not always clear whether the girl's dislike refers to female contraceptives or whether she is echoing the opinions of her boy friend. A large number (29 per cent) of boys gave replies that are best classified under the category of 'don't care'; these replies usually showed a lack of concern and a disinclination to think about birth control; rather surprisingly 12 per cent of the girls held similar attitudes. Another group held that contraceptives were not necessary for a variety of reasons. Taking these three groups together, it suggests that 56 per cent of the boys and 49 per cent of the girls have very little interest in birth control and will be slow to profit from instruction in the use of contraceptives.

A few boys (5 per cent) and girls (7 per cent) did not know enough to be able to make use of birth-control methods. Religious reasons for not taking precautions were given only rarely (6 per cent) by the girls and hardly ever (1 per cent) by the boys.

It is clear from the results reported in this section that many of the girls who are having premarital sexual intercourse are running the risk of becoming pregnant. Likewise many of the boys are not making use of birth control. Some would be more likely to take precautions if contraceptives were more readily available, but the majority are either not aware of the risks, or at the moment of sexual excitement are not disposed to consider the consequences of an unwanted pregnancy. As sexual intercourse within marriage is socially accepted, it is not too difficult to make preparations and have contraceptives available. But premarital intercourse is discouraged, and therefore when it does take place, it is often unpremeditated and clandestine; in these circumstances birth control is less likely to be practised. Unfortunately the consequences of an unwanted pregnancy are far more serious for the unmarried than for the married.

E. VENEREAL DISEASE

Until 1963 the incidence figures for the venereal diseases indicated cases and not patients; individual patients who contracted syphilis or gonorrhoea on more than one occasion during the year under review added to the total. In that year the form (V.D.(R).) on which information is supplied by all clinics was revised to provide more detailed information, including this distinction between 'cases' and 'patients'. The new form also indicated the age groups of infected patients for the first time. The ages of patients suffering from primary or secondary syphilis and from gonorrhoea are shown in table 6.13 (compiled from the Annual Report of the Chief Medical Officer of the Ministry of Health for the year 1963).

Table 6.13 *Age groups of patients suffering from infectious syphilis and gonorrhoea*

| | Primary and secondary syphilis | | | | Gonorrhoea | | | |
| | Men | | Women | | Men | | Women | |
Age	No.	%	No.	%	No.	%	No.	%
Under 16	1	—	1	1	46	—	179	2
16 and 17	16	2	20	11	389	2	617	8
18 and 19	45	5	21	12	1,484	6	1,264	17
20–24	237	26	61	35	7,450	31	2,603	35
25 and over	626	67	71	41	14,732	61	2,783	38
TOTALS	925	100	174	100	24,101	100	7,446	100

This table shows that 62 boys aged nineteen or under had syphilis and 1,919 had gonorrhoea. The contribution which immigrants make to the incidence of the venereal diseases has been studied by the Co-operative Clinical Group of the Medical Society for the Study of Venereal Diseases (1963). Information as to the countries of origin of patients who suffered 35,740 attacks of gonorrhoea in 1963 was obtained from 173 clinics. Of the men 46·3 per cent were born in the United Kingdom. Using these figures and the total number of boys aged fifteen to nineteen in the country, it can be estimated that 0·055 per cent of the boys were infected; in other words one in over 1,600 British-born teenage boys caught VD.

The incidence was higher among the girls aged nineteen and under. Forty-two girls had syphilis and 2,060 had gonorrhoea. According to the British Co-operative Clinical Groups 78 per cent of all women with gonorrhoea were born in the United Kingdom. Thus it can be estimated that 0·095 per cent of the girls aged fifteen to nineteen were infected; and so about one in a thousand British-born teenage girls get VD.

Perhaps it is not altogether surprising that young people's knowledge about venereal diseases is limited. Many sex educators find it a distasteful subject and fear that the children might be alarmed if time is spent on this disease when other information about sex is being given. Nevertheless it has been the subject of a fairly widespread propaganda campaign and several people have commented on the rise in the VD rates among young people in the last few years. This research attempted to find out how much the teenagers knew about the venereal diseases, and where they obtained this information.

First they were asked if they knew anything about VD, and 16 per cent of the boys and 13 per cent of the girls replied that they did not. Those who replied in the affirmative were asked to describe the symptoms. Now this is a difficult question to answer, particularly for girls, and it is possible that some of the young people knew, or partially knew, the symptoms but could not bring themselves to name the affected part of the body. On the other hand this question came late in the interview after a long period had been spent discussing sexual matters.

The replies to this question are shown in figure 6.7. In fact about a third of the sample was unable to describe any symptoms although they had heard of VD. The other replies were extremely varied and indicate that a large amount of misinformation is spread about this disease.

The categories listed in figure 6.7 are an attempt to summarise these various replies. A liberal interpretation would allow the first and second category (discharge and spot) as correct, and possibly the third category (rash). As there is more than one symptom for the various venereal diseases, more than one answer was recorded in several categories; strictly speaking, if all the teenagers in the sample were knowledgeable about syphilis and gonorrhoea, the figures in the first two categories would be 100 per cent in each one – in fact less than one in ten mentioned discharge as a symptom, and less than one in twenty mentioned a spot or a chancre.

Over a half of the teenagers did not know anything about the symptoms of either gonorrhoea or syphilis, and would not be able to recognise either disease if they were infected. There was no difference in this respect between the girls and the boys, and the older age groups appeared to be no better informed than the younger.

Most people (33 per cent of the boys and 30 per cent of the girls) learnt about VD from their friends; the other important sources were TV (16 per cent boys, 17 per cent girls) and books (15 per cent boys, 11 per cent girls); girls were more likely than boys to learn from their parents (3 per cent boys, 10 per cent girls) or at school (7 per cent boys, 13 per cent girls); posters were only rarely the source of knowledge (4 per cent for both boys and girls).

I

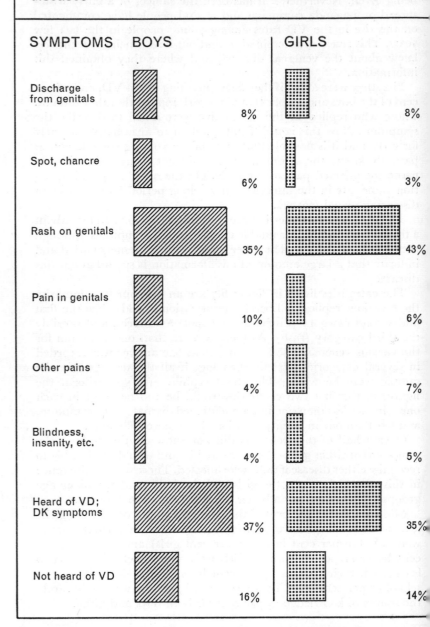

Figure 6/7
The replies of 1873 teenagers on the symptoms of venereal diseases

SYMPTOMS	BOYS	GIRLS
Discharge from genitals	8%	8%
Spot, chancre	6%	3%
Rash on genitals	35%	43%
Pain in genitals	10%	6%
Other pains	4%	7%
Blindness, insanity, etc.	4%	5%
Heard of VD; DK symptoms	37%	35%
Not heard of VD	16%	14%

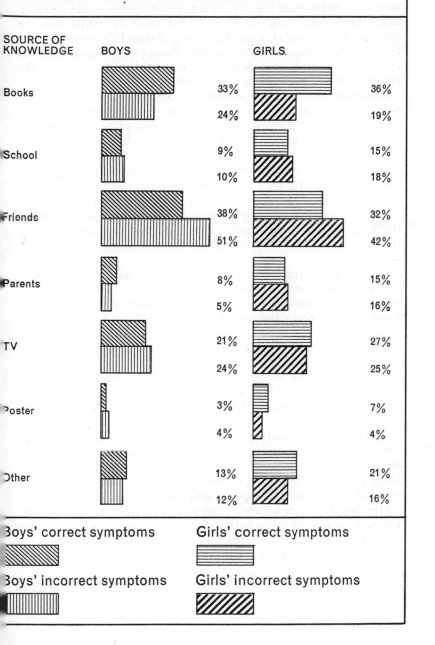

Figure 6/8
Correct and incorrect symptoms of venereal diseases
analysed by the source of the information

SOURCE OF KNOWLEDGE	BOYS	GIRLS
Books	33% / 24%	36% / 19%
School	9% / 10%	15% / 18%
Friends	38% / 51%	32% / 42%
Parents	8% / 5%	15% / 16%
TV	21% / 24%	27% / 25%
Poster	3% / 4%	7% / 4%
Other	13% / 12%	21% / 16%

Boys' correct symptoms

Girls' correct symptoms

Boys' incorrect symptoms

Girls' incorrect symptoms

In order to check the effectiveness of these sources, the replies describing the symptoms were arbitrarily divided into correct and incorrect responses, giving the teenagers the benefit of the doubt in many cases; then these two classifications were compared with the sources of information with the results shown in figure 6.8. The figures are percentages of the number of boys (or girls) giving correct (or incorrect) symptoms. Some gave more than one source, so the percentages add up to more than a hundred.

Books and friends appear to be the best source of accurate information, but friends are also the biggest source of misinformation. In the few programmes on television devoted to this subject the description of the symptoms has been correct, albeit a little vague, but the response is equally divided between correct and incorrect. Posters do not usually give much information on symptoms, but emphasise the dangers and indicate where help may be obtained. This table makes it appear as if parents and school teachers give equal amounts of reliable and unreliable information. Of course it is not the accuracy of the actual source which is being measured here, but the effect it has on the teenagers which is, after all, the important aspect.

In our sample ten boys thought they might have got VD at one period of their lives. Four went to a clinic – two of these were infected and two were not; one went to his own doctor (result not reported); the other five did nothing about it and the symptoms disappeared.

Five of the girls thought they had VD at one time or another. Three went to a clinic – one was infected and two were not; the other two said the symptoms disappeared. Of course it is quite possible that the seven boys and girls who did not go to a clinic were misinformed and were not infected; but one cannot be sure about this.

Although most young people have now heard about venereal disease there is still some ignorance about the symptoms and some doubts as to whether an infected person would go to a clinic for help. It is quite possible (although statistically improbable) that some of the teenagers we questioned had VD and were quite unaware that they were infected (and, of course, there was no way our interviewers could know). Perhaps it is a slight consolation that both boys and girls with experience of sexual intercourse were more likely to be better informed about the symptoms (see section D of chapter 10).

7 ATTITUDES

A. THE ATTITUDE INVENTORY

The rationale and construction of the attitude inventory is described in appendix 3. It was completed by 780 boys and 761 girls, and the results are given in table 7.1. To make comparison easier the five-point scale is condensed: 'agree' includes all those who indicated both *agreement* and *strong agreement*; 'disagree' includes all those who indicated both *disagreement* and *strong disagreement*.

Table 7.1 *The responses of 780 boys and 761 girls to the fifty statements on the attitude inventory*

Statement	Boys			Girls		
	Agree, %	DK, %	Dis-agree, %	Agree, %	DK, %	Dis-agree, %
1 Life is so short that having a good time is more important than anything else	47	10	43	50	7	43
2 Most parents ought to be stricter with their children	54	19	27	47	15	38
3 It always pays to be honest	75	9	16	84	4	12
4 Summer holidays without parents are more enjoyable	63	23	14	65	17	18
5 Most teenagers are bored with their jobs	36	29	35	30	22	48
6 Each person should decide for himself what is right and wrong	72	5	23	84	5	11
7 The family should spend an evening at home together at least once a week	64	17	19	75	11	14
8 Most adults say one thing and do another	41	21	38	44	16	40
9 It is best to have a good time before you are married because after that life is pretty dreary	28	18	54	27	8	65

Statement	Boys			Girls		
	Agree, %	DK, %	Dis-agree, %	Agree, %	DK, %	Dis-agree, %
10 I learn more from friends of my own age than I can learn from my parents	58	11	31	53	10	37
11 If a boy gets a girl pregnant he should be willing to marry her	66	16	18	66	15	19
12 Today's teenagers are very different from teenagers in the past	52	18	30	58	9	33
13 There is no need to teach about sex in schools, be-cause you can find out all you need to know for yourself	21	9	70	13	9	78
14 Parents should advise their children about the sort of work they should do	41	8	51	44	7	49
15 Teenage boys spend too much time thinking about their clothes and hair styles	38	12	50	34	15	51
16 People should realise their greatest loyalty is to their family	79	11	10	73	14	13
17 Girls believe today that if they are not married before they are 21 they are on the shelf	28	23	49	30	10	60
18 The average man can live a good life without religion	58	15	27	53	17	30
19 Young people should be taught all about birth control	81	13	6	83	11	6
20 TV and radio programmes have a strong influence on most teenagers	55	9	36	58	8	34
21 A girl is usually looking for a man to marry, but a boy is usually looking for sex	49	15	36	53	15	32

Statement	Boys			Girls		
	Agree, %	DK, %	Dis-agree, %	Agree, %	DK, %	Dis-agree, %
22 It should be made easier for married people to get divorced if they want to	39	15	46	30	12	58
23 In this country there is one law for the rich and another for the poor	41	15	44	32	18	50
24 Young people can only really be free if they live away from home	18	10	72	16	6	78
25 The police are unfair in their treatment of teenagers	28	13	59	19	15	66
26 When it comes to sex, there is one standard for men and another for women	31	37	32	45	28	27
27 If a girl has sex before marriage she gets a bad reputation	45	18	37	58	14	28
28 There is no harm in travelling without a ticket occasionally if you can get away with it	53	10	37	43	9	48
29 I'd rather take my holidays with my parents	19	23	58	20	23	57
30 I'd rather work for someone strict and fair, than for someone who is easy going	72	11	17	69	11	20
31 The advantages of living at home with the family outweigh the disadvantages	71	20	9	71	16	13
32 It is important for a person who gives sex education to have had some first hand experience of sex	77	14	9	66	14	20
33 I'm usually a bit bored when I stay at home in the evenings	49	6	45	39	5	56
34 The Church is the best authority to decide on matters of right and wrong	22	17	61	28	14	58

as relate
to #6

Statement	Boys			Girls		
	Agree, %	DK, %	Dis-agree, %	Agree, %	DK, %	Dis-agree, %
35 I think I'll have a better job than my father has when I am his age	59	29	12	28	38	34
36 Teenagers have sex thrown at them all the time from advertisements, films and TV	70	7	23	68	6	26
37 I would rather go to my parents for advice than to my friends	55	16	29	53	12	35
38 Sexual intercourse before marriage is all right for boys but not for girls	23	21	56	42	14	44
39 Teenagers should be able to go out in the evening without having to tell their parents where they are going	55	13	32	40	11	49
40 Very few adults really understand teenagers	54	13	33	47	14	39
41 Most boys want to marry a virgin	66	19	15	69	19	12
42 The average teenager expects to live much the same kind of life as his parents do	37	15	48	38	13	49
43 Sexual intercourse before marriage is wrong	35	20	45	62	14	24
44 All homosexuals should be severely punished	47	18	35	35	20	45
45 Foreigners should stay in their own country	30	11	59	24	10	66
46 It would be best to keep coloured people in their own districts in order to prevent too much contact with whites	25	11	64	24	13	63
47 Girls should not get married before they are 21	19	21	60	18	15	67

Statement	Boys			Girls		
	Agree, %	DK, %	Dis-agree, %	Agree, %	DK, %	Dis-agree, %
48 What teenagers do and how they dress outside their homes is their business	59	12	29	58	12	30
49 Too much freedom in the early teens leads to trouble when one gets older	50	14	36	45	12	43
50 There is more to sex than just having a good time	86	10	4	87	8	5

B. ATTITUDES TO MARRIAGE

Many of the attitudes shown in table 7.1 are interesting in themselves and require no further comment. In the remaining five
sections of this chapter some of the opinions and beliefs which
emerged during the interview will be discussed and compared with
the relevant responses in the attitude inventory.

Very few of our sample rejected the prospect of marriage; 6 per
cent of the younger boys and 3 per cent of the older boys said at the
interview that they did not want to marry; hardly any of the girls
(1 per cent in each age group) said they did not want to marry.
Another 7 per cent of the boys and 1 per cent of the girls felt unable
to answer the question. But although most of the boys and nearly all
the girls wanted to get married, over a quarter of both boys (28 per
cent) and girls (27 per cent) agreed with the statement that *it is
best to have a good time before you are married because after that life is pretty
dreary* (statement no. 9 in table 7.1).

A big difference between the sexes about the ideal age of marriage
was revealed at the interview. Among the boys 35 per cent of the
younger and 43 per cent of the older said they did not want to marry
before the age of twenty-five; the corresponding figure for girls is
9 per cent in both age groups.

The majority of boys and girls would prefer to marry after the
age of twenty-one, but the proportion is much bigger for boys than
for girls and is also bigger for older girls than for younger girls.
Over a third (38 per cent) of younger girls would like to marry
before they are twenty-one. This shows the tremendous prominence

of marriage as an immediate goal in the lives of many teenage girls. Table 7.2 gives the responses to the question during the interview and two related statements from the attitude inventory.

Table 7.2 *Opinions about the ideal age of marriage*

Item	Age-sex group	Over 21	Under 21	Don't know
At what age would you like to get married?	YB	78	9	13
	OB	83	8	9
	YG	60	38	2
	OG	70	27	3

Girls believe today that if they are not married before they are twenty-one they are on the shelf		Agree	Disagree	Don't know
	YB	28	51	22
	OB	28	47	25
	YG	30	59	12
	OG	30	62	8

Girls should not get married before they are twenty-one		Agree	Disagree	Don't know
	YB	19	61	20
	OB	20	59	21
	YG	17	67	15
	OG	19	66	14

Approximately one-third of each age-sex group believe that most girls think their marriage chances are over at twenty-one. This corresponds with the 27 per cent of older girls who would like to marry before twenty-one and the 38 per cent of younger girls. The fact that the percentage of younger girls who would like to marry before twenty-one is higher than the percentage who consider girls are on the shelf at twenty-one suggests that many younger girls would like to marry before twenty-one independently of whether or not this is the terminal age of their marriage chances. Not surprisingly a relatively small but constant percentage of all groups think girls should not marry before the age of twenty-one.

The differences between the sexes on the desired age of marriage are shown by plotting accumulated percentage curves for each age-sex group (figure 7.1). Any point on one of these curves gives the percentage of teenagers who would like to marry at or below a particular age. For most boys and nearly all girls marriage is an expected, almost inevitable, part of a person's life. But in spite of its inevitability about a quarter of the teenagers see marital life in an unfavourable light and seem to suggest that enjoyment ends when marriage begins.

Not unexpectedly most of them (62 per cent boys, 89 per cent girls) said they expected to remain faithful after marriage. However, 9 per cent of the boys and 1 per cent of the girls said they thought they would have sex with others besides their spouse after marriage. Perhaps more surprising are the 17 per cent boys and 6 per cent girls who said they were not sure when they were asked this question: Do you think you will have sex with anyone else after you are married? The others (12 per cent boys, 3 per cent girls) were unable to answer the question because they had not made up their minds about marriage.

C. ATTITUDES TO SEX EDUCATION

In figure 7.2 we bring together the responses of three interview questions and one of the attitude statements on the subject of knowledge about sex. A quarter of the boys and a third of the girls felt they should have been taught more about sex by their parents. So the boys did not get much advice from their parents, and there was not much demand for it. It is clear that more boys would rather learn about sex from their teachers than from their parents. A third of the girls had also hoped to learn more from their teachers although many more girls (86 per cent) had already received some kind of sex education at school.

The third item in figure 7.2 shows that many boys and girls want help with their sex problems from their school teachers. There are also some signs that the teenagers have not been altogether content with what little sex education they have been getting. In fact 77 per cent of the boys and even 66 per cent of the girls agreed with the statement that *it is important for a person who gives sex education to have had some first-hand experience of sex* (statement no. 32 on table 7.1). Two others statements show that the teenagers had only a limited amount of respect for adult advice. Most teenagers agreed that *I learn more from friends of my own age than I can learn from adults,* and most agreed that *very few adults really understand teenagers* (statement nos. 10 and 40 on table 7.1).

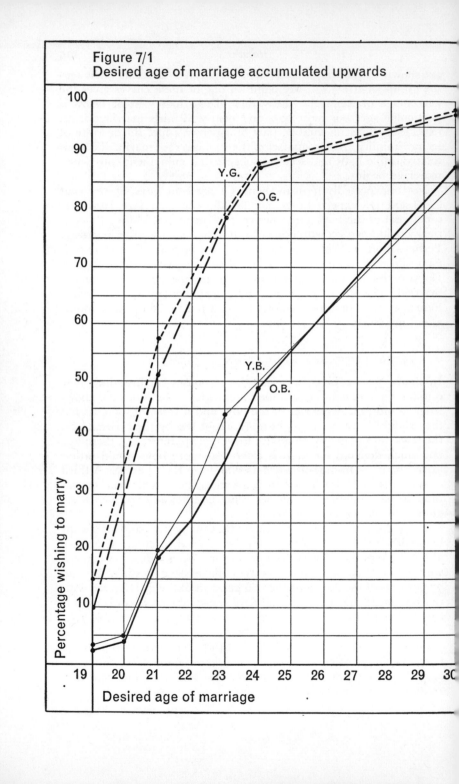

Figure 7/1
Desired age of marriage accumulated upwards

Figure 7/2
Attitude to Sex Education

Do you feel you should have been taught more about sex by your parents?

YES

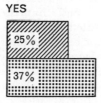

25%

37%

Do you feel you should have been taught more about sex at school?

YES

43%

35%

There is no need to teach about sex in schools, because you can find out all you need to know for yourself.

DISAGREE

AGREE

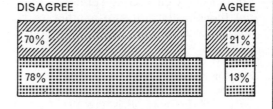

70%

78%

21%

13%

Do you feel you know all there is to know about sex?

NO

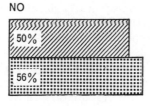

50%

56%

BOYS   GIRLS

The last item of figure 7.2 emphasises what a difficult task the teacher has to face, for nearly half the boys and girls think they know all there is to know about sex. Our later questions, particularly on birth control and venereal disease, showed that much of this confidence was misplaced and that their knowledge on sexual matters was very often limited. It was the younger adolescents who were sure that they did not have anything more to learn about sex and this over-confidence decreased as they got older.

Although it is clear that a large part of the teacher's task is to correct misinformation, this research has shown that there is a lively demand for information about sex, and there are indications that this demand is not being fulfilled.

D. INHIBITING FACTORS

All the boys who had experienced sexual intercourse were asked if they were ever afraid that the girls might become pregnant, and the experienced girls were asked if they feared pregnancy. Nearly half the boys did not worry about it; 8 per cent said they had never thought about it and 41 per cent said they did not think it would happen to their girl friend; 51 per cent boys said that they had been afraid of a possible pregnancy on one or more occasions. The attitude of the girls is quite different. Only 12 per cent said they had not thought about it and another 18 per cent said they did not worry about it. This leaves 70 per cent of the experienced girls who have feared pregnancy.

Most of the boys (66 per cent) agreed with the statement that *if a boy gets a girl pregnant he should be willing to marry her*. The same number (66 per cent) of girls agreed, but it is interesting to note that very slightly more girls (19 per cent) than boys (18 per cent) actually disagreed with this statement.

There is little doubt that fear of pregnancy is still an inhibiting factor for some people; nearly a third (30 per cent) of the experienced boys and nearly a half (44 per cent) of the experienced girls said they sometimes stopped short of complete intercourse because of the risks of pregnancy. Furthermore over half (54 per cent) the boys who had experience of genital apposition said they had refrained from sexual intercourse because of the risks of pregnancy and this applied to almost a third (31 per cent) of the girls with experience of genital apposition but not of sexual intercourse.[1]

1. Incidentally some (17 per cent) of the boys and a quarter (26 per cent) of the girls with experience of genital apposition disallowed sexual intercourse for moral reasons.

Thus 9 per cent of the boys and 7 per cent of the girls in the whole sample were using genital apposition as a form of birth control and a substitute for sexual intercourse.

A general attempt was made to find out what had stopped those who had not had sexual intercourse. Apart from those who had very little contact with the opposite sex (i.e. those in stage I), all the others who had not had experience of sexual intercourse (i.e. all those in stages II and III), were questioned about this. When they had revealed the full extent of their sexual experience, they were asked: Is there any reason why you don't go farther than this? Their replies are given in table 7.3.

Table 7.3 *Reasons for not having sexual intercourse classified into eight categories*

Reason	Boys, %	Girls, %
Fear pregnancy	24	17
Moral reasons	19	40
Religious reasons	3	5
Girl's reputation	11	9
Keep virginity	1	4
Fear VD	1	2
No reasons	14	2
DK, NK, Other	27	21
TOTAL	100	100
No. (100%)	596	769

This was a very demanding question and required the sort of response which was difficult to put into words for many of the teenagers, and beyond the capabilities of others. The possibility had not occurred to many of them, while others took it for granted that their first experience of sexual intercourse would occur after they had married. Care had to be taken not to disturb these young people or leave the impression that the interviewer was disappointed with their reply, so in 24 per cent of the cases we did not press for an answer. Another 14 per cent of the boys and 2 per cent of the girls said there was no reason why they should not go farther, implying that they would take the chance when it occurred.

An important inhibiting influence was fear of pregnancy, just as it was the most usual reason for restraint given by the experienced teenagers (stage IV and V); rather surprisingly this applied to more boys (24 per cent) than girls (17 per cent). The most usual restraint for girls (45 per cent) and an important restraint for boys (22 per cent) were moral and religious reasons, although religion was not often mentioned specifically. The girls' reputation was also an important factor about as often for the boys (11 per cent) as for the girls (9 per cent); this reinforces the suggestion made later (section F) that girls who permit premarital intercourse are disparaged by some boys, even by the boys who are seeking to have intercourse with them. This is similar to the idea that it is important for the girl to keep her virginity which was mentioned by some girls (4 per cent), but only a very few boys (1 per cent) were concerned for their own virginity. Fear of venereal disease appears to be the least important of the reasons it was possible to classify.

E. ATTITUDES TO SEX BEFORE MARRIAGE

The responses to the question and the first statement shown in figure 7.3 are very similar. Boys are more in favour of intercourse with their fiancées than girls, and also disagree more strongly that *sexual intercourse before marriage is wrong.* The older age groups are more permissive than the younger boys and girls. More teenagers reject premarital intercourse for themselves in the question, than as a general principle in the statement. Among the older boys less than a third (29 per cent) believe that sex before marriage is definitely wrong but nearly half (46 per cent) said they did not want sex with their fiancée.

Nearly half the boys appear to be in favour of premarital intercourse whereas less than a quarter of the girls hold this view. It is interesting to compare these attitudes with those expressed on sex education. Girls are more interested in learning about sex than boys, but boys are far more permissive than girls in their attitude towards sexual experience itself.

Furthermore many girls expect boys to be more experienced. Many more girls than boys believed that *sexual intercourse before marriage is all right for boys but not for girls.* Although only a minority in any group supported this double standard of sexual morality as many as 45 per cent of the younger girls and 39 per cent of the older girls agreed with this statement, compared with only 25 per cent younger boys and 21 per cent older boys. The other statement on this idea confirms that girls are prepared to endure sexual behaviour

Figure 7/3
Attitude to Sex before Marriage

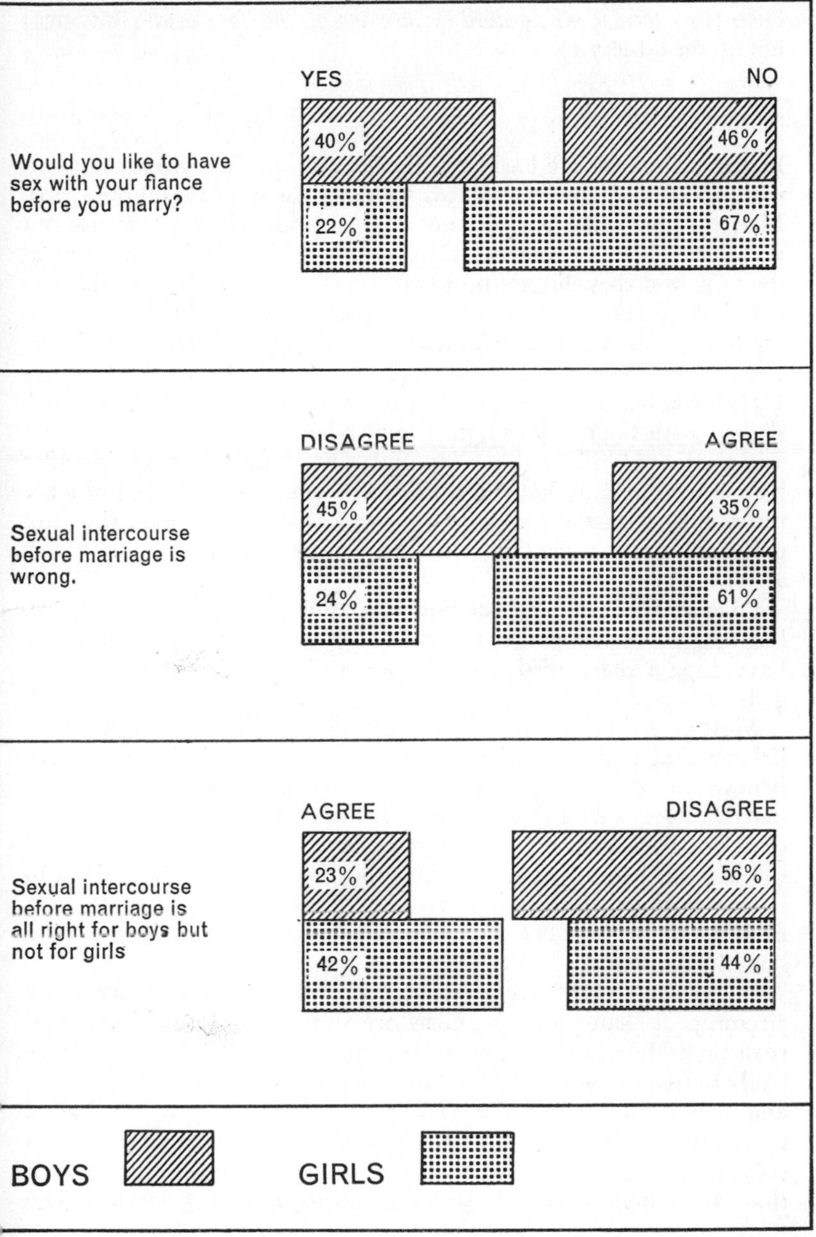

Would you like to have sex with your fiancé before you marry?

YES
40%
22%

NO
46%
67%

Sexual intercourse before marriage is wrong.

DISAGREE
45%
24%

AGREE
35%
61%

Sexual intercourse before marriage is all right for boys but not for girls

AGREE
23%
42%

DISAGREE
56%
44%

BOYS   GIRLS

K

in boys which they would not tolerate in themselves; 45 per cent of the girls compared with 31 per cent of the boys agreed that *when it comes to sex there is one standard for men and another for women* (statement no. 26 on table 7.1).

F. ATTITUDES TO VIRGINITY

Figure 7.4 reveals the basic moral dilemma that teenagers are faced with and the confusion that exists among them on moral questions. Many (45 per cent) boys are not against premarital intercourse but a majority (64 per cent) wish to marry virgins. Only a quarter of the boys said they did not mind either way and one in ten said they definitely did not want to marry a virgin. It seemed a little tactless to ask this question of girls who had already experienced sexual intercourse, but a very large number (85 per cent) of the others (stages I–III) wanted to be a virgin when they married. This conflicts slightly with the previous figure (7.3) where 22 per cent of the girls said they would like to have sex with their fiancé, but this includes people who already have had this experience; the others probably mean they wish the first experience to be with the man they are going to marry whether this be before they are married or after.

Over half (51 per cent) the boys would like to have sex experience, but two-thirds (64 per cent) want to marry virgins. Some of the boys drew a sharp distinction between girls to have sex with and girls to marry.

Most girls do not want to have sex before they marry, and they believe that their boy friends want to marry a virgin. They also believe, more often than the boys, that a girl who has sex before marriage gets a bad reputation. But many of them do not mind if their boy friend has sex elsewhere before they are married. A third (36 per cent) stated definitely that they wanted their boy friend to have sexual experience, and another quarter (26 per cent) were undecided; only 38 per cent were against their boy friend having sexual experience.

It is clear that all teenagers expect the girls to be much more circumspect than the boys. Girls are slightly more consistent and realistic in the attitudes they express on these issues. They are more likely to realise that there is a double standard for men and women, and a majority accept the view that girls who have sex before marriage get a bad reputation. They also want to be virgins when they marry and realise that this is what the boys expect; more girls than boys believe that most boys want to marry virgins. The

Figure 7/4
Attitudes to Virginity

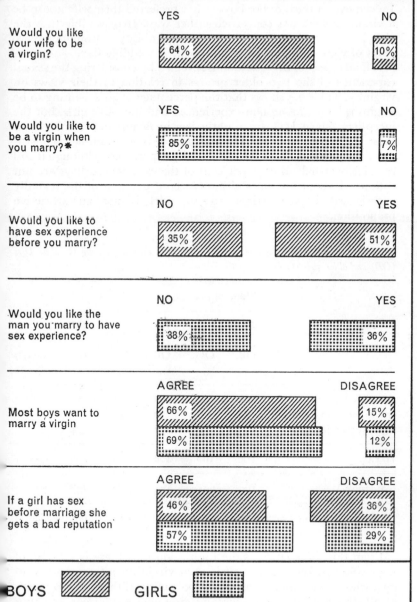

	YES	NO
Would you like your wife to be a virgin?	64%	10%

	YES	NO
Would you like to be a virgin when you marry?*	85%	7%

	NO	YES
Would you like to have sex experience before you marry?	35%	51%

	NO	YES
Would you like the man you marry to have sex experience?	38%	36%

	AGREE	DISAGREE
Most boys want to marry a virgin	66% / 69%	15% / 12%

	AGREE	DISAGREE
If a girl has sex before marriage she gets a bad reputation	46% / 57%	36% / 29%

BOYS GIRLS

* Excludes girls who have had sexual intercourse

number of girls who want to be virgins when they marry is higher than the number of boys who expect their wives to be virgins. Indeed over a third of the boys either preferred their wife not to be a virgin or were not concerned either way. It is possible that the girls have been over-estimating the desirability – from the boys' point of view – of being a virgin on their wedding day.

A final aspect of this question is revealed by considering the sexual experience of the two older groups in relation to their views on virginity. Table 7.4 shows that the percentage of girls wanting to be virgins is large among non-experienced and inceptive girls, but the inceptives (stage III) are slightly less in favour of virginity than those in stages I and II. The number of boys wanting virgins as marriage partners drops for the sexually experienced although it still remains over half. But 41 per cent of the experienced boys are not concerned about the girl's virginity. To 4 per cent of the sexually experienced boys marriage to any girl is not an attractive proposition.

Table 7.4 *Sexual experience analysed by attitude to virginity among the older boys (OB) and older girls (OG)*

	Stage of sex					
	I and II		III		IV and V	
Attitude	OB, %	OG, %	OB, %	OG, %	OB, %	OG,* %
For girl's virginity	63	92	68	85	55	—
Indifferent to virginity	32	6	30	15	41	—
Against marriage	5	2	2	0	4	—
TOTAL	100	100	100	100	100	—
No. (100%)	167	205	151	186	138	73

* Girls who had experienced sexual intercourse were not asked this question.

From this there emerges the impression that there is a group of boys who are keen to lose their own virginity but are critical of girls who provide them with this opportunity. If they wish to marry at all they are intent on marrying girls who are virgins and thus preclude marriage from their premarital sexual relationships. Girls, aware of the dangers, play a defensive role. They wish to protect their own virginity but expect boys to gain sexual experience, and find it acceptable that boys should be able to do what they rule out for themselves.

PART III
THE DIFFERENCE BETWEEN
SEXUALLY EXPERIENCED TEENAGERS
AND OTHERS

8 FAMILY BACKGROUND

A. ASSOCIATED FACTORS

The next five chapters will be devoted to investigating the association between sexual experience and other factors. In previous chapters we have noted that inceptive activities form an important part of the sexual behaviour of young people. It would be misleading to limit our definition of sexual experience only to those who have had intercourse, because this would leave out a large number of people who have experienced extensive sexual arousal during the course of inceptive activities. Accordingly we have compared other non-sexual factors with three levels of sexual activity, formed by reducing our previous scale of sexual experience as follows:

Stage I }
Stage II } the non-experienced (N)
Stage III the inceptives (I)
Stage IV}
Stage V} the experienced (E)

The *experienced* are those who have had sexual intercourse with one or more partners; these will be designated E-boys and E-girls in the following chapters.

The *inceptives* are those who have not had sexual intercourse, but have experience of breast stimulation under clothes, genital stimulation and/or genital apposition; these will be designated I-boys and I-girls.

The *non-experienced* are all those who do not fall into one of the other two groups; they will be designated N-boys or N-girls in the following chapters.

We have tested the relationship between these three levels of sexual activity and many other variables by using the χ^2 test. When the test has revealed a significant association between the level of sex activity and one of these variables, we have shown this by giving the value of p. When $p = 0.001$ it signifies that the probability of this association occurring by chance is one in a thousand; if $p = 0.01$ the chances are one in a hundred. Levels above $p = 0.05$ (20:1) are usually considered not significant. In some cases we have also reported the fact that there is no statistical relationship between sex experience and another factor because in the past other people have suggested that there might be an association. When the letters NSS in brackets are found, this indicates that the association has been subjected to a statistical test and it has been found that it is not significant.

The χ^2 test applied here assumes that this is a simple random sample whereas in fact this is a series of random samples with different sampling fractions and this would require a less rigorous test. Therefore when it is found that the difference is significant when calculated on this basis, it is reasonably certain that this difference is due to something other than chance.

These statistical tests and all the figures given in chapters 8–11 refer to the older age groups only (456 boys and 464 girls) because sexual experience is correlated with age and therefore we can partially eliminate this influence by reporting on boys and girls of about the same age, i.e. between seventeen and nineteen.

B. EARLY BACKGROUND

It has been shown (Glueck, 1952) that juvenile delinquents tend to come from broken homes and it might have been expected that precocious sexual behaviour was more likely to be found in children from homes where one of the parents is dead or absent. But this research shows that adolescents who come from broken homes are not more likely to be sexually experienced (NSS).

In this sample 9 per cent of the older boys and 12 per cent of the older girls came from broken homes. Table 8.1 divides those from broken homes into non-experienced, inceptive and experienced and compares them with a similar division of the other adolescents. This shows that sexual experience and broken homes are not related.

A broken home refers to the situation where one parent is absent when the child is very young. In another 9 per cent of the cases in this sample one of the parents died or moved away when the child was ten years old or over. Accordingly a comparison was made between those living with two parents at the time of the interview, and all those living with only one parent; but there was no association between the level of sex activity and those living with one parent or two (NSS). A similar test compared those living with two parents, and those living with stepmothers, aunts, stepfathers and foster parents; this indicated that those living with substitute parents are not more likely to have more sexual experience (NSS).

It was found that about a third (32 per cent) of the sample were living in the house where they were born; about a quarter (26 per cent) had moved home once, 17 per cent have moved twice, 13 per cent three times and 12 per cent more than three times. It has been suggested that these movements have an unsettling effect upon children as they have to get used to new surroundings, adjust to new schools and teachers, and make new friends. But this does not appear to make any difference to their subsequent sexual behaviour. A χ^2 test on the 920 older boys and girls revealed no association between the level of sex activity and the number of times they moved home (NSS).

Table 8.1 *Broken homes compared with two-parent homes and analysed by three levels of sex activity*

Type of home	Boys			Girls		
	N, %	I, %	E, %	N, %	I, %	E, %
Two-parent homes	90	91	92	87	90	85
Broken homes	10	9	8	13	10	15
TOTAL	100	100	100	100	100	100
No. (100%)	167	151	138	205	186	73

As a measurement of social class we used the Registrar-General's five classes, putting together in the first instance classes I and II, and classes IV and V. Table 8.2 shows a comparison of these three major social groups with the three levels of sex activity. For the boys there is no association between social class and sex activity, but it does appear that the higher up a girl is on the social scale, the more sexual experience she is likely to have ($p = 0.02$); although the proportion of E-girls does not vary much from class to class, the proportion of I-girls in classes I and II is much greater than in classes III, IV or V.

Class III consists of non-manual workers and skilled manual workers; these were divided so that the non-manual were added to classes I and II and the manual to classes IV and V. Once again it was found that there was no association between the level of sex activity and manual or non-manual workers for the boys (NSS), but that girls from the homes of manual workers were likely to have had less experience of inceptive behaviour ($p = 0.01$).

Another analysis was made comparing middle-class teenagers (classes I and II) with all the other classes. The results were similar;

there was no difference between the middle-class boys and the others (NSS), but middle-class girls are more likely to have had inceptive experience than the girls from other classes ($p = 0\cdot01$). The difference is accounted for solely by the large number (53 per cent) of middle-class girls with inceptive experience compared with 35 per cent in the rest of the sample. If the more straightforward, but less meaningful, comparison is made and the sample is divided between those girls who have experienced sexual intercourse and those who have not, then there is very little difference between the classes; 15 per cent of the middle-class girls have had premarital intercourse, and so have 16 per cent of the girls from other classes.

Table 8.2 *Social class analysed by three levels of sex activity*

Social class	Boys			Girls		
	N, %	I, %	E, %	N, %	I, %	E, %
I and II	25	28	23	20	35	25
III	50	50	53	56	47	57
IV and V	25	22	24	24	18	18
TOTAL	100	100	100	100	100	100
No. (100%)	167	151	138	205	186	73

Some writers (Myrdal and Klein, 1956; Bott, 1957) have suggested that the social class of the mother (assessed by her occupation before marriage) has more influence on the child than the father's social class. But in this research no association was found between sexual experience and the occupation of the mother before marriage for either boys or girls (NSS). Of course this is not a very good test because some (8 per cent) mothers did not have a job before marriage, a number of teenagers (10 per cent) did not know what work their mother did before marriage and an unknown number of middle-class mothers may have taken unskilled jobs before they got married. Even so these results seem to show that the mother's social class is not an overriding influence on sexual behaviour.

Jephcott (1962), Kerr (1964) and others have been very concerned about the effects upon the child when the mother is out at work all day. In this sample 21 per cent of the mothers went out to work full time and 32 per cent went out part time; this refers to the situation at the time of the interview when the boys and girls were already teenagers; no doubt less mothers went out to work when their children were younger.

A comparison was made between those mothers who were working full time and those who were not working, leaving out of account those mothers who worked part time. It was found that there was no association between the level of sex activity and those boys whose mothers did not work (NSS); similarly the working situation of the girls' mothers appeared to have no effect upon the extent of their sex experience (NSS).

A detailed analysis was made of the position of each teenager in the family. In fact there seemed to be no relationship between birth order and sexual experience. The oldest child was not likely to be either more or less sexually experienced (NSS); nor was the youngest child (NSS); nor was the only child in the family (NSS).

This section has reported a whole series of tests where no significant association has been found between sexual experience and home background; the only exception is the social class of the girls but not the boys. These negative results seem to us to be important because they are unexpected. An absence of family life and a disturbed childhood is given as the reason for a number of social problems, including lax morality and sexual promiscuity. Furthermore there are grounds for believing that there is a connection between a disturbed family situation and juvenile delinquency (Whyte, 1943; Cohen, 1955), adult crime (Reckless, 1961; West, 1963), mental disorder (Hollingshead and Redlich, 1958; Myers and Roberts, 1959), alcoholism (Lolli, 1961), and most forms of deviant behaviour (Clinard, 1958). But the results reported in this section suggest that teenage sexual behaviour is not associated with early background.

C. RELATIONS WITH PARENTS

The previous section reported on the circumstances surrounding the home life of the teenagers. The actual atmosphere and feeling in the home are more difficult to measure, but because they are important some attempt will be made in this section to report on the adolescents' relations with their parents and relate this to their sexual behaviour.

All the teenagers were asked: How do you get on with your father? Such a question is apt to get a non-committal reply, so the interviewers were instructed to use two standardised supplementary questions. First they asked: What do you like least about your father? Then they asked: What do you like best about your father?

Then similar questions were asked about the relationship with the mother. This procedure encouraged the teenagers to be much more communicative, and from their replies the interviewers rated them on a five-point scale. This scale appears to have some reliability as there was very little difference between the areas, or between the two age groups.

These results were analysed into non-experienced, inceptive and experienced and it was found that there was no association between the three levels of sex activity and the boys' relations with their fathers (NSS). Among the girls, however, there was a clear relationship between these two factors; girls who got on very well with their fathers were far less likely to be sexually experienced ($p = 0.001$).

The association between the level of sex activity and the relations with their mothers was significant for both boys and girls; boys who did not get on well with their mothers were more likely to be sexually experienced ($p = 0.05$); girls who got on well with their mothers were less likely to be sexually experienced ($p = 0.001$).

The teenagers were also asked if they thought their parents were happily married. Only about 5 per cent of the sample said their parents were unhappy together, while the other replies were put into three sequent categories – very happy, happy, average. Once again no relationship was found between the level of sex activity and the marital happiness of the boys' parents (NSS); but among the girls a strong association exists ($p = 0.001$).

D. HOME INFLUENCE

The background circumstances and the relationships within the home would obviously have an important effect upon the upbringing of a child. Beside these factors several other questions were asked about the home and in particular we tried to detect the amount of parental influence on the children and to ascertain parental attempts to enforce discipline.

When they were asked if their parents insisted upon knowing where they went, 43 per cent of the boys and 42 per cent of the girls implied that the situation never arose because they always volunteered the necessary information; for the others the parents of boys were rather less insistent than the girls' parents; among the boys 13 per cent of the parents always wanted to know where they were going and 24 per cent did not insist upon knowing; among the girls 32 per cent always wanted to know where they were going and 8 per cent did not insist.

This parental concern with their children's whereabouts is slightly correlated with the level of sex activity. A boy whose parents always want to know where he is going is likely to have had less sexual experience ($p = 0.02$); similarly a girl whose parents insist on knowing where she is going is likely to have had less sexual experience ($p = 0.05$).

The parents of the teenagers had met all their friends in 62 per cent of the cases among the boys, and 85 per cent of the cases among the girls. For 10 per cent of the boys and 6 per cent of the girls the parents had met hardly any of their friends. But those who introduce all or some of their friends to their parents are neither more nor less sexually experienced than those who never let their parents meet their friends (NSS).

One form of discipline that a parent is reluctant to relinquish is the time the children have to be in at night. When the teenagers were asked what time their parents expected them to be in at weekends 35 per cent of the boys and 17 per cent of the girls said their parents did not mind when they came in; but 31 per cent of the boys and 46 per cent of the girls were expected to be in before midnight, except on special occasions.

Table 8.3 *The time their parents expected the teenagers to be home at weekends analysed by three levels of sex activity*

Time expected to be home	Boys			Girls		
	N, %	I, %	E, %	N, %	I, %	E, %
Up to 11 p.m.	19	9	2	21	12	11
11–12 p.m.	22	28	13	35	27	27
After 12 p.m.	28	35	30	31	41	27
No set time	31	28	55	13	20	35
TOTAL	100	100	100	100	100	100
No. (100%)	167	151	138	205	186	73

For the purposes of comparison these answers were put into the four categories shown in table 8.3. It was found that there was a very strong association between this factor and sexual experience for the boys ($p = 0.001$) and a less strong but significant association for the girls ($p = 0.01$). The N-boys were much more strictly controlled than the E-boys; one in five (19 per cent) of the N-boys had to be in before eleven whereas hardly any E-boys were required to be in at this time. Among the girls over half (56 per cent) of the N-girls had to be in before midnight compared with about one in three (38 per cent) of the E-girls.

Also on the subject of getting home at a specified time, it was found that there was an association between sex experience and the time a teenager was required to leave a party. Not surprisingly many of the parents made a special exemption when their children were going to a party; for 63 per cent of the boys and 43 per cent of the girls no particular time was specified and the teenager was allowed to stay at the party as long as he liked. In fact it was found that those whose parents expected them to leave a party at a particular time had less sexual experience than the others, and this was true for boys ($p = 0.02$) as it was for girls ($p = 0.01$). Other questions were asked about parties and these will be reported in chapter 11.

The amount of discipline the parents attempted to impart, and the extent to which this discipline is accepted or rejected by the teenagers, are both important factors in the upbringing of a child, but this is by no means the only influence. One of the most pervasive and powerful influences is simply the amount of time the teenagers spend with their parents. There are marked differences in the ages at which adolescents cease to be constantly under the supervision of their parents. It is now recognised that the peer group has an important role in the socialisation process and, of course, the values transmitted by the peer group differ from those to be found in the parent–child interaction. It would not be surprising, therefore, if teenagers who spend only a little time with their parents have different attitudes to sex.

Girls tend to spend more time at home than boys; a third (35 per cent) of the girls said they spent more time with their family than outside the home compared with one in five (19 per cent) of the boys. Even so, over half (53 per cent) of the girls and two-thirds (67 per cent) of the boys said they spent more time outside the home; the remainder are accounted for by those who spend most of their time at home but not with their families, and those not living at home. There is a strong association between sexual experience and boys who spend most of their free time outside the home ($p = 0.001$); girls who spend most of their time away from their home are also likely to have had more sexual experience ($p = 0.02$). In terms of the three levels of sex activity, 52 per cent of the N-boys, 70 per cent of the I-boys and 82 per cent of the E-boys spent more of their time outside the home; 51 per cent of the N-girls, 38 per cent of the I-girls and 34 per cent of the E-girls spent more of their time at home.

Only 25 per cent of the boys and 30 per cent of the girls went on summer holidays with their parents; 43 per cent of the boys and 44 per cent of the girls went on holidays without their parents; the remainder did not go on holiday in the summer before the interview. When those who did not go away plus those who went away with their family are compared with those who were away from parental influence during their holidays, it is found that there is a strong association between the level of sex activity and holidays without parents among the boys ($p = 0.001$), but not among the girls (NSS). It was found that 36 per cent N-boys, 55 per cent I-boys and 64 per cent E-boys went on holidays without their parents; but 41 per cent N-girls, 53 per cent I-girls and 49 per cent E-girls went on holidays without parents.

In a few cases (5 per cent) the teenagers were without parental supervision as the parents went away and they stayed at home. It would be inadvisable to make any judgements on this situation because although some had the house to themselves and took the opportunity to throw a teenage party, others were restrained by the presence in the home of elder siblings or other relations. But we did attempt to discover if they ever got the chance to entertain their friends away from the presence of their parents.

Nearly half (45 per cent boys, 44 per cent girls) said they never had the house to themselves so that they could entertain their friends, but several (17 per cent) boys and a few (9 per cent) girls were able to do this while their parents were away, and many more (35 per cent boys, 43 per cent girls) were able to do this when their parents went out for the day or the evening; 3 per cent of the boys and 4 per cent of the girls did not live at home and so the question did not arise.

Many of the results of this research show that the behaviour of teenagers depends upon the facilities available and this factor is no exception for there is a strong association between the level of sex activity and the opportunity to entertain friends at home without parents for both boys ($p = 0.001$) and for girls ($p = 0.01$). Table 8.4 shows that boys, and to a lesser extent girls, who occasionally have the house to themselves are likely to have more sexual experience.

Table 8.4 shows that many more E-boys had the opportunity to bring back their friends to their home when their parents are not there. The I-girls had this opportunity more often than the E-girls, but both of these groups entertained without their parents far more often than the N-girls. This suggests that facilities in the home are

L

an important factor and the suggestion that teenagers will find a way to express their sexual desires whatever parental restrictions are imposed cannot be confirmed by the results of this research.

Table 8.4 *The opportunity to entertain friends at home without parents analysed by three levels of sex activity*

Facilities	Boys			Girls		
	N, %	I, %	E, %	N, %	I, %	E, %
Entertain without parents	37	52	68	42	62	55
Never has house to self	58	45	31	54	34	40
N/A, not at home	5	3	1	4	4	5
TOTAL	100	100	100	100	100	100
No. (100%)	167	151	138	205	186	73

E. PARENTAL CIRCUMSTANCES AND ATTITUDES

In the older age group 69 per cent of the boys and 60 per cent of the girls did not go to church or chapel or any form of religious meeting. Another 9 per cent boys and 11 per cent girls went less than once a month. This leaves about a quarter (23 per cent) of the boys and slightly more (29 per cent) of the girls who attend church with any kind of regularity, and rather more than half of these (14 per cent boys, 19 per cent girls) said they went every week.

Church attendance was strongly associated with the levels of sex activity both for the boys ($p = 0.001$) and for the girls ($p = 0.001$). We found that 44 per cent of the N-boys went to church at least once a month compared with 22 per cent I-boys and 11 per cent E-boys; 32 per cent of the N-girls went to church at least once a month compared with 31 per cent of the I-girls and 9 per cent of the E-girls.

However, there was very little difference between the level of sex activities and the various denominations. Table 8.5 gives the percentages at the three levels for four denominations. Neither boys nor girls from the Church of England, the Nonconformist churches, the Roman Catholic Church or the Jewish faith were more or less likely to be non-experienced, inceptive or experienced (NSS). Of course many of these young people were not interested in religion and their answer to this question merely reflected the religious affiliations of their parents.

Table 8.5 *The three levels of sex activity analysed by denominations*

Level of sex activity	Boys				
	C of E, %	N/C, %	RC, %	Jewish, %	DK/Other, %
N	39	46	34	28	29
I	34	36	29	36	31
E	27	19	37	36	40
TOTAL	100	101	100	100	100
No. (100%)	256	42	52	28	78
	Girls				
N	44	43	49	31	40
I	40	39	40	57	32
E	16	18	11	12	28
TOTAL	100	100	100	100	100
No. (100%)	291	47	75	26	25

The teenagers were also asked if their parents went to church. In 10 per cent of the homes both parents went to church; in 11 per cent only the mother regularly went to church, and in 2 per cent only the father attended church.

Rather unexpectedly there was no association between parental church-going and the levels of sex activity. So although their own church-going was very relevant to their sex behaviour, whether or not they came from a religious home did not appear to be pertinent.

This is in line with the overall impression created by comparing the level of sex activity with the home situation. The circumstances in the home do not appear to be an important influence on the young people's sexual behaviour, but the attitude and actions taken by the parents are much more important. So we find that teenagers are not much affected in this respect by the number of times they moved home, by an absent parent or a broken home, by their social class (except for girls) or their mother's job before marriage, by their position in the family, by their religious affiliation or by the church-going of their parents.

On the other hand we have seen that the relations with the parents and their marital happiness, the discipline in the home and the opportunities and facilities provided, and in particular the interest and concern of the parents for their teenage children and the amount of time they spend together, all seem to be important influences on the sexual development of the adolescent.

9 EDUCATION AND WORK

A. SCHOOL RECORD

In section G of chapter 3 we found only slight variations in the sexual behaviour of adolescents from different types of schools. The largest difference was between secondary modern and grammar schools. Boys who attended grammar schools were likely to be less experienced ($p = $ 0·01), and so were girls ($p = $ 0·001). Boys who went to private school were neither more nor less experienced, but the proportion of I-girls from private schools was greater than chance ($p = $ 0·02). Teenagers who were not N-girls or N-boys tended to be inceptive if they went to grammar or private schools, but tended to be experienced if they went to secondary modern or comprehensive schools.

There is absolutely no difference as regards the level of sex activity between girls who went to a coeducational school and those who went to a segregated school (NSS). There was a very slight tendency for the E-boys to come from a coeducational school and the N-boys and I-boys to come from a segregated school (NSS). There was no sign of an association between the level of sex activity and teenagers who went to a boarding or day school. Although there were only a few (5 per cent) boarders among the teenagers, they appeared to be neither more nor less experienced than the school children who lived at home.

In our sample 45 per cent of the older boys and 40 per cent of the older girls had taken the 'O' level GCE examination. Those who had taken this exam tended to be less experienced than the others ($p = $ 0·001 for boys; $p = $ 0·01 for girls). Table 9.1 shows that many of the I-boys and I-girls had taken GCE, but most of the E-boys and E-girls had not taken the exam. There is no difference in the level of sex activity between those who passed in five or more subjects and those who passed in four or less (NSS).

On the other hand boys who passed 'A' level GCE tended to have less experience than other boys ($p = $ 0·01), but this was not true of girls (NSS). There is probably some slight correlation between academic attainment and the level of sex activity, but a more important influence is the age they leave school.

At the time of the interview 14 per cent of the older boys and 7 per cent of the older girls were still at school. Among the others it was found that E-boys and E-girls were more likely to leave school at fifteen but those who stayed on were as likely to be inceptive as non-experienced. Table 9.2 shows that there is an association between the level of sex activity and the age they left school for boys ($p = 0.05$) and for girls ($p = 0.01$). All the teenagers in this table were between seventeen and nineteen years old.

Table 9.1 *Those who have taken 'O' level GCE and the number of subjects passed analysed by three levels of sex activity*

Number of subjects passed	Boys			Girls		
	N, %	I, %	E, %	N, %	I, %	E, %
None	55	48	75	69	55	71
1–4	18	18	9	8	19	13
5+	27	34	16	23	26	16
TOTAL	100	100	100	100	100	100
No. (100%) *	149	130	116	156	176	67

* This question was not asked in the same form in London C and therefore replies from this area have been excluded.

It is interesting to note that those who have attained higher academic standards and those who stay on at school tend to be inceptive but not experienced. A similar tendency was found among middle-class teenagers (chapter 8). For some reason working-class teenagers who leave school at the statutory minimum age do not remain at the inceptive stage for long; but middle-class teenagers and those who stay on at school appear to get more satisfaction from inceptive behaviour.

All the teenagers, whether they had left school or not, were asked if they liked school. Their replies were classified into three categories. About a half (57 per cent boys, 48 per cent girls) said they liked being at school; another third (30 per cent boys, 29 per cent girls) said they had mixed feelings; fewer boys (13 per cent) than girls (23 per cent) said they disliked school.

Teenagers who disliked being at school were much more likely to be E-boys ($p = 0.01$) or E-girls ($p = 0.001$). Only 11 per cent of the N-boys said they disliked school compared with 22 per cent of the E-boys; 17 per cent of the N-girls said they disliked school compared with 38 per cent of the E-girls.

Two-thirds (63 per cent) of the boys and nearly half (45 per cent) of the girls said they had no special problems at school. Others mentioned such things as the teachers (12 per cent), the work (10 per cent), the discipline (7 per cent) and many other things. There is an association between the level of sex activity and those who had problems at school. Among the boys 30 per cent of the non-experienced, 36 per cent of the inceptives and 46 per cent of the experienced had school problems of one kind or another ($p = 0.02$). A similar tendency was found among the girls ($p = 0.01$); 48 per cent of the N-girls, 56 per cent of the I-girls and 70 per cent of the E-girls had special problems at school. Thus many of the teenagers were pleased to leave school as soon as possible, and these were often the ones who would have the most sexual experience.

Table 9.2 *School leaving age analysed by three levels of sex activity*

Age left school	Boys			Girls		
	N, %	I, %	E, %	N, %	I, %	E, %
14–15	48	41	58	59	46	60
16	21	25	28	22	31	32
17–19	13	18	8	10	17	5
At school	18	16	6	9	6	3
TOTAL	100	100	100	100	100	100
No. (100%)	167	151	138	205	186	73

Some of the teenagers continued with their formal education after they had left school; 23 per cent of the boys were attending evening classes at the time of the interview; most (18 per cent) were taking vocational subjects that were directly related to their work, but few (3 per cent) were going to evening classes in general education, and a few (2 per cent) were going to classes to get further information about hobbies or leisure pursuits. Not so many girls went to evening classes; altogether 12 per cent attended, made up of 7 per cent going to classes on vocational subjects, 1 per cent on general education and 4 per cent on leisure pursuits. There appears to be no relationship between the level of sex activity and attendance at evening class (NSS).

A comparison was made between those who went to evening class twice a week or more often, and those who went once a week or less. But it was found that there was no association between the level of sex activity and the number of times a teenager attended evening class (NSS). It has been suggested that those who continue with their education have less sex experience because they have less free time, and this may be the case for those still at school; but it does not seem to apply to those who go to evening classes who have the same amount of sex experience however many classes they attend.

Although there are small signs of difference in intelligence (as shown by the type of school and exam results) between the sexually experienced and the others, the main differences seem to be personality factors; E-boys and E-girls had more problems at school, had lost interest, and wanted to leave as soon as possible.

B. OCCUPATIONAL RECORD

In our sample 80 per cent of the boys and 82 per cent of the girls were in full-time employment; 2 per cent and 5 per cent respectively were unemployed. This left 14 per cent of the boys who were at school, 4 per cent at university; 7 per cent of the girls were still at school with 6 per cent at university or technical college.

Boys who were working were more likely to be sexually experienced ($p = 0 \cdot 01$). Only 8 per cent of the E-boys were at school or college. Among the girls those with experience seemed more likely to be unemployed, but the numbers are small (NSS); 5 per cent of the N-girls, 3 per cent of the I-girls and 10 per cent of the E-girls had left school but were out of work at the time when they were interviewed. The number of girls at work did not differ (82 per cent at all three levels), but 14 per cent of the N-girls, 16 per cent of the I-girls and 8 per cent of the E-girls were at school or college, which shows a trend similar to that found among the boys although the numbers are too small for it to be statistically significant (NSS).

A quarter (29 per cent) of the boys were in non-manual jobs and half (51 per cent) were in manual jobs. With the girls it was the other way round; half (57 per cent) were doing non-manual work and a quarter (24 per cent) were doing manual work. Although it was possible to detect a slight tendency for non-manual workers to be inceptive and manual workers to be experienced, in fact the association between the levels of sex activity and manual or non-manual jobs was only just significant for girls ($p = 0.05$), and not significant for boys (NSS).

When the teenagers were asked if they liked their job, a large number (52 per cent boys, 44 per cent girls) said they were very content, others (22 per cent boys, 26 per cent girls) were fairly content but had some reservations, and only a few (7 per cent boys, 10 per cent girls) said they did not like their job. It has often been said that one of the causes of teenager misbehaviour is boredom; if this is the case, then it would appear that the boys and girls are bored during their leisure, for the vast majority seem to be happy in their work.

Among the girls there was a slight tendency for the least contented to be the most experienced ($p = 0.05$), but this tendency was not apparent among the boys (NSS); indeed as many as 57 per cent of the E-boys said they were very content with their job compared with 54 per cent of the N-boys and 45 per cent of the I-boys who said they were very content; among the girls who were very content with their work, 48 per cent were N-girls, 44 per cent were I-girls and 32 per cent were E-girls.

Table 9.3 *The number of jobs analysed by three levels of sex activity*

Number of jobs	Boys			Girls		
	N, %	I, %	E, %	N, %	I, %	E, %
1	41	50	35	40	34	19
2	20	16	25	20	26	18
3	9	6	12	18	13	25
4+	7	6	19	6	10	25
N/A	23	22	9	16	17	13
TOTAL	100	100	100	100	100	100
No. (100%)	167	151	138	205	186	73

Job contentment notwithstanding, 20 per cent of the boys and 28 per cent of the girls had been in three or more jobs in the short time in which they had been in employment. Table 9.3 shows the number of jobs the teenagers have had at each level of sex activity; those who are still at school or have only had part-time or vacation jobs are put together in the last category (N/A).

The more experienced a boy is, the more jobs he is likely to have had ($p = $ 0·01), and there is a similar association between sex experience and the number of jobs for girls ($p = $ 0·001). Half the E-girls and nearly a third (31 per cent) of the E-boys had been in more than two jobs; only 7 per cent of the N-boys have had four or more jobs, compared with 19 per cent of the E-boys; only 6 per cent of the N-girls have had four or more jobs compared with 25 per cent of the E-girls.

Table 9.4 *The amount received in wages analysed by three levels of sex activity*

Weekly wages	Boys			Girls		
	N, %	I, %	E, %	N, %	I, %	E, %
Up to £5	15	13	7	13	14	13
£5–£7	30	33	25	37	43	33
£7–£9	16	18	25	26	20	19
£9–£12	8	11	17	4	3	15
£12+	6	2	16	0	1	3
Unemployed	3	2	3	5	3	10
At school	22	21	7	15	16	7
TOTAL	100	100	100	100	100	100
No. (100%)*	149	130	116	156	176	67

* This question was not asked in the same form in London C and therefore the replies from this area have been excluded.

The teenagers were asked how much was in their pay packet last week. Thus their pay was calculated for the period immediately before the interview and the results given in table 9.4 refer to the amount of money received after deductions for tax and insurance. On this basis we found that a minority (13 per cent boys, 14 per cent girls) were earning under five pounds a week, the majority (48 per cent boys, 60 per cent girls) were earning between five and nine pounds a week and the others (19 per cent boys, 7 per cent girls) were earning over nine pounds a week – a few of the boys (3 per cent) in this latter group were making fifteen pounds a week or more. Average earnings of boys and youths at the time the interviews were carried out was about seven pounds and ten shillings.

There is an association between the level of sex activity and the weekly wage for boys ($p = 0.01$) and for girls ($p = 0.02$). For the boys the dividing line seems to be about nine pounds; the N-boys are much more likely to receive a wage below that figure, and most of the high wages are paid to E-boys. The difference between the N-boys and the E-boys would be even more striking were it not for the I-boys who, in this case, are not in a midway position; in general they seem to make rather less than the N-boys. Thus it can be seen that the difference in wages between boys who have experienced sexual intercourse (E-boys), and those who have not (N- and I-boys), is very great indeed.

The trend is very similar for the girls. Although the girls are paid less than the boys overall, the dividing line is still around nine pounds; below that line the differences are not so great; very few N-girls earn more than nine pounds a week, but one in five of the E-girls are paid more than this. As with the boys, the I-girls are much more like the N-girls than the E-girls and it becomes clear that the experienced girls make much more money than the inceptive or non-experienced girls.

A special effort was made during the interview to get an estimate of the amount of money each individual had left to spend. Starting from the amount received in wages, we found out and deducted the amount paid in rent or given to the parents to pay for their keep; we further deducted any other unavoidable or regular outgoings such as fares and other commitments, but not money paid for hire purchase or into a clothing or Christmas club. This was worked out between the teenager and the interviewer until they arrived at an agreed sum that was left to spend in an average week. For teenagers still at school the sum was calculated after deductions had been made from the pocket money allowed by parents or the grant in the case of students at college.

The amount of spending money available to these teenagers aged seventeen to nineteen spread over a wide range. For 5 per cent of the boys and 4 per cent of the girls there was less than ten shillings a week; at the other end of the scale 7 per cent of the boys and 2 per cent of the girls had more than seven pounds a week to spend. But the majority had between one and four pounds each week; 39 per cent of the boys and 39 per cent of the girls had under two pounds; 37 per cent of the boys and 43 per cent of the girls had between two and four pounds; 24 per cent of the boys and 18 per cent of the girls had over four pounds to spend each week. The amount of spending money available to the teenagers in each of the three levels of sex activity is given in table 9.5.

There is a very strong association between spending money and the level of sex activity. Boys who have a lot of money to spend are much more likely to be experienced ($p = 0.001$); and this is also true of girls ($p = 0.02$). Only 5 per cent of the N-boys and 3 per cent of the I-boys have over six pounds a week to spend, but 24 per cent of the E-boys have this amount. Only 16 per cent of the N-girls and 18 per cent of the I-girls have over four pounds to spend, but 30 per cent of the E-girls have this amount to spend.

Table 9.5 *Money left to spend analysed by three levels of sex activity*

Money to spend	Boys			Girls		
	N, %	I, %	E, %	N, %	I, %	E, %
Under 10s.	5	5	3	8	1	1
10s. to £1	12	14	3	11	7	16
£1–£2	27	29	15	24	28	15
£2–£4	43	32	36	41	46	38
£4–£6	8	17	19	12	13	21
£6+	5	3	24	4	5	9
TOTAL	100	100	100	100	100	100
No. (100%) *	149	130	116	156	176	67

* This question was not asked in the same form in London C and therefore the replies from this area have been excluded.

It is possible that many of the factors noted in this chapter are interconnected. It might be argued that teenagers who left school at fifteen had more sexual experience because there were more opportunities and facilities for sex after they had started work. But we believe it is a kind of restlessness that impels the E-boys and E-girls to leave school.

Perhaps one might expect the E-boys and E-girls to be earning more because they have had a longer working career. In fact it is the blind alley jobs that pay the highest wages in youth employment. It might also be said that the sexually experienced teenagers had more jobs because they were in employment over a longer period; if they left school at fifteen, they would have been at work for about three years by the time we interviewed them, whereas others who left school at seventeen or sixteen would have been at work for only one or two years, and so would have had less time to change jobs as often. But even allowing for this there is a large difference between the number of times the experienced teenagers changed their jobs, and the relatively few times the others changed; and this seems to indicate that a kind of vocational restlessness is associated with sex activity among teenagers.

10 GROUPS

A. GROUP MEMBERSHIP

As the child grows up he becomes less dependent on his family and mixes with friends outside the home. In our sample the amount of time spent at home depended upon the age of the teenager. Among the younger age groups a third (33 per cent) of the boys and almost half (45 per cent) of the girls spent more time with their families than outside the home; but among the older teenagers, only a fifth (19 per cent) of the boys and a third of the girls (35 per cent) spent more time at home.

There was an association between the level of sex activity and the amount of time spent away from their families; E-boys were much more likely to spend more of their free time outside the home ($p = $ 0·001) and so were the E-girls ($p = $ 0·02). This association is independent of the age influence because it will be remembered that in this part of the report (chapters 8–11) only the older age groups are being used to test the relationship of sex activities with other factors.

Questions about groups are not always successful because the interviewee is not always clear what is meant. The boundaries of such groups tend to be nebulous and their membership is constantly changing. First of all we asked about their leisure activities (reported in the next chapter) and then we asked about the people with whom they spent most of their time after work or school and at weekends. Assuming that a group comprised three or more people including the person being interviewed, we found that about three-quarters (74 per cent) of the older boys and about two-thirds (64 per cent) of the older girls went round with a particular group of friends.

There is an association between the level of sex activity and group membership both for boys ($p = $ 0·01) and for girls ($p = $ 0·05). Table 10.1 shows that N-boys and N-girls are less likely to go round in groups. Table 10.1 also shows that those who were in mixed groups were most likely to be sexually experienced; furthermore many of the boys who went round in single sex groups were also sexually experienced, but this was not often the case with the girls. The association between the level of sex activity and those who were in mixed groups is stronger for girls ($p = $ 0·01) than it is for boys (NSS).

The influence of the group varied considerably from one person to another. Among the boys nearly half (49 per cent) met the group at least three times a week, and a fifth (19 per cent) met daily. The girls tended to meet less frequently; a quarter (26 per cent) met three or more times a week, but only 7 per cent said they met every day. The association between the level of sex activity and the time spent with the group is strong for boys ($p = 0.02$), but not so strong for girls (NSS).

Table 10.1 *Group membership and the type of group analysed by three levels of sex activity*

Type of group	Boys			Girls		
	N, %	I, %	E, %	N, %	I, %	E, %
No group	35	24	19	41	30	36
All boys	45	48	44	—	—	—
All girls	—	—	—	20	16	8
Mixed	20	28	37	39	54	56
TOTAL	100	100	100	100	100	100
No. (100%)	167	151	138	205	186	73

Most teenage groups have a recognised meeting-place where they foregather at least at the start of an evening. Often it was in one of their homes (18 per cent), at a youth club (7 per cent) or at school (2 per cent). Other groups met in commercial premises such as bars (12 per cent), dance halls (8 per cent) or coffee bars (6 per cent). A few (4 per cent) said they met outside, another 12 per cent mentioned other meeting-places and the remaining 31 per cent were not members of a group.

We found there was a difference in the level of sex activity between those who met in their homes or youth clubs, and those who met in dance halls, coffee bars or premises licensed to sell alcohol for both boys ($p = 0.02$) and girls ($p = 0.01$). Both N-boys and N-girls were more likely to meet at home or in youth clubs, and E-boys and E-girls were more likely to meet in commercial premises.

B. THE INFLUENCE OF THE GROUP

As the adolescent spends more and more time in a teenage group, he begins to adopt opinions and beliefs obtained from his friends, and sometimes these attitudes are in conflict with the opinions and beliefs of his parents.

All the teenagers were asked if they would prefer to talk over a personal problem with their parents or with someone else. Over half (54 per cent) said they would go to their parents for advice, but 20 per cent of the boys and 30 per cent of the girls said they would go to someone of their own age. It was found that N-boys are much more likely to go to their parents for advice ($p = 0.01$) and this was also true of N-girls ($p = 0.05$).

Some of the teenagers said they would seek advice from their brothers or sisters, or adults other than their parents, but 11 per cent of the boys and 3 per cent of the girls said that if they had a personal problem they would keep it to themselves and not tell anyone. There seemed to be no association between these self-sufficient or lonely people, and their level of sex activity.

Later in the interview a similar question was asked, except that this time the problem was specified as something to do with sex. In these circumstances the E-girls were even less likely to go to their parents for advice ($p = 0.001$). The E-boys were also less likely to seek advice from their parents ($p = 0.01$).

An indirect attempt was made to see if their standards of sexual behaviour were influenced by other teenagers. Everyone was asked: Do you think your friends have more or less sex experience than you? Not surprisingly 34 per cent of the boys and 29 per cent of the girls answered that the behaviour of their friends varied – some had more, some less. But the others gave fairly definite replies. About a third (30 per cent boys, 31 per cent girls) thought their friends had about the same amount of experience, and about the same number (27 per cent boys, 35 per cent girls) thought their friends had more sex experience; only 7 per cent of the boys and 5 per cent of the girls thought their friends were less experienced. Most teenagers, whatever their level of sex activity, felt their friends were having as much sex as they were, if not more.

C. CLOSE FRIENDS

In section E of chapter 4 we noted that teenagers who start dating at an early age were more likely to have sexual intercourse. In fact there is a strong association between the age of the first date and the level of sex activity for boys ($p = 0.001$) and for girls ($p = 0.001$). There is a similar association between the age of the first kiss and sex activity for boys ($p = 0.001$) and girls ($p = 0.001$). But the age when they start dating is not the only significant association; there also appears to be an association between the duration, and so the strength, of the relationship. The E-boys were much more likely to date a girl over a long period ($p = 0·001$) and so were the E-girls ($p = 0·01$).

Over a third of the boys (38 per cent) said they had a steady girl friend at the time of the interview, and still more (58 per cent) girls said they had a steady boy friend. We did not attempt to define what was meant by steady when we asked this question, but we did ask them how long they had been going out with their steady girl or boy friend. In fact 2 per cent of both boys and girls had been going out with their steady for less than a month, while 8 per cent of the boys and 6 per cent of the girls had been going out less than three months. On the other hand there were some long relationships, for 15 per cent of the boys and 27 per cent of the girls had been going out for over a year.

We felt that any relationship which had been going on for more than three months could reasonably be called steady. On this definition 30 per cent of the boys and 52 per cent of the girls were going steady. Not altogether surprisingly there is a strong association between the boys with steady girl friends and their level of sex activity ($p = 0·001$). There is a similar association between girls with boy friends and the level of sex activity ($p = 0·01$).

More specifically the teenagers were asked if they were in love. Over a quarter (29 per cent) of the boys and exactly half (50 per cent) of the girls said they were in love at the time the interview took place; a further 21 per cent of the boys and 15 per cent of the girls had been in love in the past, leaving half (50 per cent) the boys and a third (35 per cent) of the girls who said they had never been in love. There is a strong association between those who have been in love and the level of sex activity ($p = 0·001$ for both boys and girls).

The girls were much more likely to say they were engaged; 16 per cent of the girls said they were engaged at the time the interview took place compared with 4 per cent of the boys. This suggests there is a misunderstanding between many courting couples; the girl feels sure that they are going to get married, but the boy thinks that he has not yet committed himself. But another reason for the difference is that many teenage girls marry boys who would be too old to qualify as teenagers for this research. In 1962 21 per cent of all the girls aged nineteen in England and Wales were married, but only 4 per cent of the nineteen-year-old boys were married.[1] Over a quarter (27 per cent) of the older girls said they hoped to be married

1. From the Registrar-General's *Review* of 1962.

M

before they were twenty-one compared with only 8 per cent of the older boys. Even more (38 per cent) of the younger girls hoped to marry before they were twenty-one compared with 9 per cent of the younger boys. Marriage is a much more immediate prospect for a teenage girl than it is for a teenage boy.

Among the girls who said they had steady boy friends, 15 per cent were having sexual intercourse with them; among the girls who were engaged, 37 per cent were having sexual intercourse with their fiancés. Among the boys with steadies, 41 per cent were having sexual intercourse with their girl friends; among the few boys who were engaged, 39 per cent were having sexual intercourse with their fiancées. This suggests that a large number of the sexually experienced teenagers have premarital intercourse with very close friends, and often with the person they will eventually marry. This is confirmed by the fact that a third of the E-boys and three-quarters of the E-girls had sexual intercourse with one partner only in the last year, and 25 per cent of the E-boys and 65 per cent of the E-girls have never had intercourse with more than one partner.

In addition to the engaged couples who decide to have sexual intercourse before their wedding day, there are also courting couples who decide to get married when it is found that the girl is pregnant. This further increases the number of experienced teenagers who only have premarital intercourse with the person they will marry. It seems likely that much of the premarital sexual activities of teenagers is not promiscuous behaviour.

D. FRIENDS AS A SOURCE OF INFORMATION

Precocious boys who learn about sex at an early age are more likely to be sexually experienced by the time they are eighteen ($p = 0.001$); only 14 per cent of the N-boys knew the facts of life before the age of twelve compared with 34 per cent of the E-boys; and 48 per cent of the N-boys were over fourteen before they found out compared with 31 per cent of the E-boys. This association between the levels of sex activity and early knowledge about sex does not seem to apply to girls (NSS).

But the source of this information is more important for girls than for boys. Table 10.2 shows that girls who first heard about the facts of life from their parents are more likely to be N-girls or I-girls ($p = 0.05$); there appears to be a similar tendency for the N-boys but the figures are smaller (NSS). Those who get their first information about sex from their teachers are also more likely to be N-girls ($p = 0.01$), but this is not true for boys (NSS).

Classified under the category *other* are clergymen, other adults, work-mates, siblings and books (see section A of chapter 6). By far the largest number of people learnt the facts of life from their school friends and this was strongly associated with the level of sex activity for both girls ($p = 0.001$) and boys ($p = 0.001$).

Table 10.2 *The source of the first information about sex analysed by three levels of sex activity*

Source of information	Boys			Girls		
	N, %	I, %	E, %	N, %	I, %	E, %
Parent	13	7	7	32	30	16
Teacher	13	8	12	25	13	14
Friends	49	74	63	30	49	56
Others	25	11	18	13	8	14
TOTAL	100	100	100	100	100	100
No. (100%)	167	151	138	205	186	73

Girls who had never received any advice about sex from their parents at any time were more likely to be E-girls ($p = 0.05$); 26 per cent of the N-girls, 30 per cent of the I-girls and 41 per cent of the E-girls had never received any advice about sex from their parents. This did not apply to the boys (NSS); two-thirds (67 per cent) of the boys, whatever their level of sex activity, had never received any advice about sex from their parents.

In section B of this chapter it was found that the more experience a girl had, the less likely she was to go to her parents for advice about sex ($p = 0.001$); 59 per cent of the N-girls, 42 per cent of the I-girls, but only 22 per cent of the E-girls would go to their parents. The experienced boys were also less likely to seek advice from their parents ($p = 0.01$); 58 per cent of the N-boys, 46 per cent of the I-boys and 36 per cent of the E-boys said they would go to their parents. So the teenagers who are most likely to have a serious sex problem are also those who are least likely to go to their parents for help.

Sex education seems to have had remarkably little effect on the subsequent sex behaviour of the teenagers. Rather less than half the boys received sex education at school. Those who were given some form of sex education were neither more nor less experienced in their sexual activities (NSS). More girls received sex education, but there is no association between those who received it and the level of sex activity (NSS). Nearly half the older boys (47 per cent) and girls (43 per cent) thought they should have been told more about sex at school, but this desire for more information was equally prevalent in all three levels of sex activity (NSS).

About half the boys felt they knew all there was to know about sex; just as many of these were N-boys, I-boys or E-boys (NSS). Among the girls the percentage who felt they knew all about sex was about the same for N-girls (47 per cent) or E-girls (52 per cent); it was the I-girls who were the least confident for only 36 per cent of those felt they knew all there was to know ($p = 0.05$).

In chapter 6 it was reported that only a few teenagers would be able to identify venereal disease. It was found that boys with good knowledge about VD were much more likely to be experienced ($p = 0.001$), and this was also true of the experienced girls ($p = 0.01$). We found good knowledge about VD in 8 per cent of the N-boys, 11 per cent of the I-boys and 27 per cent of the E-boys; 9 per cent of the N-girls, 12 per cent of the I-girls and 20 per cent of the E-girls appeared to be correctly informed about VD. Among the boys with experience of sexual intercourse 35 per cent revealed slight knowledge of VD and 38 per cent appeared to have no knowledge at all. Among the experienced girls 52 per cent revealed slight knowledge and 28 per cent had no knowledge. It appears, therefore, that three-quarters of the boys at risk and four out of five girls at risk would not know if they had been infected.

It has already been reported (section D, chapter 6) that the majority of teenagers with experience of sexual intercourse do not use contraceptives; 25 per cent of the E-boys and 61 per cent of the E-girls never used any method of birth control. It is difficult to know if this is due to lack of knowledge or lack of concern. But this section has shown that knowledge on sexual matters is not a prerequisite of premarital intercourse.

The sexually active teenagers tended to find out about sex from their friends and to eschew information or advice from their parents. Sex education given in the schools does not seem to have inhibited sex activities nor does it seem to have encouraged it 'by putting ideas into their heads' as some have feared. Many teenagers think they know all about sex whether they have had practical experience or not. In fact those with sexual experience are slightly more informed, but good knowledge about sexual matters is far from widespread.

The results reported in this chapter have shown that teenage groups are an influence on sexual behaviour. The sexually experienced girl is likely to be in a mixed group and the experienced boy is likely to spend a lot of time with his group. Those who meet in commercial premises are more often sexually experienced than those who meet in youth clubs or in their own homes. Boys who are non-experienced tend to think that their friends have more sex than they do ($p = 0.05$); this, combined with the strong pressures towards conformity in teenage groups, must be one of the influences that lead a boy on to sexual experimentation.

Boys and girls who are courting have more sex experience. Many of the teenagers marry the only person with whom they have had sexual intercourse, either because they feel premarital intercourse is only permissible between couples about to be married, or because an unexpected pregnancy leads to marriage.

II LEISURE

A. YOUTH CLUBS

The type and number of youth clubs varied considerably in the seven areas where the research was carried out. In one of the London boroughs there were hardly any facilities, but in the area we designated South A, there was one of the largest and best-equipped youth clubs in the country. In the whole sample a third of the younger boys and younger girls were members of youth clubs. In the older groups 23 per cent of the boys were still members, but only 11 per cent of the girls. The girls seemed more inclined to drift away from youth clubs as they got older.

Although most of the older boys were not in a youth club, many of them were members of some kind of club or association such as a sports club (13 per cent), jazz club (4 per cent), political club (1 per cent), pre-service unit (1 per cent) or the scouts (1 per cent). The girls were less likely to join these kinds of associations although 5 per cent were in jazz clubs and 4 per cent in sports clubs.

There was no association between youth club membership and the level of sex activity (NSS). E-boys and E-girls were just as likely to be club members as not. Nor was there any difference between the boys who went to segregated clubs and those who went to mixed youth clubs (NSS). There were not enough girls in segregated clubs to be able to make this comparison.

Club members were asked when they last went to their club and this revealed a difference between the girls and boys. Although as many E-girls were still members, they tended to visit the club less often ($p = 0.01$). Only 10 per cent of the E-girls who were members had visited their clubs within the last seven days compared with 17 per cent of the I-girls and 24 per cent of the N-girls. But this association between the level of sex activity and frequency of attendance at clubs did not apply to the boys (NSS).

Much thought has been given by youth workers to the problem of the so-called unclubbables. Experiments have been made with special types of youth clubs and social centres in an attempt to attract the type of boy who would not be interested in joining an ordinary youth club. It has been felt that the limitation of the ordinary youth club has been that it only attracts the type of boy who would keep clear of trouble in any event. But so far as sex behaviour is concerned the unclubbables do not stand apart.

Although youth clubs have undoubtedly had some success in other problem areas, there does not seem to be much evidence to support the view of some youth leaders that premarital sexual intercourse can be prevented by persuading the boys to join a club. There is no difference in sexual behaviour between the boys who are not in a club, and those who are in mixed clubs where it is hoped they will meet 'the right type' of girls, and those who are in segregated clubs where they will not meet any girls at all.

There are some indications that experienced girls are the first to leave youth clubs as they get older. This may be because a girl with a steady boy friend may wish to spend most of her free time with him away from the club. But in any case girls are less interested in youth clubs by the time they reach the age of eighteen and the influence of the club diminishes rapidly.

B. OTHER SPARE-TIME ACTIVITIES

Most boys are interested in sport and although this interest tends to diminish after they leave school, nearly two-thirds (64 per cent) of the older boys had played some kind of sport during the four weeks before the interview; about a third (30 per cent) of them were still keen on sport and had played more than once in the week before the interview. The girls were less interested, but over half (52 per cent) the older girls had played some kind of sport in the last month and 15 per cent had played twice or more in the week before the interview.

Boys who did not play any sport at any time were more likely to be sexually experienced ($p = 0.02$); 34 per cent of the N-boys, 26 per cent of the I-boys and 43 per cent of the E-boys did not play sport at all. However, among the majority who played sport at some time, there was no difference between those who played frequently and those who hardly ever played (NSS).

Much the same tendencies are to be found among the girls. Girls who played no sports at all tended to be sexually experienced ($p = 0.05$); 37 per cent of the N-girls, 36 per cent of the I-girls and 54 per cent of the E-girls had given up sport altogether. But there seemed to be very little difference between those who played often and those who hardly ever played (NSS).

Over a third (38 per cent) of the older boys had some form of transport; 10 per cent had a motor-cycle, 9 per cent had a motor-scooter and 19 per cent either had a car of their own or the use of their parents' car. But there was no association between the level of sex activity and the boys who used any of these forms of transport

(NSS). Those who had cars or motor-cycles were not more experienced than those who did not have them. Nor was there any difference between the motor-cyclists and those with scooters.

Audience research by the commercial companies has shown that the segment of the population least interested in television is the teenage group, but since the advent of the pop music programmes especially designed to attract the teenage viewer, it seems likely that the influence of TV is growing. Everyone was asked what they had done on the evening before the interview and on the previous Saturday. Table 11.1 gives the full list of the replies. Some people did several things on these two evenings and all their activities were recorded, so the totals add up to more than 100 per cent.

Television was mentioned more than any other activity by boys

Table 11.1 *Activities reported on the evening before the interview and on the previous Saturday evening*

	Boys		Girls	
Activities	Weekday evening, %	Saturday evening, %	Weekday evening, %	Saturday evening, %
Television	31	18	27	18
Visited friends	14	8	19	14
Drink in pub	10	16	7	13
Studied at home	9	4	4	5
Sport	9	4	2	2
Records/radio	7	5	12	6
Cinema	5	9	7	9
Coffee bar	5	5	5	5
Youth club	5	1	2	0
Friends at home	5	4	11	7
Motor-cycle	4	2	1	1
Other club	4	6	2	4
Walk	3	4	2	1
Dance	3	8	4	11
Read a book	2	2	4	2
Party	1	7	0	7
Meal out	1	2	2	4
Concert/theatre	0	1	2	1
Other	25	23	19	19

and girls on weekdays and weekends. The other frequent activities for boys on weekdays is visiting, drinking, studying and sport; at the weekend it is a pub, a cinema, a dance or visiting friends. The most frequent activities after watching TV for girls on weekdays are visiting friends, listening to records and entertaining friends at home; at weekends they are visiting, drinking, dancing and the cinema.

Table 11.1 shows that a third (31 per cent) of the boys and a quarter (27 per cent) of the girls watched television at some point of the weekday evening and even on Saturday night, when most teenagers would expect to be out of the home, 18 per cent had seen television for at least part of the evening. When they were asked how many evenings a week they watched television, 10 per cent of both boys and girls said they watched six or seven nights a week. Among the others, 31 per cent of the boys and 38 per cent of the girls watched between three and five nights a week; 43 per cent boys and 42 per cent girls watched once or twice; and 16 per cent boys and 10 per cent girls hardly ever or never watched television. But there was no association between the level of sex activity and the number of nights a week they watched television (NSS).

Teenagers go to the cinema more often than most people. In this sample 9 per cent went more than once a week and another 32 per cent went every week; another 27 per cent of the boys and 34 per cent of the girls went less than once a week but more than once a month. Only 31 per cent of the boys and 25 per cent of the girls went less than once a month.

Although there is little difference between the amount boys and girls went to the cinema, there is a difference in the association between this and the level of sex activity. Table 11.2 shows that experienced boys go to the cinema more often ($p = 0.001$), but cinema-going and sexual experience are not related for girls (NSS).

But the person they usually accompanied to the cinema is significant for girls as well as boys. Many of the boys (46 per cent) said they usually went to the cinema with their girl friend and even more of the girls (62 per cent) went with their boy friend. There is a strong association between the level of sex activity and those who went to the cinema with their girl or boy friends ($p = 0.001$ for boys and girls). The numbers are high for I-boys and I-girls, as well as for E-boys and E-girls. The darkness inside a cinema provides one of the few semi-private places where a boy and girl can go to make love.

The last activity considered in this section is dancing. The teenagers were asked when they last went to a dance and this included dances at youth clubs and jazz clubs as well as at commercial dance halls. Although pop music and new forms of dancing are thought of as endemic to the teenage world, in fact the frequencies are not as high as might be expected. Only 4 per cent of the boys and 6 per cent of the girls went dancing three or more times a week. Among the boys a quarter (26 per cent) went dancing at least once a week, a third (37 per cent) went less often, and the rest (37 per cent) hardly ever or never went to a dance. The girls went a bit more often; 31 per cent went at least once a week, 40 per cent went less often, and 29 per cent hardly ever or never went. As with the cinema, there is an association for boys ($p = 0.001$), but not for girls (NSS), between dancing and the level of sex activity.

Table 11.2 *The last visit to the cinema analysed by three levels of sex activity*

Cinema last visited	Boys			Girls		
	N, %	I, %	E, %	N, %	I, %	E, %
Up to 7 days ago	40	42	54	43	47	48
Up to 2 weeks ago	13	26	9	17	19	15
Up to 4 weeks ago	14	12	17	17	16	16
Hardly ever, never	33	20	21	23	18	21
TOTAL	100	100	101	100	100	100
No. (100%)	167	151	138	205	186	73

Again as with the cinema, the person they went with to the dance was more important for the girls than the number of times they went. Although many (31 per cent) girls went to dances with other girls, and some (11 per cent) went in a mixed group, the largest proportion went with their boy friends. These girls who went dancing with their boy friends were more likely to be experienced than those who went with other people ($p = 0.05$).

This association was not found among the boys. Although 23 per cent usually took their girl friend with them when they went dancing, these boys were not likely to be more experienced than those who went with other boys (37 per cent) or in a mixed group (10 per cent). So for a boy the level of sex activity for both cinema-going and dancing is associated with the number of times he goes, but for a girl it depends whether she goes with her boy friend or not. As we have already noted (section C of chapter 10) girls with steady boy friends tend to be more experienced whether they go to cinemas and dances or not, and this may be influencing the association which we found for girls. But the clear-cut association between sex experience and both cinema-going and dancing among the boys is unaffected by the person they went with, and can be taken as a sign of gregariousness, a characteristic which will be discussed in chapter 13.

C. PARTIES

Although by no means the most frequent teenage activity, we made special and detailed inquiries about parties because it has been alleged that many of these teenage gatherings are specifically arranged to facilitate sexual activities. Those teenagers who admitted getting drunk, often said it was at a party; 32 per cent of the older teenagers said they had got drunk at a party, compared with 17 per cent at a public house, 4 per cent at their own home, 3 per cent at someone else's home; 5 per cent mentioned other places and 39 per cent had never been drunk.

In chapter 8 it was noted that about half (52 per cent) of the boys and girls sometimes had the house to themselves, and it can be assumed that in many of these cases it was possible to throw a party. At all events teenagers who could entertain at home were often the experienced teenagers. But of course teenagers can go to many parties given by friends even if they are unable to hold a party at their own home without the supervision of their parents.

Only 11 per cent of the boys and 7 per cent of the girls said they had never been to a party. But parties vary enormously from the staid to the riotous. We tried to define what we meant by a party by asking about the age of the other people at the last party they attended. If it was obviously not a children's or a family party, and if it was not supervised by parents, then by our definition it was a *teenage* party if most of the people were the same age as the interviewee, and an *adult* party if most of the people there were older.

We found that the last party attended by 57 per cent of the boys and 41 per cent of the girls was a teenage party, and for 11 per cent of the boys and 26 per cent of the girls it was an adult party. So girls were more likely than boys to go to parties where most of the other people were older. Boys who attended teenage or adult parties were as likely to be I-boys as E-boys, but were less likely to be N-boys ($p = 0.01$). Girls who went to teenage or adult parties were most often I-girls, not so often E-girls or N-girls (NSS). The teenagers were also asked how often they had been to a party when there were no parents in the house. There was an association between the level of sex activity and the number of times a boy or girl had been to a party without parental supervision ($p = 0.001$ for boys and girls).

In chapter 8 it was noted that there was an association between the level of sex activity and the time a teenager was expected back from a party ($p = 0.02$ for boys, and $p = 0.01$ for girls). More specifically those who attended teenage or adult parties were asked how many of the parties had lasted past midnight. Table 11.3 shows that this is quite a common occurrence for half the E-boys, and for a quarter of the I-boys, I-girls and E-girls. There is a strong association between the level of sex activity and the number of times they went to parties which lasted past midnight ($p = 0.001$ for boys and girls).

Table 11.3 *Attendance at parties which have lasted past midnight analysed by three levels of sex activity*

Number of parties lasting past midnight	Boys			Girls		
	N, %	I, %	E, %	N, %	I, %	E, %
10+	2	24	51	7	22	25
3–10	11	16	14	19	18	19
1–2	14	24	11	14	17	18
Never	20	13	6	22	17	15
No parties*	53	23	18	38	26	23
TOTAL	100	100	100	100	100	100
No. (100%)	167	151	138	205	186	73

* This refers to those who have not been to teenage or adult parties.

A similar association is found between the level of sex activity and those who have been to all-night parties ($p = 0.001$ for boys and girls) although this happened much more infrequently. Among the boys 15 per cent had been to an all-night party more than twice, and nearly all of them were E-boys. Among the girls 11 per cent had been to an all-night party more than twice, half of them E-girls and half I-girls. But there were many experienced and inceptive boys and girls who had not been to this kind of party.

This detailed consideration of teenage party-going shows that it is not the number of parties attended but the type of party that appears to be associated with sexual experience. Not surprisingly parties without parental supervision tend to be more permissive. There is also a strong association between sex experience and the length of time the party goes on.

Although this section has shown that sex experience is associated with party-going and especially a particular type of party, it is possible to exaggerate the importance of this. Only 3 per cent of the older boys (10 per cent of all E-boys) met their first sexual partner at a party and only 2 per cent (7 per cent of all E-boys) had their first experience of sexual intercourse at a party; 2 per cent of the older girls (8 per cent of the E-girls) met their first sexual partner at a party and 2 per cent (7 per cent of the E-girls) had their first experience of sexual intercourse at a party.

D. DRINKING AND SMOKING

All of the boys in the younger age group of boys were under eighteen and so legally prohibited from obtaining alcoholic drinks in a public house. In fact over a hundred (21 per cent) went to a pub at least once a week. In the older age group which we are considering in this chapter, 27 per cent were under eighteen. Over half (57 per cent) the older boys had been to a bar in the week before the interview, another 13 per cent in the previous month and another 14 per cent in the last six months; 16 per cent had never been to a bar.

Girls do not go out drinking quite so often, but the number who had been to a public house recently was not very much smaller; 43 per cent had been to a bar in the week before the interview, another 20 per cent in the previous month and another 17 per cent in the last six months; 19 per cent had never been to a bar.

According to the boys they usually went to a bar with friends of the same sex (65 per cent), less often with a mixed group (7 per cent), relatives (6 per cent) or their girl friends (5 per cent). According to the girls they usually went with their boy friends (46 per cent), in a mixed group (23 per cent) or with relatives (12 per cent). The discrepancy is probably accounted for by the fact that during a typical week the boys go with their male friends on one day and with their girl friend on another occasion.

There is a strong association between the level of sex activity and the number of times a boy or girl goes to a public house ($p = 0\cdot001$ for both groups). Table 11.4 shows that E-boys went much more often and N-boys went much less often, and the same is true for girls.

The usual drink for the boys was beer or stout (73 per cent) with cider (9 per cent), spirits (8 per cent) and soft drinks (6 per cent) coming a long way behind. The usual drink for the girls was spread over a wider range; 28 per cent usually had spirits, 20 per cent soft drinks, 20 per cent beer, 18 per cent cider (including champagne perry) and 13 per cent port or sherry wines.

Table 11.4 *The last visit to a public house analysed by three levels of sex activity*

Bar last visited	Boys			Girls		
	N, %	I, %	E, %	N, %	I, %	E, %
Up to 7 days ago	44	57	75	31	47	68
Up to 4 weeks ago	16	16	8	18	24	19
Up to 6 months	17	15	9	18	19	10
Never, hardly ever	24	12	9	33	10	3
TOTAL	101	100	101	100	100	100
No. (100%)	167	151	138	205	186	73

They were asked if they had 'ever been a bit drunk'. No further definition was given and the teenager was left to answer according to his own estimation of whether he had been drunk or not. A third (33 per cent) of the boys said they had never been drunk, another third (34 per cent) said they had been drunk once or twice and the other third (33 per cent) said they had been drunk from three to ten times. No one said he had been drunk more than ten times. Fewer girls admitted to being drunk; 44 per cent had never been drunk, 38 per cent once or twice and 18 per cent three or more times.

Perhaps it will not be a surprise to find that there is a strong association between the level of sex activity and the number of times a person has been drunk ($p = 0.001$ for boys and girls), but the extent of the association, as shown in table 11.5, may be surprising. It can be seen that only a few N-boys or N-girls have been drunk more than twice, but over half the E-boys and nearly half the E-girls have been drunk three or more times in their own estimation. Conversely only a few (11 per cent) of the E-boys and E-girls have not been drunk.

The rise of Espresso coffee bars in the last decade has been much appreciated by the teenage population as it provides one of the few indoor places where they can meet. In the previous chapter it was noted that it was one of the places where teenage groups meet. Over a third (37 per cent) of the boys and a quarter (28 per cent) of the girls had been to a coffee bar in the week before they were interviewed, and another 18 per cent of the boys and 15 per cent of the girls had visited one in the previous month. Although there is no association between the level of sex activity and the last time the girls went to a coffee bar (NSS), this association does hold for boys ($p = 0.01$). A quarter (28 per cent) of the N-boys, a third (36 per cent) of the I-boys and half (50 per cent) the E-boys had been to a coffee bar within seven days of the interview.

Table 11.5 *The number of times drunkenness was admitted analysed by three levels of sex activity*

No. of times been drunk	Boys			Girls		
	N, %	I, %	E, %	N, %	I, %	E, %
Never	54	30	11	61	38	11
1–2	32	36	33	33	41	44
3–10	14	34	56	6	21	45
TOTAL	100	100	100	100	100	100
No. (100%)	167	151	138	205	186	73

During the pilot research we encountered a small group of teenagers who were experimenting with drugs and we learnt about clubs and coffee bars where drugs could be obtained. But the number of teenagers involved is a very small proportion of the whole. Although we were interviewing during the height of the purple-heart craze, in fact we found only 1 per cent of the boys and even fewer girls in the random sample had taken any kind of drug in the four weeks before the interview, and only 3 per cent of the boys and 2 per cent of the girls had ever tried taking drugs. We were left with the impression that the number of teenagers taking drinamyl had been exaggerated, while only a very few had taken marihuana and none in our sample had tried any of the addictive drugs. The numbers are too small to relate drug-taking to sex behaviour.

Not many teenagers seem to be interested in gambling. Among the boys 10 per cent did the pools, 9 per cent placed bets on the dogs or horses about once a week and another 9 per cent gambled with cards or dice. There was no association between gambling and the level of sex experience (NSS). Although 7 per cent of the girls did the pools, there were not enough gamblers in the sample to look for associations with sex behaviour.

In this sample 45 per cent of the boys and 55 per cent of the girls did not smoke. Another 5 per cent of the boys and 8 per cent of the girls said they only had one or two cigarettes a day, and 14 per cent and 18 per cent had less than ten. So over a third (36 per cent) of the boys had more than ten cigarettes a day (5 per cent smoked over twenty) and nearly one in every five girls (19 per cent) had more than ten a day (2 per cent smoked over twenty).

There is a clear association between the level of sex activity and the number of cigarettes smoked in a day ($p = 0.001$ for boys and girls). Table 11.6 shows that the experienced teenagers were likely to smoke more than the inceptives, and the inceptives more than the non-experienced. Practically all the girls who smoked over twenty a day were experienced, and so were half the boys who smoked this amount.

Table 11.6 *The number of cigarettes smoked a day analysed by three levels of sex activity*

Cigarettes per day	Boys			Girls		
	N, %	I, %	E, %	N, %	I, %	E, %
None	58	45	27	65	51	35
Under 10	21	20	17	19	33	26
10–20	17	32	47	16	15	27
21+	4	3	9	0	1	12
TOTAL	100	100	100	100	100	100
No. (100%)	167	151	138	205	186	73

E. DELINQUENCY

Our results confirmed the well-known fact that boys are much more likely to get into trouble than girls. Only 7 per cent of the girls had got into trouble with the police and in only 3 per cent did this involve a court appearance. On the other hand nearly half (47 per cent) the boys said they had been in trouble with the police and nearly a quarter (24 per cent) had made an appearance before a court. Most (16 per cent) of them had made only one court appearance, but a few (3 per cent) had appeared twice and one in twenty (5 per cent) had made more than two appearances.

Boys who have made an appearance in court are more likely to be sexually experienced ($p = 0.001$). Table 11.7 shows that a third (39 per cent) of the E-boys compared to a tenth (11 per cent) of the N-boys had appeared before a court. There is also an association between the number of court appearances and the level of sex activity ($p = 0.001$). Table 11.7 suggests that those who made one appearance only are as likely to be I-boys as E-boys. But those who make two or more court appearances are much more likely to be E-boys. The same tendency can be seen among the girls although the numbers are much smaller.

Table 11.7 *The number of court appearances analysed by three levels of activity*

Number of appearances in court	Boys			Girls		
	N, %	I, %	E, %	N, %	I, %	E %
None	89	75	61	99	99	87
One	7	21	22	1	1	8
2+	4	4	17	0	0	5
TOTAL	100	100	100	100	100	100
No. (100%)	167	151	138	205	186	73

Of course there are all sorts of reasons why a boy might be charged with committing an offence, some more serious than others. In this sample 12 per cent were charged with traffic offences and 6 per cent with other relatively unimportant offences; but 9 per cent were on charges of stealing property and 2 per cent on charges involving violence against other people; less than 1 per cent were charged with a sexual offence.[1] We added the stealing, violence and sexual

1. As some boys committed more than one type of offence, the percentages add up to more than the 24 per cent who had made court appearances.

N

offences together and compared them with the other offences, but we found no association between these two groups of offences and the level of sex activity (NSS).

We made a note of the court action for each offence committed. We were aware that the sentence given by the juvenile magistrates depended on a wide variety of factors, not least the attitudes of the magistrates themselves. But for the purposes of this research we assumed that those who were sent to approved schools, detention centres, remand homes, borstals and put on probation had committed more serious offences than those who were fined, bound over, given an absolute or conditional discharge. However, we found no association between these two groups of sentences and the level of sex activity (NSS). This seems to confirm the previous finding that the type of offence is less important than the number of offences of all kinds.

But a large number of offences committed by young people do not come to the notice of the police. After we had asked these questions about delinquency we added a more general question: Have you ever done anything which might have got you into trouble if you had been found out? We defined trouble as anything that could have led to being charged by the police. We have no way of testing the validity of a question like this, but a large number of boys and girls seemed ready to admit one or more misdeeds.

Altogether 55 per cent of the boys and 20 per cent of the girls admitted breaking the law in some way. For both boys and girls the admitted offence was most often stealing, and traffic offences were also mentioned frequently by boys.

The answers were classified into four categories as in table 11.8. Although these answers are the spontaneous disclosures of the teenagers without being pressed, even so we found a clear association between the level of sex activity and the number of offences admitted for boys ($p = 0.001$) and for girls ($p = 0.01$). Most of the N-boys said they had not done anything which might have got them into trouble, and most of the E-boys said they had. The girls show much the same kind of pattern and this is the only time that it has been possible to show a statistical association with female delinquency and sex activity. This may be because the figures for female delinquency are too small in our sample to show tendencies which are similar to those of the boys. But offences committed by girls are not only much less frequent, but are usually of a different type.

This chapter has indicated that sex experience in boys is often associated with 'outgoing' activities such as dancing, cinemas, coffee bars, drinking in public houses, parties; even the association with delinquency might be accounted for by high spirits, among the first offenders at any rate; the main exception is sport and even here there are many sexually experienced boys who take an active interest in sport.

Table 11.8 *The frequency of admitted misconduct analysed by three levels of sex activity*

Frequency of misconduct	Boys			Girls		
	N, %	I, %	E, %	N, %	I, %	E, %
Often	4	3	17	1	3	5
Sometimes	19	19	25	6	5	16
Once or twice	18	34	29	8	11	11
Never	59	44	29	85	81	67
TOTAL	100	100	100	100	100	99
No. (100%)	167	151	138	205	186	73

For girls it depends less upon where they go, more upon whom they go with. Most girls go to cinemas, dances, clubs, coffee bars whatever their level of sex activity; this is because they go to these places with other girls if they do not go with boy friends. It is noteworthy that the number of visits to public houses is the only one associated with sex experience, because this is an exception to the previous list of places, for girls rarely go into a bar with other girls and almost always go with boy friends. Therefore the really important factor so far as a girl's sexual experience is concerned is whether she has a steady boy friend or not. Sexually experienced girls are inclined to be romantic; sexually experienced boys tend to be cavalier.

12 PERSONAL FACTORS

A. THE ANALYSIS OF THE ATTITUDE INVENTORY

A higher order factor analysis was carried out on the responses to the fifty statements on the attitude inventory. Thus it was possible to organise these statements into three levels of attitude dimensions. At the first-order level each factor is still specific and depends on one or two statements only. Attitude dimensions at this level approximate in their simplest form to the shades of opinion existing between two opposite views on a particular topic. An example of this is favourable and unfavourable attitudes towards religion. At the next level the factors become more generalised, and each dimension extends over a wider range of topics. In some cases the second-order dimension summarises those at the first-order level and religion may appear as one of a number of items associated with morality. The third-order level produces even broader generalisations and the fifty statements are reduced to two or three basic attitude dimensions. This level is of interest because it may lead on to a picture of personality.

This research was primarily interested in the factors associated with sexual experience. Factor analysis condensed a large number of attitude statements into a smaller number of basic variables each of which could be studied in relation to sexual experience. At the first-order level the relationship between sexual experience and attitudes to specific topics could be studied and at the third-order level ideas arise about personality and sexual experience.

The method used is described in section C of appendix 3. The analysis produced the following factors:

Boys
- 15 first-order factors
- 5 second-order factors
- 2 third-order factors

Girls
- 16 first-order factors
- 6 second-order factors
- 3 third-order factors

In order that the discussion of these factors and their relationship with sex experience is clear, we will define three concepts that will be used throughout the rest of this chapter.

Loading. This is a measure of the association between a factor and one of the fifty statements on the attitude inventory. A positive loading signifies agreement with the statement and a negative loading signifies disagreement.

Scores. This can be calculated for each individual on each factor. It is a measure of the extent to which the individual shows the factor in the attitudes he expresses. A high score or a low score on a particular factor will mean that the individual's opinions are predictable on all statements with high loadings in that factor.

Identification. We have identified and named each factor in terms of the statements which have the highest loadings in it. The name indicates the attitudes which are held by those teenagers who score highly on the factor. These names are printed in italics.

For example, *antipathy towards religion* is a factor which exists for boys and girls (factor II for boys and IV for girls). The two statements with the highest loadings are no. 18 in table 7.1 ('The average man can lead a good life without religion') and no. 34 ('The Church is the best authority to decide on matters of right and wrong'). A high score[1] on this factor would indicate agreement with the former statement and disagreement with the latter. Thus it is identified as *antipathy towards religion*.

Analysis of variance was used to determine whether or not there was any significant variation between factor scores of teenagers of differing sexual experience. In this case the five stages of sex experience were used (section G of chapter 3) instead of the three levels of sex activity (as used in chapters 8–11). It was then possible to determine whether or not the mean factor score for all teenagers varied significantly across all five stages.

The main aim of this analysis was to determine whether or not sexually experienced teenagers had much higher or much lower scores on certain factors. The technique of the analysis involved calculating the variance ratio (F)[2] for each factor and comparing this value with the theoretical value of F in Fisher and Yates tables for the relevant number of degrees of freedom. At any par-

---

1. The score is determined from the opinions expressed on every single attitude tatement although those that have the highest loading are the defining ones. A much wider measure of 'religiousness' is thus obtained than would be the case if only one statement on religion was considered in isolation.

2. The variance ratio = the variance between stages of sexual experience divided by the variance within classes of sexual experience.

ticular significance level, if the calculated value of F is greater than the value of F in the tables, then one can infer that there is a significant variation in factor scores between the stages of sexual experience at that particular level of significance. This is indicated by giving the value of p, as explained in section A of chapter 8.[1]

The attitude inventory was not constructed with any view as to what basic attitude dimensions existed for teenagers. The statements were chosen for their topicality and relevance to subjects of interest to the research; so the analysis was not being used to refute or confirm hypotheses derived from a psychological theory. The aim was to place teenage attitudes in a simplified framework which could be studied in relation to sexual experience.

B. FIRST-ORDER FACTORS

Tables 12.1 and 12.2 show the first-order factors for boys and girls. Statements with loadings greater than 0·5 are given below the factor title. The numbers refer to the numbered statements of the attitude inventory to be found in table 7.1. In addition the values for F and the significance levels are given.

In most cases only one or two statements have very high loadings (above 0·7) on each factor. All other statements have much lower loadings on the factor, and in most cases the loading is very close to zero. In this respect simple structure is shown in a very clear form. The analysis has isolated those statements which have most in common and has eliminated the rest in varying degrees. It is thus simple to name most of the factors in terms of the high-loading statements. But four factors, two in each table, have not been named. These are factors which are loaded highly on only one statement or on two statements grouped in such a way as to make interpretation virtually impossible. We have called these *incidental factors* (Thurstone, 1949). The most probable explanation of their existence is that they are artefacts of the design of the attitude inventory and the analysis has simply made them apparent. They have been included in tables 12.1 and 12.2 together with their high-loading statements, but no attempt has been made to label them.

Only two of the boys' first-order factors have insignificant F values. These are 1/2 and *preference for living at home*. The first is an incidental factor, while the other covers the two statements concerned with the advantages and disadvantages of living at home.

1. Thus at the $p = 0.001$ level, the odds are 1,000:1 against this occurring by chance alone. Similarly at the $p = 0.01$ level the odds are 100:1 against the theoretical value of F being exceeded by chance alone.

Table 12.1 *Boys' first-order factors giving the statement number and highest loading for each factor and showing F values and significance levels (p)*

No.	Factor name, statement number and loading	F value	p value
I	Belief in controls on teenagers		
	6 (−0·80), 39 (−0·67), 48 (−0·65)	4·46	0·01
II	Antipathy towards religion		
	18 (+0·79), 34 (−0·77)	11·87	0·001
III	Respect for adult standards		
	8 (−0·75), 40 (−0·71)	3·29	0·05
IV	Dislike of holidays with parents		
	4 (+0·85), 29 (−0·85)	27·10	0·001
V	I/1		
	50 (+0·82), 13 (−0·61)	3·48	0·01
VI	Tolerance towards foreigners		
	46 (−0·94), 45 (−0·93)	3·25	0·05
VII	Opposition to premarital sexual intercourse		
	27 (+0·89), 41 (+0·71)	8·09	0·001
VIII	I/2		
	26 (−0·69), 10 (−0·58)	0·60	NSS
IX	Preference for home activities		
	7 (+0·72), 5 (+0·52)	6·03	0·001
X	Belief in a new teenage culture		
	12 (+0·76), 17 (−0·64)	6·08	0·001
XI	Support for double standard of morality		
	38 (+0·72), 21 (+0·70)	9·67	0·001
XII	Lack of ambition		
	35 (−0·78), 42 (+0·57)	5·96	0·001
XIII	Moral scepticism		
	23 (+0·69), 3 (−0·67), 30 (−0·58)	28·36	0·001
XIV	Preference for living at home		
	24 (−0·79), 31 (+0·63)	0·82	NSS
XV	Support for moral standards		
	28 (−0·65), 22 (−0·64)	5·75	0·001

Notes: The statement number refers to those given on table 7.1. All loadings greater than 0·5 are given in brackets after each statement number. I/1 and I/2 are incidental factors. The number of boys in each stage are:

Stage I   = 117   Stage II = 285
Stage III = 223   Stage IV = 36
Stage V   = 119

Table 12.2 *Girls' first-order factors giving the statement number and highest loadings for each factor and showing F values and significance levels* (p)

	Factor name, statement number and loading	F value	p value
I	Dislike of adult interference		
	40 (+0·66), 48 (+0·63), 25 (+0·52)	5·58	0·001
II	Dislike of holidays with parents		
	4 (+0·82), 29 (−0·74)	20·32	0·001
III	Tolerance towards foreigners		
	46 (−0·89), 45 (−0·85)	1·45	NSS
IV	Antipathy towards religion		
	34 (−0·86), 18 (+0·84)	6·88	0·001
V	Desire for good time		
	9 (+0·73), 1 (+0·54)	0·76	NSS
VI	Opposition to premarital intercourse		
	27 (+0·75), 41 (+0·74), 43 (+0·71)	42·57	0·001
VII	I/3		
	35 (−0·87)	4·69	0·01
VIII	Support for teenage freedom		
	14 (−0·72), 49 (−0·69)	10·06	0·001
IX	Distaste for mass media		
	20 (+0·87), 36 (+0·67)	0·37	NSS
X	Dislike of other teenagers		
	5 (+0·76), 15 (+0·47), 2 (+0·46),		
	42 (+0·44)	2·19	NSS
XI	I/4		
	28 (+0·72)	6·26	0·001
XII	Belief in a moral authority		
	6 (−0·87), 32 (−0·47)	5·43	0·001
XIII	Antipathy towards family loyalty		
	16 (−0·66), 31 (−0·64)	7·86	0·001
XIV	Belief in a double standard of sexual morality		
	26 (+0·91), 38 (+0·55)	4·51	0·01
XV	Preference for friends' advice		
	10 (+0·82), 37 (−0·77)	3·61	0·01
XVI	Dislike of home restrictions		
	17 (+0·75), 24 (+0·66)	8·09	0·001

Notes: The statement number refers to those given in table 7.1. All loadings greater than 0·5 are given in brackets after each statement number. I/3 and I/4 are incidental factors. The number of girls in each stage are:

Stage I = 47   Stage II = 338   Stage III = 286
Stage IV = 58   Stage V = 32

The result of the analysis shows that boys at all levels of sexual experience do not differ in their scores on these two factors.

For the girls four factors have insignificant *F* values. These are *tolerance towards foreigners, desire for good time, distaste for mass media* and *dislike of other teenagers*. Girls who are highly prejudiced against foreigners are no more or less sexually experienced than those who are free of prejudice. For boys the value of *F* is significant at the 0·05 level for the *tolerance towards foreigners* factor. However, the relationship between this factor and sexual experience is not a simple one. Figure 12.1[1] shows that stage III boys had the highest mean factor score, and this implies that they are less prejudiced towards foreigners than any other group. The most prejudiced group of boys appears to be stage V. These slight differences do not appear for the girls on this factor as shown in figure 12.2.

For the boys one other factor has a significant *F* value at the 0·05 level. This is *respect for adult standards*. As figure 12.3 shows, boys who

Mean scores for first order factors at each stage of sex experience

Fig 12/1   Fig 12/2
BOYS   GIRLS

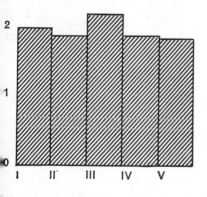

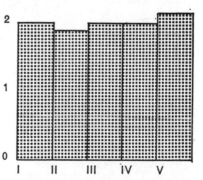

Tolerance towards foreigners   Tolerance towards foreigners

1. The distribution of the mean scores across the five stages of sex experience is shown in figures 12.1 to 12.27. For the purpose of illustrating the variation in factor scores between the stages of sexual experience, the origin on the diagrams has been shifted from 0 to −2. Shifting the origin means they all appear in the positive direction. The mean score now equals +2.

score highly on this factor (i.e. who disagree with the belief that very few adults understand teenagers and that most of them are hypocrites) tend to be inexperienced sexually. Stage I boys score relatively highly on this factor whereas most of the others have scores which are close to the mean (mean = 2 with origin shifted). Boys who have never had any physical contact with girls will tend to have more respect for adult standards.

Mean scores for first order factors at each stage of sex experience

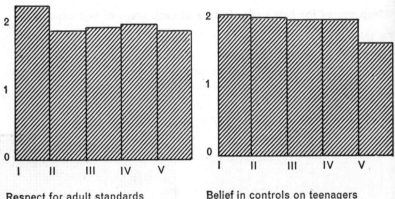

Fig 12/3
BOYS
3

Respect for adult standards

Figure 12/4
BOYS
3

Belief in controls on teenagers

Two of the boys' factors are significant at the 0·01 level. One is an incidental factor (I/1) and the other is *belief in controls on teenagers.* Figure 12.4 shows the stage V boys have a much lower score than the boys in the other stages who have factor scores quite close to the mean. This shows that stage V boys tend to agree that each person should decide for himself what is right and wrong, and that teenagers should be able to do what they want, dress as they like and go where they want without interference from adults.

Three of the girls' factors have significant associations with sex experience at the 0·01 level. One is an incidental factor (I/3). Another is *belief in double standards of morality* in which the stage IV girls score highest followed by stage III and stage V girls (figure 12.5). These girls tend to agree that there are different sexual standards for men and women and that premarital intercourse is all right for boys but not for girls. This may seem to be a surprising result in view of the fact that these stage IV and V girls have actually had intercourse themselves. But it is clear that when an experienced girl signifies agreement with these two statements, she is in fact making a complaint (or a wry comment); she is not agreeing that this is a satisfactory state of affairs. The other factor at this level is *preference for friends' advice* and this is a factor which isolates stage I girls from the rest (figure 12.6). Most of the groups have scores which are close to the mean with stage III this time slightly ahead of the rest. Stage I girls on the other hand have a relatively low score; they would tend to turn for advice to their parents rather than their friends and they reject the idea that a person can learn more from friends than from parents.

Mean scores for first order factors at each stage of sex experience

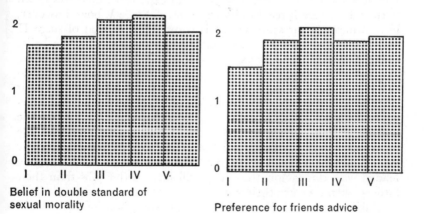

Figure 12/5
GIRLS

Belief in double standard of sexual morality

Fig 12/6
GIRLS

Preference for friends advice

All the other first-order factors for boys and girls have F values which are significant at the 0·001 level. At this stage much stronger relationships between the factors and sexual experience begin to appear and there are indications that in some cases besides varying between the stages of sexual experience the factor scores are also correlated with sexual experience as well. In one sense the size of the F value for each factor is a measure of the strength of the relationship between it and the stages of sexual intercourse. A very large F value indicates a considerable variation in mean factor score across the stages of sexual experience and a very high probability against this variation occurring through chance alone. This may or may not imply the existence of a strong linear correlation between the factor and sexual experience. Correlation exists when the mean factor score increases or decreases linearly as sexual experience increases.

With this in mind the remaining first-order factors will be considered in groups according to the size of the F values (given in tables 12.1 and 12.2). First those factors with F values which are not very much greater than the theoretical value at the $p = 0 \cdot 001$ level (i.e. 4–6) are considered. There are four of these for each sex. These are followed by factors with higher F values ranging from 7 to 11; there are three of these for each sex. Finally, the two factors having exceptionally high F values (over 20) for boys and girls are discussed.

The distribution of the mean factor scores between stages of sexual experience for the four boys' factors having F values ranging from 4 to 6 are shown in figures 12.7 to 12.10. Figure 12.7 shows an unusual relationship between *lack of ambition* and sexual experience. Factor scores decrease steadily as sexual experience increases down to stage IV where it reaches its lowest level. Stage V boys, however, have a mean factor score which is comparable to that of stage II and III. High scores on this factor are associated with the belief that the average teenager expects to lead much the same kind of life as his parents. Stage IV boys appear to be most strongly opposed to this idea. One explanation of this result lies in the possibility that stage IV contains a larger proportion of boys who are having intercourse with their girl friends and fiancées than stage V. It is possible that these boys who may be actively considering marriage are determined to lead a better life than their parents. They also show more ambition when they agree with another statement, highly loaded with this factor, that they will have better jobs than their fathers when they are their age.

A different aspect of home life and the work situation is shown in figure 12.8. Stage I boys appear to have the strongest *preference for home activities*. They tend to believe that most teenagers are bored with their jobs and that the family should spend one evening together each week. Stage III, IV and V boys all tend to oppose

Mean scores for first order factors at each stage of sex experience

Fig 12/7
BOYS

Lack of ambition

Fig 12/8
BOYS

Preference for home activities

Fig 12/9
BOYS

Belief in a new teenage culture

Fig 12/10
BOYS

Support for moral standards

these views. Figure 12.9 shows the association between *belief in a new teenage culture* and sexual experience. This factor associates the view that today's teenagers are different from those in the past and that girls today believe they are on the shelf at twenty-one. Stage V boys believe this most strongly and stage II boys tend to be most opposed to the idea.

On *support for moral standards* stage V boys have the lowest scores (figure 12.10). Most of the other classes of sexual experience seem to contain scores which are close to the mean, with a tendency for stage I boys to have the highest scores. This means that stage V boys tend to believe in easier divorce, and that there is no harm in travelling without a ticket if you can get away with it. No other group has such predictable views on these topics.

Of the girls' factors with F values in the 4–6 range, one is probably of the incidental type $(I/4)$. The distribution of the mean factor scores for the other three are shown in figures 12.11 to 12.13. Stage V girls have the highest mean scores on *dislike of adult interference*, and stage I have the lowest. This means that stage V girls tend to believe that adults misunderstand teenagers and that the police are unfair to them. They also tend to think that teenagers should be free to do what they want and dress as they like.

Antipathy towards religion is related to sexual experience in the manner shown by figure 12.12. Increasing antipathy towards religion is associated with increasing sexual experience. Thus the stage V girls are the group most antipathetic towards the Church and the stage I girls have the most favourable view of it.

On *belief in a moral authority* stage I and stage II girls have the highest scores (figure 12.13). They tend to believe in an external moral code independent of one's own personal experience and judgement; and they disagree that each person should decide for himself what is right and wrong. Stage IV and V girls take the opposite view.

For the next range of F values (7–11) the distributions of the mean scores of the three boys' factors are shown in figures 12.14–12.16. Stage V boys are less in favour of religion than other boys; they tend to believe that the average man can live a good life without religion and to disagree that the Church is the best authority on matters of right and wrong (figure 12.14). Unlike the girls the group which follows them next in 'anti-religiousness' is the stage III boys; these boys tend to be more antipathetic in their attitudes towards religion than the boys in stage IV. For a significant proportion of stage IV boys sexual experience with one partner is not necessarily combined with antagonistic views towards religion. These are

Mean scores for first order factors at each stage of sex experience

Fig 12/11
GIRLS

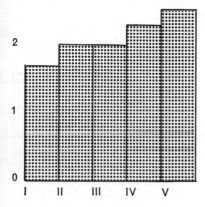

Dislike of adult interference

Fig 12/12
GIRLS

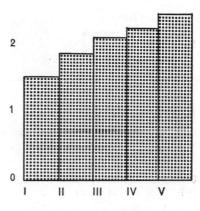

Antipathy towards religion

Fig 12/13
GIRLS

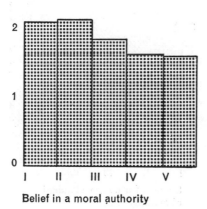

Belief in a moral authority

Mean scores for first order factors at each stage of sex experience

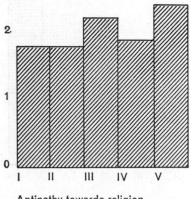

Fig 12/14
BOYS

Antipathy towards religion

Fig 12/15
BOYS

Opposition to premarital intercourse

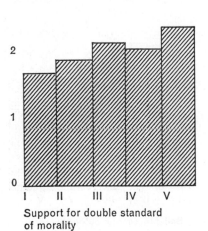

Fig 12/16
BOYS

Support for double standard of morality

probably boys who have only had intercourse with their steady girl friends or fiancées.

The relationship between *opposition to premarital intercourse* is a simpler one (figure 12.15). The boys who are at stages I and II are the ones who believe most strongly that most boys want to marry virgins and that girls who have sex before marriage get bad reputations.

Scores on *support for double standards of morality* increase as sexual experience increases (figure 12.16). Thus stage V boys tend to believe more strongly than any other group that girls look for marriage whereas boys look for sex, and that sexual intercourse before marriage is all right for boys but not for girls. This is in contrast to the previous factor *opposition to premarital intercourse*; stage V boys may not be so insistent that boys want to marry virgins but they do believe that sex before marriage is for boys, and not for girls.

Figures 12.17 to 12.19 illustrate the distributions of mean factor scores for girls in the 7–11 range of F values. *Antipathy towards family loyalty* is most strongly felt by stage V girls; they are less inclined to agree that one owes one's greatest loyalty to the family and see more disadvantages in living at home. Stage IV girls follow them on this factor and the other three groups are all fairly close to the mean. *Support for teenage freedom* (figure 12.18) shows a similar tendency. Experienced girls tend to reject the idea that parents should advise their children about the sort of work they do, and disagree with the view that too much freedom in the early teens leads to trouble when one gets older.

A third aspect of this question is shown in *dislike of home restrictions*. This is expressed in the belief that freedom only exists away from home and that girls believe they are on the shelf at twenty-one; some girls see marriage as a means of getting away from home. There appears to be an increasing support for these views as sexual experience increases. It seems from these three results that sexual experience for girls is associated with an increasing desire for freedom and independence from the family.

The remaining first-order factors all have very high F values (over 20). One of these is common to both sexes. It is *dislike of holidays with parents*. As can be seen from figures 12.20 and 12.21 experienced boys and girls tend to be opposed to taking their holidays with their parents. Stage IV and V girls both have high mean scores which are fairly close to each other on this factor. For boys, however, those at Stage V have a high mean score, whereas those at stages IV and III are lower, with stage III very slightly

o

Mean scores for first order factors at each stage of sex experience

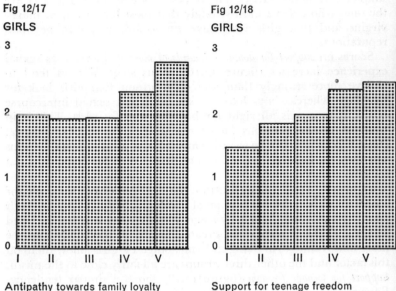

Fig 12/17
GIRLS

Antipathy towards family loyalty

Fig 12/18
GIRLS

Support for teenage freedom

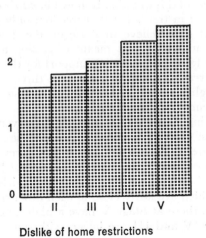

Fig 12/19
GIRLS

Dislike of home restrictions

ahead of stage IV. This result for boys has similarities to the earlier one for *antipathy towards religion* and suggests that in some ways stage III boys may be more like stage V than stage IV boys in their attitudes.

The desire of teenagers to take their holidays with friends rather than parents seems to be a significant turning-point in their lives. It is one of the major stepping-stones to teenage independence from the family, particularly for girls. The fact that the desire is associated with the sexual experience of the teenagers who hold it shows that the move towards friends and away from the family has much wider implications than simply a desire for more freedom. This should not be interpreted to mean that once a teenager expresses a desire to have his holidays alone he is on the brink of experiencing sexual intercourse. What it does suggest is that sexually experienced teenagers tend to desire independence to a greater extent than non-experienced ones and the area of their lives where this is exemplified is in taking holidays. Not all the experienced teenagers who want to take their holidays apart from their parents do in fact go away on holiday with friends (section D of chapter 8). It is the desire, not the accomplishment, that is associated with sex experience.

The other factor for boys with a very high *F* value is *moral scepticism*. Figure 12.22 shows that experienced boys score highly on it. It suggests that experienced boys tend to take a cynical view of society. They believe that there is one law for the rich and another for the poor and they deny that it always pays to be honest. They would also rather work for an easy-going boss than one who is strict and fair.

Finally the factor with the highest *F* value of all is the girls' factor *opposition to premarital intercourse*. Figure 12.23 shows that sexually experienced girls have very low scores on this factor. This means that they tend to reject the view that girls acquire bad reputations by having sexual experience. They also disagree that intercourse before marriage is wrong and do not believe that most boys want to marry a virgin. This result is of course the most predictable association of all.

C. SECOND-ORDER FACTORS

At the second-order level the difference between high and low loadings is less marked and there are a larger number of statements with relatively high loadings (0·35–0·5) for each factor. This makes

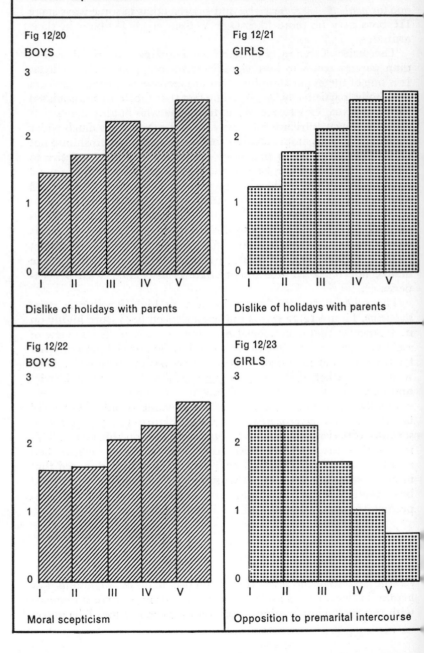

Mean scores for first order factors at each stage of sex experience

Fig 12/20
BOYS
Dislike of holidays with parents

Fig 12/21
GIRLS
Dislike of holidays with parents

Fig 12/22
BOYS
Moral scepticism

Fig 12/23
GIRLS
Opposition to premarital intercourse

it more difficult to identify them. However, at this stage of the analysis broad dimensions of social attitude begin to appear and these can be identified by the statements which are clustered within each of them.

Tables 12.3 and 12.4 show the second-order factors for boys and girls. Statements with loadings greater than 0·35 are given below the factor title. The numbers refer to the numbered statements of the attitude inventory to be found in table 7.1. In addition the values for *F* and the significance levels are given.

All the boys' and four of the girls' second-order factor scores vary significantly across the five stages of sexual experience at the 0·001 level. Another girls' factor has an *F* value which is significant at the 0·01 level and the remaining one has an *F* value which is insignificant.

The second-order factors were produced by factor-analysing the matrix of correlation between the first-order factors. Because of this most of them appear as broad summaries of the factors on the lower level. There are two exceptions.

The first of these is the boys' factor *distaste for mass media*. This is highly loaded on the two statements which defined the first-order factor IX for the girls. Statements on the mass media had relatively low loadings on the boys' first-order factors. This boys' second-order factor covers a slightly wider range of topics than the girls' factor IX even though the defining statements are the same.

The only other factor which appears for the first time at the second-order level is the girls' factor *opposition to sex instruction*. Girls who score highly on it tend to express negative views on sex education and experience. They believe that there is no need to teach about sex in schools and disagree that young people should be taught all about birth control. Also highly loaded on this factor is the view that girls should not get married before twenty-one. Both these factors are associated with sex experience.

The other second-order factors are similar to the first-order factors, and they are related to sex experience in the same way The distribution of the mean scores across the stages of sex experience for all the second-order factors are shown in figures 12.24 and 12.25. As the results shown in these figures are similar to those found for the first-order factors, it is not necessary to discuss each one in detail.

The results may be summarised as follows: Boys who are sexually experienced tend to oppose restrictions on their behaviour and accept the idea that teenagers are alienated from the adult world; they also believe that different standards exist in sex for boys and

Table 12.3 *Boys' second-order factors giving the statement numbers with the highest loadings for each factor and showing F values and significance levels (p)*

No.	Factor name, statement number and loading	F value	p value
I	Support for teenagers		
	15 (−0·54), 49 (−0·51), 47 (−0·39), 2 (−0·38), 7 (−0·36)	25·47	0·001
II	Distaste for mass media		
	20 (+0·43), 36 (+0·47), 19 (+0·35)	6·28	0·001
III	Respect for adults		
	8 (−0·53), 5 (−0·39), 40 (−0·48), 10 (−0·36), 23 (−0·36), 37 (+0·35)	10·07	0·001
IV	Support for boys' sexual freedom		
	21 (+0·46), 38 (+0·43), 1 (+0·42), 32 (+0·40), 19 (+0·38), 43 (−0·35)	16·97	0·001
V	Support for moral restrictions		
	11 (+0·49), 3 (+0·39), 44 (+0·40), 43 (+0·36)	15·20	0·001

Table 12.4 *Girls' second-order factors giving the statement numbers with the highest loadings for each factor and showing F values and significance levels (p)*

No.	Factor name, statement number and loading	F value	p value
I	Antipathy towards family		
	16 (−0·59), 7 (−0·50), 31 (−0·46), 37 (−0·45), 3 (−0·42), 42 (−0·36)	28·83	0·001
II	Opposition to sex instruction		
	19 (−0·51), 47 (+0·48), 13 (+0·39)	14·12	0·001
III	Tolerance towards other people		
	46 (−0·51), 45 (−0·50), 44 (−0·47), 9 (−0·44), 1 (−0·39), 11 (−0·36)	1·54	NSS
IV	Belief in personal moral responsibility		
	32 (+0·44), 50 (+0·40)	22·64	0·001
V	Belief in double standards		
	23 (+0·44), 26 (+0·43)	3·70	0·01
VI	Opposition to girls' sexual freedom		
	21 (+0·39), 27 (+0·39)	14·21	0·001

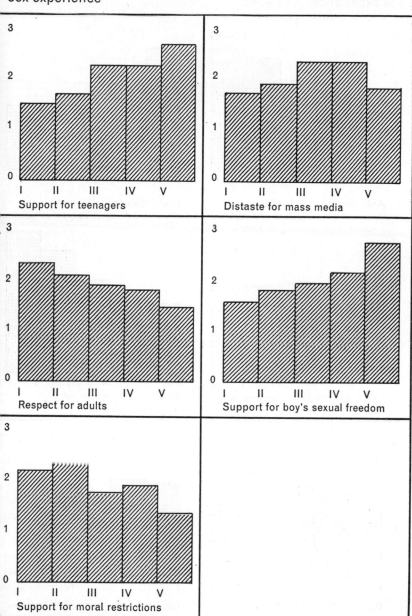

Figure 12/24

Mean scores for boys second order factors at each stage of sex experience

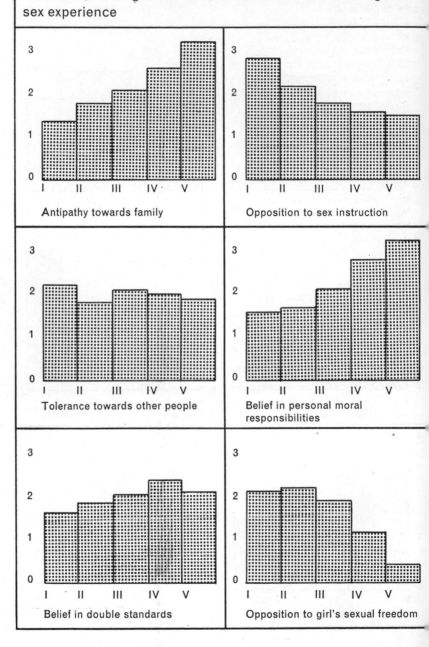

Figure 12/25

Mean scores for girls second order factors at each stage of sex experience

Antipathy towards family

Opposition to sex instruction

Tolerance towards other people

Belief in personal moral responsibilities

Belief in double standards

Opposition to girl's sexual freedom

girls and that nothing is so important in life as enjoyment; and they have permissive moral views which are shown in their equivocal attitude towards honesty and in their belief that a boy who makes a girl pregnant should not have to marry her. Experienced girls on the other hand tend to be against family loyalty and family activities; they feel that girls should be taught more about sex and believe in making their own decisions; they dislike the idea of a double sexual standard and believe that girls should be allowed more sexual freedom.

D. TEENAGE ATTITUDE STRUCTURE

Before considering the relationship between the third-order factors and sex experience, this section will describe the overall attitude structure revealed by the factor analysis. At the third-order level the difference between high loadings and low loadings becomes even smaller than for the second-order factors. Each factor has loadings over 0·3 and under 0·5 on a larger number of statements.

Two factors for the boys and two for the girls are listed in tables 12.5 and 12.6, together with all the statements with loadings of over 0·3.

A third factor for the girls was brought out by the analysis, but it is not listed with the others because only one of the statements has a loading over 0·3. This was a negative loading on the statement in favour of birth control. In addition there were four statements with loadings above 0·2. A study of these five statements will show that it is difficult to interpret this factor.

19. Young people should be taught all about birth control (−0·30).
50. There is more to sex than just having a good time (−0·28).
13. There is no need to teach about sex in schools because you can find out all you need to know yourself (0·25).
30. I'd rather work for someone who is strict and fair than for somebody who is easy-going (−0·24).
34. The Church is the best authority to decide on matters of right and wrong (0·24).

This factor is also closely correlated (0·77) with the second-order factor *opposition to sex instruction*. Most girls are in favour of sex education[1] and the factor analysis seems to have sorted out the few who are not, and found that they are also pro-Church, anti-birth

1. Young people should be taught all about birth control: 83 per cent agree, 11 per cent DK, 6 per cent disagree. In favour of sex education in schools: 81 per cent agree, 6 per cent DK, 13 per cent disagree (from table 7.1).

Table 12.5 *Boys' third-order factors*

I Teenage ethnocentrism

  1 Life is so short that having a good time is more important than anything else (0·42).

48 What teenagers do and how they dress outside their homes is their business (0·40).

  9 It is best to have a good time before you are married because after that life is pretty dreary (0·39).

40 Very few adults really understand teenagers (0·37).

45 Foreigners should stay in their own country (0·36).

46 It would be best to keep coloured people in their own districts to prevent too much contact with whites (0·35).

10 I learn more from friends of my own age than I do from my parents (0·35).

25 The police are unfair in their treatment of teenagers (0·35).

33 I'm usually a bit bored when I stay at home in the evenings (0·33).

44 All homosexuals should be severely punished (0·33).

39 Teenagers should be able to go out in the evening without having to tell their parents where they are going (0·31).

  8 Most adults say one thing and do another (0·30).

II Restrictiveness

11 If a boy gets a girl pregnant he should be willing to marry her (0·47).

  3 It always pays to be honest (0·43).

43 Sexual intercourse before marriage is wrong (0·43).

34 The Church is the best authority to decide on matters of right and wrong (0·39).

44 All homosexuals should be severely punished (0·38).

16 People should realise that their greatest loyalty is to their family (0·37).

---

control, anti-strictness and anti-sex. We know this applies to only a very small number of our sample and it appears to have little meaning. Consequently a detailed interpretation of this factor would be of doubtful validity and therefore it will not be discussed further.

The boys' factor with the largest number of statements with high loadings has been labelled *teenage ethnocentrism*. There is a similar factor for girls; in fact eight statements are common to both groups. *Teenage ethnocentrism* reveals the extent to which teenagers are for their own group and opposed to all other groups. There is an emphasis on enjoyment and having a good time. Adult institutions are looked upon unfavourably. Ethnocentric teenagers are against

Table 12.6 *Girls' third-order factors*

I Teenage ethnocentrism

46 It would be best to keep coloured people in their own districts to prevent too much contact with whites (0·42).

45 Foreigners should stay in their own country (0·40).

1 Life is so short that having a good time is more important than anything else (0·40).

9 It is best to have a good time before you are married because after that life is pretty dreary (0·39).

33 I am usually bored when I stay at home in the evenings (0·38).

12 Today's teenagers are very different from teenagers in the past (0·33).

48 What teenagers do and how they dress outside their homes is their business (0·33).

39 Teenagers should be able to go out in the evenings without telling their parents where they are going (0·31).

10 I learn more from friends of my own age than I do from my parents (0·30).

II Restrictiveness

30 I'd rather work for someone who is strict and fair than for someone who is easy-going (0·38).

43 Sexual intercourse before marriage is wrong (0·37).

2 Most parents ought to be stricter with their children (0·35).

7 The family should spend one evening at home together at least once a week (0·35).

3 It always pays to be honest (0·34).

11 If a boy gets a girl pregnant he should be willing to marry her (0·33).

16 People should realise that their greatest loyalty is to their family (0·33).

49 Too much freedom in the early teens leads to trouble when one gets older (0·32).

29 I'd rather take my holidays with my parents (0·30).

44 All homosexuals should be severely punished (0·30).

foreigners, coloured people, the police, homosexuals and marriage. They scorn advice from adults, resent interference in their affairs and take a hedonistic view of life.

The other factor common to both groups has been named *restrictiveness*. This represents the attitude dimension associated with opinions on honesty, control of teenagers and a strict moral code at one end, to permissiveness on all these topics at the other end. Both boys and girls who score highly on this factor believe that it always pays to be honest. They have strong views on sexual morality. They are opposed to premarital intercourse and think that if a boy gets a girl pregnant he should be willing to marry her. Family loyalties are also stressed by the strongly restrictive teenagers. Homosexuals are also condemned and this exemplifies the difference between ethnocentrism and this factor; in the ethnocentric context homosexuals are seen as another out-group; in terms of restrictiveness, however, homosexuality is seen as immoral behaviour.

Religious feeling is also a measure of restrictiveness for boys, but this is less strong for girls. Control by parents over their children is important for the restrictive girls. For boys restrictiveness is associated with restraint and respect for a strict moral code. Girls have more statements with relatively high loadings, suggesting that morality for them covers a wider area of their lives; the restrictive girl is both moral in her views and also is strongly in favour of family life.

E. THE THIRD-ORDER FACTORS AND SEXUAL EXPERIENCE

The scores of the third-order factors varied significantly between the classes of sexual experience at the $p = 0.001$ level. The F values for each of them are shown on table 12.7 and the distribution of the mean factor scores across sexual experience are shown in figures 12.26 and 12.27.

Table 12.7 *F values and significance levels (p) for the third-order factor scores classified by sex experience*

Group	No.	Factor name	F value	p value
Boys	I	Ethnocentrism	16·00	0·001
	II	Restrictiveness	35·61	0·001
Girls	I	Ethnocentrism	6·23	0·001
	II	Restrictiveness	42·27	0·001

For both boys and girls the highest F value was obtained for *restrictiveness*. As boys and girls increase their sexual experience they tend to become more permissive in their attitudes. For the girls restrictiveness decreases steadily as sexual experience increases, but for boys the anomaly of the stage IV boys again appears; these boys tend to be slightly more restrictive in their attitude than those at

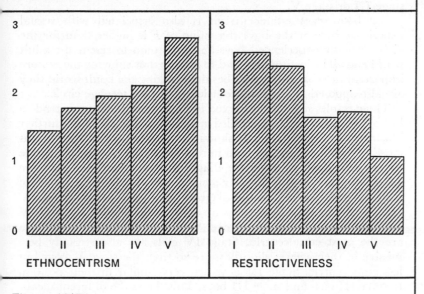

Figure 12/26
Mean scores for boys third order factors at each stage
of sex experience

ETHNOCENTRISM

RESTRICTIVENESS

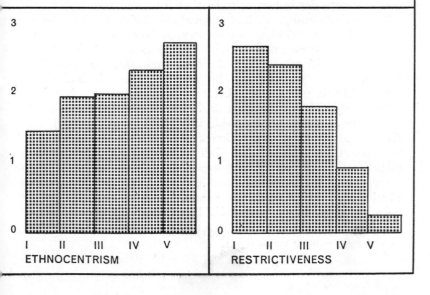

Figure 12/27
Mean scores for girls third order factors at each stage
of sex experience

ETHNOCENTRISM

RESTRICTIVENESS

stage III. As suggested earlier this may be due to a stronger element of steadiness in their sexual relationships than is found in boys at stage III or stage V.

For both sexes ethnocentrism is also associated with sexual experience but for the boys the value of F is higher than for the girls. Sexually experienced boys and girls tend to resent the adult world and all its institutions, and to believe that enjoying life is more important than anything else. Besides disliking the adult world they are also opposed to all groups outside their own teenage circle.

These results suggest that sexually experienced teenagers tend to be both ethnocentric and permissive in their attitudes. This is further illustrated in figure 12.28. It shows the position which the various levels of sexual experience hold in relation to the two basic attitude dimensions. Each point on the diagram represents the mean score on each of these two factors for teenagers in the different classes of sexual experience.[1] From the diagram it can be seen that stage V girls are the most permissive group of all in their attitudes. Stage V boys are not nearly as permissive. Stage V teenagers of both sexes are the most ethnocentric. Stage IV girls are also strongly permissive in their views; slightly more so than the stage V boys but less ethnocentric. Stage IV boys are very similar in their position to stage III girls and stage III boys. This shows the different meaning of sexual experience for boys and girls. For a girl to go as far as stage III she becomes almost as permissive in her attitudes as boys who have actually had sexual intercourse. Similarly a stage IV girl is more permissive in her attitudes than a stage V boy.

For the boys and girls who have had very little experience of sex, their positions in relation to the two dimensions are more similar. Stage I girls are the group which have the most restrictive views of all. This again illuminates the different meaning of sexual experience for boys and girls. A boy who has never had any physical contact with a girl will not be so restrictive in his attitudes.

On ethnocentrism the boys and girls hardly differ at all. The more experienced they are, the farther along the ethnocentric scale they are to be found. The difference between the sexes is confined to the restrictive/permissive scale. Experienced girls are both ethnocentric and permissive; experienced boys are also ethnocentric, but not so permissive; in fact boys may be relatively restrictive in their attitudes in comparison with girls and yet still have had experience of premarital intercourse with one partner.

1. Unlike figures 12.1 to 12.27 the scores on figure 12.28 are in standard form i.e. with mean = 0 and variance = 1.

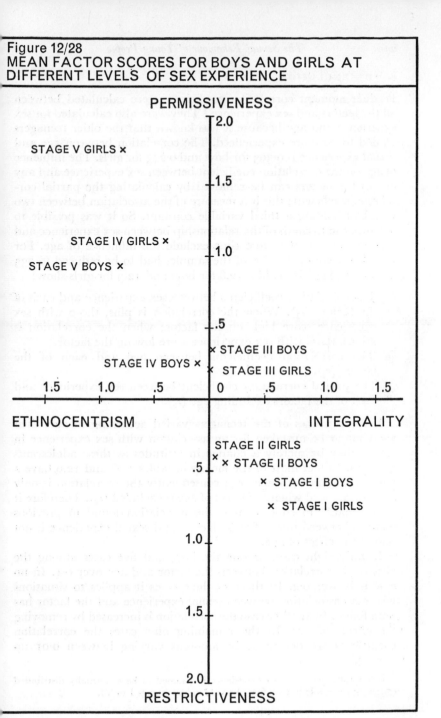

Figure 12/28
MEAN FACTOR SCORES FOR BOYS AND GIRLS AT DIFFERENT LEVELS OF SEX EXPERIENCE

PERMISSIVENESS

2.0

STAGE V GIRLS ×

1.5

STAGE IV GIRLS ×

1.0

STAGE V BOYS ×

.5

× STAGE III BOYS
STAGE IV BOYS × × STAGE III GIRLS

1.5   1.0   .5   0   .5   1.0   1.5

ETHNOCENTRISM   INTEGRALITY

STAGE II GIRLS
× × STAGE II BOYS
.5
× STAGE I BOYS
× STAGE I GIRLS

1.0

1.5

2.0
RESTRICTIVENESS

F. THE EXCLUSION OF AGE

Product moment correlation coefficients were calculated between all the factors and sex experience.[1] They were also calculated for sex experience and age because it was known that the older teenagers tended to be more experienced. The correlation between age and sexual experience is 0·393 for boys and 0·243 for girls. The influence of age on the correlation coefficient between sex experience and any one of the factors can be removed by calculating the partial correlation coefficient; this is a measure of the association between two variables holding a third variable constant. So it was possible to measure the strength of the relationship between sex experience and a factor, and at the same time exclude the influence of age. For technical reasons the size of the samples had to be reduced to 735 boys and 724 girls. Tables 12.8 for boys and 12.9 for girls show:

(a) The correlation coefficients between sex experience and each of the factors (r_1). When the correlation is plus, those with sex experience score high on the factor; when the correlation is minus, those with sex experience score low on the factor.

(b) The correlation coefficients between age and each of the factors (r_2).

(c) The partial correlation coefficient between sex experience and each of the factors excluding age (r_3).

If the attitudes of the teenagers varied according to age, then what might be mistaken for an association with sex experience in reality may be merely a change in attitudes as these adolescents grew up. In fact most of the factors in tables 12.8 and 12.9 have a low correlation with age (r_2); consequently the correlation is only slightly changed when the effect of age is excluded (r_3). Therefore it is reasonable to suppose that the association found in previous sections between most of these factors and sexual experience is not due to the effect of age.

In only eight cases among the boys and five cases among the girls is the correlation between the factor and age over 0·1. In no case is it over 0·2. In three of these cases it applies to situations where no association between sexual experience and the factor has been found. In another case the correlation is increased by removing the effects of age. In the remaining nine cases the correlation coefficients are decreased by amounts varying between 0·01 up to 0·03.

1. For these purposes sex experience is assumed to be a normally distributed continuous variable having five observed values (stages I to V).

Table 12.8 *The partial correlation of each of the boys' factors with sex experience excluding the influence of age*

Order	No.	Factor	r_1	r_2	r_3
First	I	Belief in controls on teenagers	−0·140	+0·012	−0·157
	II	Antipathy towards religion	+0·205	+0·118	+0·174
	III	Respect for adult standards	−0·072	+0·020	−0·087
	IV	Dislike of holidays with parents	+0·344	+0·123	+0·324
	V	I/1	+0·015	+0·073	−0·015
	VI	Tolerance towards foreigners	−0·015	+0·044	−0·035
	VII	Opposition to premarital intercourse	−0·194	−0·095	−0·171
	VIII	I/2	−0·034	+0·128	−0·092
	IX	Preference for home activities	−0·163	−0·025	−0·167
	X	Belief in a new teenage culture	+0·143	−0·042	+0·173
	XI	Support for double standard of morality	+0·212	+0·076	+0·199
	XII	Lack of ambition	−0·105	−0·090	−0·076
	XIII	Moral scepticism	+0·342	+0·109	+0·327
	XIV	Preference for living at home	+0·061	+0·049	+0·046
	XV	Support for moral standards	−0·149	+0·146	−0·227
Second	I	Support for teenagers	+0·333	+0·094	+0·323
	II	Distaste for mass media	+0·036	+0·108	−0·007
	III	Respect for adults	−0·206	+0·011	−0·228
	IV	Support for boys' sexual freedom	+0·267	−0·008	+0·294
	V	Support for moral restrictions	−0·238	−0·116	−0·211
Third	I	Ethnocentrism	+0·264	−0·036	+0·303
	II	Restrictiveness	−0·379	−0·131	−0·359

The exclusion of age reduces the correlations of *dislike of holidays with parents* for boys and girls. This is understandable as one would expect older teenagers to be keener on holidays alone, simply because of their greater independence from the family. In fact it is surprising that the association between this factor and sex experience remains so strong when age is held constant: $r_3 = 0.324$ for boys, and $r_3 = 0.270$ for girls.

Age has a much stronger association with *antipathy towards religion* for boys than for girls. As boys get older they tend to become more antipathetic towards the Church and this means the association

P

Table 12.9 *The partial correlation of each of the girls' factors with sex experience excluding the influence of age*

Order	No.	Factor	r_1	r_2	r_3
First	I	Dislike of adult interference	+0·144	−0·068	+0·166
	II	Dislike of holidays with parents	+0·304	+0·195	+0·270
	III	Tolerance towards foreigners	+0·061	+0·005	+0·062
	IV	Antipathy towards religion	+0·191	+0·013	+0·194
	V	Desire for good time	+0·002	−0·163	+0·043
	VI	Opposition to premarital intercourse	−0·397	−0·039	−0·400
	VII	I/3	+0·158	+0·087	+0·142
	VIII	Support for teenage freedom	+0·209	+0·001	+0·215
	IX	Distaste for mass media	−0·008	−0·022	−0·003
	X	Dislike of other teenagers	−0·068	+0·151	−0·109
	XI	I/4	+0·060	+0·024	+0·056
	XII	Belief in a moral authority	−0·158	−0·096	−0·139
	XIII	Antipathy to family loyalty	+0·126	+0·046	+0·118
	XIV	Belief in a double standard of sexual morality	+0·111	+0·107	+0·088
	XV	Preference for friends' advice	+0·094	−0·050	+0·110
	XVI	Dislike of home restrictions	+0·173	−0·068	+0·196
Second	I	Antipathy to family	+0·315	+0·021	+0·319
	II	Opposition to sex instruction	−0·245	+0·037	−0·262
	III	Tolerance towards other people	+0·018	+0·130	−0·015
	IV	Belief in personal moral responsibility	+0·304	+0·089	+0·292
	V	Belief in double standards	+0·121	+0·077	+0·106
	VI	Opposition to girls' freedom	−0·235	−0·003	−0·242
Third	I	Ethnocentrism	+0·162	−0·064	+0·183
	II	Restrictiveness	−0·413	−0·075	−0·408

between their views on the Church and sexual experience becomes weaker when the effect of age is excluded; removing age makes very little difference for the girls.

Age does not appear to have much effect on any of the other seven correlations and excluding it has the effect of slightly reducing the correlations, but the associations remain significant at the 0·001 level.

Of all the girls' factors for which correlation coefficients were calculated, *restrictiveness* had the highest correlation of all. As a girl's sexual experience increases there is a strong tendency for her factor score to decrease. The correlation between age and this factor is relatively low and excluding it makes little difference to the association with sexual experience. A high correlation also exists for the boys on *restrictiveness*. Here the association with age is slightly stronger. There is a greater tendency for younger boys to have high scores than for the younger girls. This has the effect of reducing r_1 when age is excluded, but it still remains very high.

For boys there is a high association between *ethnocentrism* and sexual experience demonstrating the tendency of sexually experienced boys to be more ethnocentric in their views than inexperienced ones. This factor has a small negative correlation with age. Thus younger boys tend to be slightly more ethnocentric than older ones. When age is held constant the association between sexual experience and the factor is strengthened. Girls' *ethnocentrism* is also associated with sexual experience and age acts in the same direction, so that the correlation is increased when it is excluded.

These results show that the sexual experience of boys and girls is closely associated with the restrictive–permissive dimension of their social attitude. For boys, however, sex is seen less in the context of what is right and wrong than it is for girls. It is also connected with an ethnocentric view of life – a hedonistic self-centredness associated with antagonism towards everything outside the teenage world. As the analysis of variance showed (figure 12.28), as sexual experience increases the teenage girl gets very strongly permissive in her attitudes and fairly ethnocentric as well. The teenage boy also gets more ethnocentric and not quite as permissive.

G. THE EXCLUSION OF OTHER VARIABLES

Excluding age does not radically affect the size of the correlations between these factors and sexual experience. Several of the other responses to questions asked at the interview had high correlations with sexual experience. Table 12.10 gives these correlations and it can be seen that all but three of them have high correlations for both sexes. The extent to which boys like or dislike their mothers does not appear to be strongly associated with their sexual experience (affection for mother is −0·095), whereas for girls there is an association (−0·229). Social class and type of school[1] are included

1. This was scaled on the basis: All age + secondary modern = 1. Technical + comprehensive = 2. Grammar = 3. Private school = 4.

because of their importance in sociological classification. It is of interest to observe that neither of them have high correlations with sexual experience for boys or girls (see chapter 8). Because of this they have not been included in the table of partial correlations (table 12.11).

Table 12.10 *Correlation of a number of variables with sexual experience*

Variable	Boys, r_b	Girls, r_g
Money to spend	0·449	0·238
Church attendance	−0·202	−0·215
Time back in the evening	0·384	0·212
Proportion of time out of home	0·298	0·265
Frequency of dancing	0·330	0·119
Affection for mother	−0·095	−0·229
Wages	0·360	0·153
Cinema attendance	0·174	0·135
Enjoyment of school	−0·201	−0·142
Type of school	0·105	0·010
Social class	0·044	−0·003

Note: r_b is correlation of boys' variables with sexual experience. r_g is correlation of girls' variables with sexual experience.

Table 12.11 lists the ten most important factors for boys and girls, and shows the partial correlations which were obtained when nine of the variables in table 12.10 are removed in turn from the correlation between the factor and sexual experience. Thus table 12.11 shows how far the correlations between these ten factors and sex experience have been influenced by nine other variables.

It can be seen that most of the correlations maintain their high level when each of the variables is excluded. The correlations which are in italics are those which are the lowest for each factor. The variables that appear to have the most influence are wages which increased the correlation five times and decreased it once and time back in the evening which increased the correlation twice and decreased it twice.

None of these partial correlations seriously weakens the association of the factor with sex experience and in many cases the result is expected. Thus the factor *support for teenagers* is most influenced by the time the boy spends out of the family home; and *antipathy to family* is most influenced by how well the girl gets on with her

Table 12.11 *Partial correlation between key factors and sexual experience excluding each variable in turn*

Factor	Correlation with sex experience	Partial correlation with sex experience after each of these variables has been excluded								
		Money	Church	Time back	Out of home	Dances	Mother	Wages	Cinema	School
Boys										
Dislike of holidays with parents	(0·344)	*0·276*	0·317	0·311	0·288	0·300	0·339	0·291	0·323	0·321
Moral scepticism	0·342	0·311	0·323	0·293	0·330	0·327	0·335	(0·350)	0·330	0·311
Support for teenagers	(0·333)	0·286	0·307	0·286	*0·281*	0·293	0·326	0·311	0·320	0·310
Ethnocentrism	0·264	0·203	0·218	(0·271)	0·196	0·240	0·259	*0·188*	0·239	0·234
Restrictiveness	−0·379	−0·359	−0·351	−0·313	−0·362	−0·361	−0·370	(−0·408)	−0·371	−0·357
Girls										
Dislike of holidays with parents	(0·304)	0·284	0·298	0·282	0·263	0·290	0·260	0·292	0·293	0·297
Opposition to pre-marital intercourse	−0·397	−0·387	−*0·371*	−0·380	−0·383	−0·394	−0·390	(−0·401)	−0·394	−0·390
Antipathy to family	0·315	0·315	0·290	0·305	0·275	0·302	0·255	(0·321)	0·311	0·301
Ethnocentrism	0·162	0·153	*0·114*	(0·170)	0·135	0·148	0·115	0·141	0·156	0·140
Restrictiveness	−0·413	−0·406	−0·390	−0·393	−*0·379*	−0·404	−0·379	(−0·421)	−0·406	−0·401

Note: Correlations shown in italics are the lowest for each factor after the exclusion of one of the variables; correlations in brackets are the highest for each factor.

mother. The correlation of *dislike of holidays with parents* is decreased by all the variables, especially by the amount of spending money received in the case of the boys, and by the relationship with the mother in the case of the girls. *Moral scepticism* is most influenced by the time a boy comes back home in the evening, and *opposition to premarital intercourse* is most influenced by the number of times a girl goes to church.

When the size of the girls' wage packets is held constant, the association between *restrictiveness* and sexual experience is slightly strengthened. Although the correlation is reduced by frequency of church attendance (as in *opposition to premarital* intercourse), the strongest influences on the restrictive factor is the time spent out of the home and the relationship with the mother. The more restrictive the girl is, the more time she spends at home, the better she gets on with her mother, and the less sexually experienced she is.

For boys the pattern is similar. The correlation between sexual experience and *restrictiveness* increases when wages are held constant, but the variable which causes the largest decrease in this correlation is the time the boy gets back in the evening. The different functions of the 'time back' for boys and time 'out of home' for girls throw further light on differences in *restrictiveness* for the two sexes. 'Time back' can be seen as a disciplinary measure of parental control over a teenager; whereas time 'out of home' is more a measure of independence from the family. This bears out in behavioural terms the earlier suggestion that for girls restrictive moral views are associated with family loyalties, but for boys these views are more closely associated with restraint and controls on teenage behaviour.

The factor which appears to be under a strong influence from the variables is *ethnocentrism*. For both boys and girls its correlation with sexual experience is altered considerably by excluding several of the variables. For boys the variable having the strongest influence is wages and for girls the biggest influence is church attendance. The more a boy earns the more ethnocentric he is in his views; when wages are held constant there is less likelihood of sexually experienced boys being strongly ethnocentric. The ethnocentric girl rarely attends church; when this variable is excluded, then the correlation between sexual experience and ethnocentrism drops to 0·114 which is the lowest correlation in table 12.11, but still not insignificant.

The results given in this section show the way in which several of the basic classifying variables (obtained from questions at the interview) are related to the most important factors (obtained from the attitude inventory). Although variations do occur in the correlations between the factors and sexual experience when each of these variables is excluded, in no case is the alteration a major one, and all the correlations remain significant at the 0·01 level. From this one can conclude that these factors do have a strong association with sexual experience independently of any other influence.

H. SEXUAL EXPERIENCE AND PERSONALITY

It should be made clear that all the correlations which have been discussed in the previous sections simply indicate the association which exists between two variables, i.e. the extent to which sexual experience varies in a similar way to a factor. The existence of an association means that one can predict, at a certain level of probability, the outcome of one variable from the other one. However, these variables are all independent of each other and even though a high correlation may exist one is not justified in inferring from this that one variable is the cause of the other variable. For example, one cannot infer from the correlation coefficient alone that having sexual experience causes a teenager to dislike taking his holidays with his parents; nor can one infer the reverse, namely, that when a teenager decides that he does not want to take his holidays with his parents, this is going to cause him to become sexually experienced. But when high correlations do exist, a causal relationship is always possible. The explanation of the relationship in terms of cause and effect must be a theoretical one and it is at this point that psychological theories of personality are of value.

This study of the responses to fifty attitude statements has enabled us to identify two basic factors which are strongly related to sexual experience. One factor we have been able to plot along a *permissive–restrictive* scale; the permissive boy attempts to reject adult controls and institutions and the permissive girl tries to escape the influence of her family. The other basic factor we have called *teenage ethnocentrism* which is a rejection of the adult world.

Eysenck (1954) has suggested that two basic social attitude dimensions exist and are related to personality in different ways. One dimension is 'tough-mindedness' as opposed to 'tender-mindedness' and this is highly correlated with 'extroversion' as opposed to 'introversion'.[1] People who are tough-minded in their attitudes are also extroverted in their behaviour. Those who are tender-minded are introverted. In terms of Eysenck's theory these

1. These terms, popularised by Jung, are now used by many psychologists. The extrovert is sociable, active, outgoing, impulsive, talkative and optimistic. The introvert is reserved, thoughtful, unsociable, passive, quiet and careful.

characteristics have a hereditary basis and the environment simply determines the form in which they manifest themselves.

If one can assume that there are only two basic dimensions of social attitudes, then ethnocentrism may be tough-mindedness in a teenage context. Tough-minded adults would certainly agree with the ethnocentric teenager that life is so short that having a good time is more important than anything else. They would also dislike foreigners, homosexuals and anyone who does not conform or tries to interfere. They would not, of course, share the teenager's antagonism to the adult world. If this suggestion is correct, then teenage ethnocentrism may be similar to extroversion. The ethnocentric teenager, besides feeling alienated from the adult world, may be highly extroverted as well.

Eysenck calls his other attitude dimension 'radicalism–conservatism'. This does not have such a clear association with hereditary personality characteristics, but consists largely of reactions to the influences which the individual has experienced throughout his life. Radicalism–conservatism is very similar in many ways to the permissive–restrictive dimension of our research. The difference lies mainly in the fact that the attitudes Eysenck studied in this context were largely concerned with political questions. Some of his statements on moral topics however were very similar to ours and it appears that our strongly permissive teenager would be radical in Eysenck's terms and our strongly restrictive teenager would be conservative.

Eysenck (1953, 1960) proposes that extroverts condition (in the Pavlovian sense) less easily than introverts, partly due to the nature of the nervous systems they have inherited. In consequence they are less bothered by guilt and shame when they break the rules of society (on the family or community level). In other words their consciences are much weaker and they are less inhibited in their social activity. In view of this one would expect extroverts to be more sexually experienced than introverts. Sex in psychological terms is one of the basic drives motivating human behaviour. The control of this drive is one of the most elementary conditioning processes which commences very early on in a person's life. The extrovert who is less susceptible to the conditioning process will more easily abandon his inhibitions and take the opportunity to have sexual experience when it arises.

From this one can conclude that a degree of extroversion is a prerequisite for premarital sexual experience. The introverted individual would find it more difficult to lose his inhibitions as far as sex is concerned; it would be far harder for the introvert to surmount the barriers of conscience and the ensuing guilt which is associated with it.

However, extroversion alone is not sufficient to determine the extent of a teenager's sexual experience. Sex is one of the subjects which is central in the arena of controversy which exists in modern society. As with politics and religion there is a so-called radical or progressive view of it which is opposed by a conservative or re-actionary one. In terms of Eysenck's theory, what determines the opinions one holds on topics which fall within the scope of this dimension are all the influences which one has encountered through-out one's life. The process by which one acquires ideas in these areas is the other form of learning, namely, the instrumental type. Most of the learning which is acquired through the mediation of language is instrumental. At the conceptual level it involves assimilating ideas, thinking about them, and accepting some and rejecting others depending on whether or not they fit in with the views which one has been developing all one's life.

In this section we are making the tentative suggestion that permissiveness–restrictiveness has many similarities with Eysenck's radical–conservative dimension. The highly permissive teenager is similar to the highly radical one, except that the topics on which he expresses his permissive opinions are mainly concerned with morality.

This chapter has shown that permissiveness is more strongly associated with sexual behaviour than any other variable, and as figure 12.28 has shown the sexually experienced teenager also tends to be ethnocentric as well as highly permissive in his views.

In Eysenck's terms, extroversion coupled with influences which have produced a radical view of life will be the personality charac-teristics most likely to lead to pre-marital sexual intercourse. The first-order factors and the second-order factors which are associated with sex experience are also manifestations of extroversion and radicalism in more specific areas of the teenager's life. They are of special interest because they reveal the extent to which the teenager desires freedom from the family and so is provided with opportunities and facilities to have sexual experience.

We have attempted to make some tentative suggestions about the personality types which are most likely to lead to sexual experience in teenagers. The suggestions are tentative because this is not the place to get involved in the controversies about theories of per-sonality. We have used Dr Eysenck's terms, but it would have been possible to use others.

Personality is only one of the determinants of sexual behaviour.

The opportunity for contact with the opposite sex and the facilities to make use of that opportunity are just as important as personality. This chapter indicates that there are probably certain personality characteristics which lead some teenagers to create the opportunities and to take advantage of the available facilities.

PART IV
SUMMARY AND DISCUSSION

13 PROFILE OF THE EXPERIENCED TEENAGER

A. RATING SCALES

This research concentrated upon the task of obtaining quantitative and measurable material because only a few researches on sex behaviour have provided this type of information. Up to this point of this report we have left out most of the qualitative material because many other books on teenagers have been based on general impressions. But during the course of a long interview there is little doubt that our interviewers often got a very vivid qualitative impression of the girl or boy. The difficulty is to convert this valuable material into a form which can be handled statistically. It was decided that this could best be done by making inferential assessments on a few general topics (section D of appendix 2).

By bringing together all the answers on a particular subject it is possible to rate each individual on a simple four- or five-point scale, using anchor definitions for each point on the scale. Inevitably this is not a precise measuring instrument; by definition, qualitative material is very difficult to measure. Despite training and supervision during the course of the research, we found inconsistencies between the different interviewers; some tended to rate towards one end of the scale, others towards the centre; in one scale (appearance) about 75 per cent of our sample were rated up at the top end of the scale. Despite these inconsistencies the assessments give an overall evaluation which complements the more specific measurable items and five of the scales turned out to be highly correlated with sex experience.

At the end of the interview each teenager was rated on a five-point scale of appearance, ranging from handsome to ugly. There appears to be a strong association between good looks and sex experience for boys ($p = 0.001$) and, rather unexpectedly, a less strong association for girls ($p = 0.05$). A similar rating was made of the response of the teenager during the interview on a five-point scale ranging from talkative to reserved; there was no association for girls but there appears to be a strong association between sex experience and loquaciousness for boys ($p = 0.001$).

Three of the scales which reflected more general impressions were found to have strong associations with sex experience. One of them was an attempt to bring together the answers to sixteen questions by rating them on a scale named *intensity of family influence*. It was found that those who were most influenced by their families were the least experienced ($p =$ 0·001 for boys and girls). Similarly the *intensity of group influence* scale based on the answers to twenty-one questions was associated with sexual experience for boys ($p =$ 0·01) and girls ($p =$ 0·001). Finally an important five-point scale, based on the answers to twenty questions, indicated the extent to which each individual had available the *facilities* which made sexual activities impossible, difficult or easy. This scale was strongly associated with sex experience for both boys ($p =$ 0·001) and girls ($p =$ 0·001).

B. UNDISTINGUISHABLE FEATURES

The two sections following this one will describe the characteristics which discriminate the sexually experienced teenagers from the others (as detailed in chapter 8–12). These two sections on their own might give the impression that experienced teenagers are quite different from other boys and girls of the same age. In fact there are many more features where there is no difference between experienced and other teenagers than there are features where a difference can be detected. Consequently it is important to emphasise that it is not possible to draw a clear-cut profile of the experienced teenager, for the distinctions are often blurred and the similarities may be just as important as the differences. This is especially the case as regards the basic background features where differences might have been expected.

The boys in our sample, aged seventeen to nineteen, who had experience of premarital intercourse came from all sections of the community and from all social classes. They were not more likely to be the sons of manual or non-manual workers. Nor did we find any difference between the two groups when we considered the social class of the mother. Their position in the family had no effect; they did not tend to be the oldest, or the youngest, or the only child in the family.

It made no difference if they came from a church-going home, and there was no difference as between those in the Church of England and Nonconformists, Roman Catholics or Jews.

The background of the boys seems to have little effect, and early experience, found to be influential in other areas of behaviour, did not appear to produce changes in sexual behaviour. Experienced boys were not more likely to come from broken homes where the father was dead or absent; the parents' marital happiness or the number of times they have moved home had no effect. Mothers who went out to work or the relations with the father were not important; only where there were poor relations with the mother were the boys more likely to be experienced.

There were only slight variations in the sexual behaviour of boys from different types of school; experienced boys were most likely to come from secondary modern schools and least likely to come from grammar schools; there was hardly any difference between state schools of all types and independent schools; there was a slight tendency for experienced boys to come from coeducational rather than segregated schools, but no difference between day and boarding schools.

Sex education did not seem to prevent premarital intercourse or to encourage it. The experienced boys, like the other boys, wished they had been told more about sex at school and by their parents. About half of each group felt they now knew all there was to know about sex. Experienced boys started work before the others and had more jobs, but they did not appear to be less contented in their work.

Youth clubs did not seem to have much effect on sexual behaviour. Neither the number of visits in a month, nor the type of club was an influencing factor. Experienced boys did not spend any less or more time watching TV, and were not less or more likely to own a motor-cycle, scooter or have the use of a car.

Thus the sexually experienced boy did not come from a deprived home, nor was he handicapped in any other way. He seems to have had much the same start in life as the others and there are no signs in early childhood which can be used to predict the later sexual behaviour of the teenager.

C. DISCRIMINATING FEATURES

Although the early family life and background of experienced boys appear to be unexceptional, when the present family situation is considered, it is possible to detect a difference. This is particularly true of questions related to parental discipline. The parents of the less experienced boys knew where they spent their leisure and insisted that they returned home in the evenings at a definite time. Age itself is related to parental discipline; as a boy gets older he is less amenable to discipline and also more likely to be sexually experienced.

The rating scale on family influence showed a strong association with sex experience. This influence did not extend to religion as we found that the extent of parental church-going had no influence on sex behaviour. But experienced boys do not go to church and their attitudes are out of sympathy with religious thinking.

Where there is less parental discipline there are probably more opportunities for sexual behaviour. Experienced boys were more often out of the home, and when they were at home they more often had the house to themselves. They were more likely to go to parties where there was no supervision by adults and to parties that lasted after midnight, and perhaps all night. It was made clear in the factor analysis that they would prefer to take their holidays away from their parents and many of them did this. Experienced boys either have, or create, the opportunities and facilities for more extensive sex behaviour.

The school careers of the sexually experienced boys were less satisfactory. They were more likely to be sent to a secondary modern school and they did not pass many exams; this may be more a matter of personality than intelligence because we found that the experienced boys who did take GCE 'O' level passed in just as many subjects as the other boys. But the experienced boys disliked school and had many more problems at school. And many of them left school as soon as they could.

As they left school earlier, they also went to work at an earlier age. This may partly account for the fact that they had many more jobs than the non-experienced and inceptive boys; but it is doubtful if this wholly accounts for the larger number of jobs which the experienced boys had; there are also signs of restlessness and lack of ambition (factor XII).

They received larger wages than the other boys and they had more money to spend. This is partly because they were older, but this does not fully explain the difference; the correlation between money to spend and sex experience is 0·45, and when the influence of age is excluded, it is reduced to 0·32, but this is still a high correlation. The teenagers earning very high wages were nearly all experienced boys and this may be connected in some cases with physical energy and strength. Another indication of this vigour is shown in the association with sport. Experienced boys are less likely to be interested in sport, but the few who are interested play as often as the other boys.

Their desire to leave school and go to work may also be related to physical development. It is well known that the age of puberty varies considerably (Tanner, 1961) and in the early stages of the research we tried to devise some way of recording the age at the start of puberty for each individual, but the practical difficulties were too great. So we had to be content with asking the boys if they remembered when their voice broke. Some boys had difficulty in remembering this, and in other ways it was not a very satisfactory question, but it did reveal an association with sex experience; from this slight evidence it appears that boys who reach puberty at an early age tend to have more sexual experience ($p = 0.05$).

There were other signs that physical developement might be an important influence. Experienced boys found out about the facts of life before the other boys; they also started dating at an earlier age and they had their first kiss before the other boys. It is also possible that the association between lack of parental discipline and sexual experience is related to physical maturity; the boy of seventeen who looks like an adult may resent attempts to prevent him behaving like an adult.

One of the strongest influences on a teenager's behaviour in any sphere is the desire to be like other teenagers, and sexual activities are no exception. Experienced boys spend more time in teenage groups and seek advice from friends rather than parents. They are influenced by other teenagers and by the entertainment industry and the flourishing commercial market directed towards teenage spending. Conformity with other teenagers is very important. Experienced boys are more likely to support the teenage mythology (section C of chapter 1) and are more likely to be against adult standards and outsiders of any kind. As the factor analysis showed they are the embodiment of teenage ethnocentrism.

Many boys think their friends are having more sexual experience than they are themselves. When this urgent desire to conform is combined with the fact that the most enthusiastic advocates of the teenage mythology are already sexually experienced, it becomes clear that the pressures put upon the other boys to extend the range of their sexual activities are very great indeed.

Experienced boys go out more than the others. They go to cinemas, dances, coffee bars and pubs. It is particularly the commercial premises that they like; sports clubs, youth clubs and evening institutes do not hold the same attraction. It is interesting that cinemas, dances and coffee bars are significantly associated with sexual experience for boys but not for girls. This suggests that it is not because they expect to pick up girls in these places; it is more a measure of sociability or outgoingness. (Pubs are the exception for they are significantly associated with sex for both boys and girls; this is because girls rarely go into pubs alone and are taken in by their boy friends.)

This outgoingness seems to be part of a vigorous and hedonistic search for a good time. Not only did they go to bars more often, but

Q

they also got drunk more often. They went out with a group more often and were rated as the most talkative by the interviewers. Not only did they appear before a juvenile court more often, but they were also more prepared to admit other misdeeds. It is notable that juvenile delinquency of all kinds is associated with sexual experience, but we did not find a tendency for the experienced boys to commit the more serious offences such as stealing or violence. Their transgressions often seem to be the result of thoughtless verve and liveliness.

But there is little doubt that their attitudes as well as their activities were exceedingly permissive and even indulgent. They were sceptical about adult moral standards and opposed any kind of restrictions; most of them favoured premarital intercourse for boys, but were less sure about the propriety of intercourse for unmarried girls. Although somewhat intolerant of attitudes outside the teenage world, considerable licence is allowed inside this group on most moral issues not excluding sexual behaviour.

The profile of the sexually experienced teenager falls short of the popular image of the jazz crazy, fast living, fun loving immoral youth. Although he does not exactly fit this picture, the sexually experienced teenager can be identified in four main areas of activity:

Facilities. Although family background was not very different, lack of interest or discipline from the parents meant that the teenager found more opportunities for sex behaviour.

Physical development. The rate of human growth varies considerably and sexual behaviour seems to be connected with energy, strength and physical development, as well as with chronological age.

Conformity. The teenage mythology is now an important element in all adolescent behaviour, and those who are sexually experienced are especially liable to combine this teenage ethnocentrism with antagonism to outside adult standards.

Permissiveness. A lively gregariousness combined with a tolerant attitude to all moral questions seems to be the most universal feature of sexually experienced boys under the age of twenty.

D. EXPERIENCED GIRLS COMPARED WITH BOYS

When the sexually experienced girls were compared with the other girls in the sample, many of the same discriminating features were found, but there were some notable differences. In general the experienced girls did not have less favourable backgrounds than the other girls, but there was a difference in family relations. There was no difference in the number who came from broken homes, who moved homes more often, whose mothers were working, whose parents went to church; nor was the religious denomination, the position in the family, or social class a discriminating feature. (Although inceptive girls tended to be higher up the social scale, there was no difference between experienced girls and the others in the social class of the father or the mother.)

But experienced girls more often reported poor relations with both the father and the mother, and there were more reports of marital difficulties among the parents. It will be remembered that there was a difference in the third-order *restrictive* factor between boys and girls (section D of chapter 12). Boys who scored high on this factor favoured restraints and controls without reference to family, but girls stressed the importance of family influence and loyalty. In the analysis of the attitude inventory three of the girls' first-order factors were *antipathy to family loyalty, dislike of home restrictions* and *preference for friends' advice*. All these factors were highly correlated with sexual experience, but did not appear at all among the boys' first-order factors.

It is clear that experienced girls have gone much farther than experienced boys in rejecting family influences. Relations with both parents were often strained and they were less likely to receive advice on sexual matters from their parents, and when they did get this advice, they were more likely to reject it.

In matters of parental discipline the experienced girls were like the experienced boys. These girls did not tell their parents where they were going, did not have to be in at a definite time, spent more time outside the home and more often entertained their friends at home when their parents were out. Like the boys, their home situation provided them with more opportunities and facilities for sexual activities.

The religious influence is the same with girls as it is with boys. The experienced girls were less likely to go to church and less likely to hold views which were favourable to religion, but they were just as likely to come from church-going homes.

The school records of the two experienced groups were very similar. Like the boys, the girls were more likely to have been to a secondary modern or comprehensive school, and were unlikely to have taken GCE; they disliked school, had more problems, and left at an earlier age. Sex education appears to have had no influence on them either way.

As with the boys, these girls had more jobs, were paid higher wages, and had more money to spend; unlike the boys they were more often discontented at work, more often unemployed, and more often in manual jobs than the other girls.

Like the boys, the school and work record of these sexually experienced girls suggests that their physical development is more advanced than it is for the other girls in the sample. They started dating and kissing at an earlier age; they were more likely than the others to have a steady boy friend; and more often they claimed to be in love, although not everyone will regard this claim as a sign of physical development.

The tendency towards teenage conformity was just as strong among the experienced girls as it was among the experienced boys. These girls were more likely than the other girls to go around in a mixed group, to spend more time with the group, and to meet on commercial premises.

More girls than boys received advice about sex from their parents, but the experienced girls, like the experienced boys, nearly always said they would go for advice to friends of their own age rather than parents or other adults. The experienced girls tended to hold attitudes that indicated support for teenage freedom and had a high score on teenage ethnocentrism.

The gregarious outgoingness noted among the experienced boys is not quite so apparent among the experienced girls. They did not go to the cinema, dances or coffee bars any more than the other girls. The important difference for girls is the person they go with; experienced girls were much more likely to go to these places with a boy than with another girl. Experienced girls were also less likely to play sports and they visited youth clubs less often although just as many of them were members of youth clubs.

In all other ways the experienced girls were as permissive as the experienced boys, indeed our third-order factor showed them to be more permissive. Like the boys, they went to bars more often, got drunk more often, and smoked more cigarettes. They went to more unsupervised parties, often where most of the other people there were adults, and these parties lasted past midnight and sometimes all night.

Although far fewer girls than boys had ever been in trouble with the law, those who had appeared before a court were more likely to be sexually experienced. They also admitted more misdeeds than the other girls. Not surprisingly they disagreed with the attitudes that support premarital virginity and they were not opposed to sexual intercourse before marriage. They also disputed the double standard of morality which makes premarital intercourse permissible for boys but not for girls.

The main difference between teenage girls and boys who have sexual experience is that a girl is more influenced by her family. She must overcome these family pressures and derogate her family loyalty before she can be persuaded to agree to premarital intercourse. Apart from this the discriminating factors are very similar and depend on the facilities available, the physical development, the desire to conform to the teenage mythology and the ease with which the young person can adopt a permissive attitude to moral issues; this permissiveness is essentially a personality characteristic which appears to combine with an outgoing hedonism in boys, and a rejection of family influences in girls.

I4 VALIDITY

A. SOURCES OF ERROR

People who had heard about this research often asked the very relevant question: How do you know that the teenagers have been telling you the truth? The answer is that we do not know; the best we could do was to make it as easy as possible for them to tell us the truth. No social researcher can be absolutely certain that his results convey a completely accurate picture of the population he has sampled. Problems of validation are common to all researches, and are particularly pertinent to a research into sexual behaviour. No topic is more personal and private than the sexual activities of the individual, and a person who gives truthful and straightforward answers about his shopping habits or voting intentions may well hesitate before he decides to be equally frank about his sex experiences. This may seem axiomatic, but it is surprising how many surveys on sexual behaviour assume that people will answer all the questions with candour. We did not make this assumption.

From the start of this research we considered the validity of the material to be the most important problem. That is why the discussion about the validity is not part of the introduction or in the appendix, but comes here before the final chapter. As our results are the reported experiences of the individuals in the sample, ultimately their truthfulness depends upon the teenager and the interviewer. But much can be done before to ensure that the design of the research increases the validity.

Inadequate sampling is a source of error and we took considerable pains to obtain a good sample, although it is not perfect. Our sample covered several areas, but we did not visit any rural areas and we did not go to Scotland. But our interviewees were found by random sampling methods and it is likely that no particular groups or types of teenagers were left out, except possibly those girls and boys who were always on the move and did not stay in any one place long enough to get on the sampling frame: such people may be a significant segment of the young adult population, but are a rarity among boys and girls of nineteen and younger; in only 4·8 per cent of the homes on our lists were there teenagers living away from home.

Any sample, even one taken by a production engineer from mass produced goods, is subject to sampling error, but this margin of error can be estimated statistically. Outside checks confirmed that our sample was representative; for example, the expected number of married teenagers occurred in our sample and the weighting procedure explained in section H of chapter 3 made hardly any change in our original results.

Indeed we are prepared to assert that no other research on sexual behaviour has used a better sample; this is not a boastful claim of assiduousness or skill, but simply the result of being provided with enough money and time to do the sampling thoroughly. But sampling is only the first step; it is also necessary to gain the cooperation of those participating in the research.

B. THE BIAS CAUSED BY REFUSALS

Every investigator dealing with human samples knows that he is very unlikely to get a 100 per cent response. It is almost inevitable that a certain percentage of those selected will not agree to an interview. The most that can be done is to keep the number of refusals down to a minimum, and to find out as much as possible about those who refuse.

The non-response rate excluding refusals was large in three of the seven areas due to inadequacies in the sampling frame (see section A of appendix 7). These inadequacies can create considerable difficulties in administrative procedure, but they are dependent on factors having no relation to the subject matter of the research and therefore they probably do not introduce any serious bias into the results.

But refusals may well distort the results and it was essential to impress upon the interviewers the importance of minimising the number of refusals. This was done during the training of the interviewers (section B of appendix 6) and during the fieldwork when the interviewers were required to persist even with the more reluctant teenagers (section B of appendix 5). The attempt to arrange an interview was only abandoned if an outright refusal had been given or if it was clear that the teenager did not intend to cooperate. The interviewers were all briefed with strong arguments in favour of the research and were also taught how to justify the personal questions in the interview whenever the parents or teenagers queried them.

The results of these efforts was that the refusal rate was kept down to under 15 per cent. But three in every 20 teenagers could not be persuaded to help and this may seem a high proportion. But it is much lower than the results obtained by most researches into sexual behaviour. Only a third of the questionnaires were returned in Chesser's (1956) survey, while Bromley and Britten (1938) had a refusal rate as high as 80 per cent. Others, like Kinsey (1948, 1953), have relied entirely on volunteers and therefore are unable to estimate the effects of refusals.

The highest rate of refusals was 18 per cent in South B, while the lowest was 10 per cent in North A. The A (middle-class) areas produced fewer refusals than the B (working-class) areas; there were fewer refusals in the North than elsewhere, and the rate of refusals tended to rise during those periods when there was public criticism of teenage activities. The parents of the girls refused on behalf of the teenager in about a quarter of the cases. But in two out of three refusals the interviewer actually met the teenager (section C of appendix 7). Thus in many cases we were able to get full information about the reasons for refusing.

The most usual reason for refusing was lack of interest. It was sometimes impossible to persuade a teenager to give up an hour of his time for a research which would not benefit him directly. The number who refuse for this reason depends on many things, none of which need necessarily be connected with the subject matter of the research. The introductory letter, time of day, and everything in the interviewer's approach were all very important, but in every survey there will usually be a residual number who cannot be persuaded to take part. Moser (1958) expects this group to be somewhere between 3 per cent and 5 per cent in most general interview surveys. In this research those who specifically said they were not interested were just under 3 per cent; if we add those who gave no particular reason for refusing, the rate is about 6 per cent. The one thing that all members of this apathetic group have in common is their lack of cooperation. This may be associated with a personality attribute, such as excessive shyness or aggressiveness, which in turn may be associated with sex experience, but any conclusions about their possible sexual behaviour based on this assumption would be very speculative. It is not unreasonable to assume that as a group their sex experiences are distributed in the same way as for the interviewed sample.

The other reason for refusing was that they guessed that questions were going to be asked about things they did not want to discuss. Many teenagers or their parents guessed that the interview would contain questions on sex experience. Some teenagers had heard distorted accounts or had picked up incorrect information about the research from misleading newspaper stories. Others had confused it with other studies on sexual behaviour reported in the press.

The teenager who felt that he was bound to be asked about his sexual behaviour would adopt an attitude towards the research which would depend largely on his attitude towards sex and his experience of it. At one end of the scale a sexually experienced teenager who felt guilty or ashamed of his sex experience might refuse to be interviewed; at the other end of the scale the immature adolescent with no sexual experience of any kind might view the prospect of answering questions about sex as too embarrassing to contemplate, and again a refusal would be the obvious solution to his difficulty. So the foreknowledge that questions about sex were to be asked would introduce a bias, but it is not certain which way this would influence the results.

It is indeed possible that knowing the interview was about sex would be an incentive to take part for some boys. It is difficult to gauge the extent to which these factors operate. It seems reasonable to guess that some experienced girls are likely to refuse because they are ashamed; at the same time it is a reasonable guess that some inexperienced girls are likely to refuse because they would be embarrassed. The fact that the younger age groups, and particularly the younger girls, were the most likely to refuse (section D of appendix 7) suggests that there is a greater tendency for the inexperienced and embarrassed to refuse rather than the experienced and ashamed.

A few parents also refused because they had heard that some of the questions were about sex; but this would have less relevance, because the fact that a parent feels he should protect his child from questions about sex is not necessarily an indication that the child is naïve or inexperienced, as our interviewers found out when some of the parents were persuaded to change their minds.

The reasons given by those who refused have not really helped us to decide if their absence from the interviewed sample has produced a distortion in the results. We also attempted to calculate the effect of the refusals by sending a refusal form to everyone who would not agree to an interview (section E of appendix 7). We were surprised and pleased that 78 boys and 84 girls returned these forms. Therefore exactly half those who refused told us a little about themselves.

In table 14.1 the boys and girls who returned the refusal form are compared with those who were interviewed in the sample. There are very few important differences between the groups. More of those who returned the refusal form were now at work, and fewer of them had been to grammar or private schools, and fewer had taken the GCE exam. These three items are all associated with sex

Table 14.1 *Those who returned the refusal form (RRF) compared with those who were interviewed in the sample (IS)*

	Boys		Girls	
	RRF, %	IS, %	RRF, %	IS, %
Type of school				
Secondary modern and comprehensive	68	63	65	63
Grammar	15	22	12	23
Technical	2	4	4	2
Private	4	8	5	8
Other, NK	11	4	14	4
Educational attainment				
GCE 'O' level	14	33	20	27
Others	86	67	80	73
Type of job				
Professional, managerial	6	8	1	2
Skilled	35	31	6	6
Semi-skilled, non-manual	6	5	11	4
Semi-skilled, manual	8	7	8	12
Routine non-manual	10	8	46	41
Unskilled	14	9	6	6
At school, NK	20	31	21	30
Number of jobs				
One	44	40	51	36
2–4	31	26	28	32
5+	5	5	2	3
NK and N/A	20	30	19	29
Church-going				
Every week	12	17	18	21
Occasionally	14	17	27	24
Never	72	65	50	55
NK	1	0	5	0
Club membership				
Yes	56	60	44	46
No	44	40	56	54
Dancing				
One a week or more	26	23	30	29
Less than once a month	24	30	34	39
Hardly ever and never	50	47	35	32
No. (100%)	78	934	84	939

experience, and this suggests that those who refused may be more experienced.

But the other results from the refusal form do not confirm this suggestion. There was no real difference in the occupations or the number of jobs, or in church-going, or in the number of times they went out dancing. All these items are associated with sex experience. If those who had refused to be interviewed were more likely to be sexually experienced, we would have expected to find differences in these items.

The results from the refusal form suggest that it was the under-educated and uninquisitive teenager who would not agree to an interview. These boys and girls could see no point in a research of this kind and were not prepared to give up their time to help. Unless apathy is closely correlated with sex experience, and chapter 13 leads us to believe the opposite, we doubt if these refusals have had much effect on our results.

C. COMPARISONS WITH OTHER RESEARCHES

Table 14.2 lists the other researches where it has been possible to calculate the accumulative incidences of premarital intercourse for teenage boys. We define accumulative incidence as the number of people in the total sample who have engaged in this activity by a given age.

Table 14.2 *Accumulative incidence of premarital intercourse by teenage boys as reported by five researches*

Research	Range of sample	Age	Acc. In. %
Hohman, 1947	American soldiers	16	36
,, ,,	,, ,,	18	63
Kinsey, 1948	American males	16	52
,, ,,	,, ,,	17	61
,, ,,	,, ,,	18	71
Kirkendall, 1961	American students	17	40
,, ,,	,, ,,	18	54
Christensen, 1962	Danish students	20	62
,, ,,	American students	20	50
THIS RESEARCH, 1965	British males	16	14
,, ,, ,,	,, ,,	17	26
,, ,, ,,	,, ,,	18	34

All but one of the researches available for comparison are American. All of them show accumulative incidence figures higher than we have obtained. This suggests that the incidence of pre-marital intercourse is higher in Denmark and the United States than it is here.

Hardly any of the researches on the sexual behaviour of girls give enough information about the age at the time of first inter-course for us to be able to calculate the accumulative incidence. In table 14.3 we have listed seven other surveys which showed the extent of premarital intercourse, but it is not easy to compare these figures with ours because they include women of twenty and over who first experienced intercourse before they were married.

Table 14.3 *The extent of premarital intercourse as recorded in eight researches*

Research	Range of sample	Incidence, %
Davis, 1929	College educated. Average age 37	11
Hamilton, 1929	Patients. Average age 30	35
Terman, 1938	Mostly college. Average age 36	37
Bromley, 1938	College educated. Average age 40	24
Landis, 1940	Patients. Ages 22–35	27
Chesser, 1956	British females. Average age 18–21	21
Christensen, 1962	Danish students. Average age 20	57
,, ,,	American students. Average age 20	20
THIS RESEARCH, 1965	British girls. Ages 15–17	6
,, ,, ,,	British girls. Ages 17–19	16

Kinsey (1953) pointed out that the first experience of premarital intercourse often takes place in the year or two before marriage, and much of it is confined to the fiancé in the period just before marriage. Consequently the incidence depends upon the age of marriage. Girls who marry at an early age tend to have premarital intercourse when they are younger than the women who marry later. Therefore there is a close correlation between age at first premarital intercourse and age at marriage. This means that table 14.3 does not give much information about teenage premarital intercourse although it does show quite clearly that it is a common phenomenon with females of all ages.

Chesser's survey is the only other study in table 14.3 that was carried out in Great Britain. About 21 per cent of his youngest groups of informants had experienced premarital intercourse, and 49 per cent of all those with premarital experience had started before the age of twenty-one; so it appears that about 10 per cent of the single girls were sexually experienced at the age of twenty. This compares with our figure of 17 per cent at the age of eighteen.

We were only able to calculate the accumulative incidence for girls under nineteen from Kinsey's report. Table 14.4 compares these figures with the percentages we found at three age levels.

Table 14.4 *Accumulative incidence at three age levels of premarital intercourse in teenage girls as reported by the Kinsey research and this research*

Age	Kinsey, %	This research, %
16	7	5
17	10	10
18	13	17

This shows that our incidence for girls is higher than that found by Kinsey. This is surprising considering that the incidence for boys found by Kinsey was much higher than our results. This also means that the difference between boys and girls is much greater in Kinsey's research than it is in this one.

D. EXTERNAL CHECKS

None of the previous researches into sexual behaviour cover the same ground; most of them are unrepresentative or study a different segment of the population; all of them are investigations carried out in different countries at different times. Consequently it is not really possible to check our results against the results of previous researches.

Nor is it possible to find much in the way of external checks from the official records. Indeed if the information on sex behaviour was available from government sources there would be no point in doing the research. But we should try to use the small amount of official information that is available.

For example the official records of illegitimate births can be used as an approximate indication of the minimum incidence of premarital sexual intercourse. Wimperis (1960) found that 'unmarried mothers are far from being a psychologically average cross section of society' and in consequence it seems probable that they differ in some respects from other girls who are having premarital intercourse. But every unmarried mother has had sexual intercourse at least once and therefore the illegitimacy figures can serve as an approximate baseline for a research into the incidence of premarital sexual intercourse.

Table 14.5 is based upon information obtained from the Registrar General's *Statistical Review* for 1962. We have taken the national figures rather than those for the specific areas where we interviewed because a large number of unmarried mothers go away from where they live to have their babies. For example, 58 per cent of the unmarried mothers seen by the five large Moral Welfare Associations in London in 1960 were either not born in this country or had been resident in London for less than one year (from the report of the Medical Officer of Health for London, 1960). Therefore the figures in table 14.5 refer to the illegitimate births which were recorded in England and Wales in 1962 and the incidence of illegitimacy is defined as the percentage of girls in a particular age group who had illegitimate babies.

Table 14.5 *The incidence of illegitimacy in England and Wales in 1962*

Age	No. of single girls	No. of illegitimate births	Incidence of illegitimacy, %
15	419,370	919	0·2
16	324,060	1,782	0·6
17	310,100	3,041	0·9
18	296,020	3,820	1·3
19	249,240	4,367	1·8
15–19	1,598,790	13,929	0·9

Ten of the 939 girls in our sample had given birth to an illegitimate baby or were pregnant at the time of the interview; this represents an incidence of 1·1 per cent which compares with the national average incidence for the fifteen to nineteen age group of 0·9 per cent.

The national incidence of illegitimacy for girls aged sixteen and seventeen is 0·8 per cent and these are the ages which most nearly correspond to our younger age group, taking into account the fact that conception precedes illegitimacy by about nine months. In our sample 6 per cent of the younger girls admitted experience of sexual intercourse. The national incidence of illegitimacy for girls aged eighteen and nineteen is 1·6 per cent and these are the ages which most nearly correspond to our older age group where 16 per cent had premarital sexual intercourse. Thus our results are eight times as large as the baseline in the younger age groups and are even farther above the baseline among the older girls.

Another indication of the incidence of premarital sexual intercourse is the national figure for the number of legitimate births which occurred within the first eight months of marriage. It can be assumed that these maternities were the result of premarital sexual intercourse and so their incidence can be used as an approximate baseline in the same way as the illegitimacy figures.

Table 14.6 refers to births which occurred within eight months of marriage to girls in 1962 and the incidence of maternities legitimised by marriage is defined as the percentage of all girls in a particular age group who are married and had babies which were conceived before marriage. Thus in spite of the fact that these figures relate to girls who were married at the time the records were made, they refer to sexual intercourse which occurred when the girls were unmarried.

Table 14.6 *The incidence of maternities occurring within the first eight months of marriage in England and Wales in 1962*

Age	No. of single girls	Maternities within eight months	Premarital conceptions, %
15	419,370	10	0·0
16	324,060	2,026	0·6
17	310,100	6,921	2·2
18	296,020	10,875	3·5
19	249,790	11,524	4·3
15–19	1,598,790	31,356	1·9

The average incidence for girls aged sixteen and seventeen is 1·4 per cent which is well below the 6 per cent of our younger girls who have had premarital sexual intercourse. The average for those girls aged eighteen and nineteen is 3·9 per cent which is below the 16 per cent of our older girls who have experienced sexual intercourse.

The national figures for conceptions before marriage were used so that they could be added to the illegitimacy figures. If we add the overall average for illegitimacy (0·9 per cent) to the overall average for conceptions before marriage (1·9 per cent) we find that at least 2·8 per cent of all single girls aged fifteen to nineteen have had experience of sexual intercourse. In fact we found that 11 per cent of all such girls in our sample had experienced sexual intercourse.

Among the older girls 16 per cent of our sample had experienced sexual intercourse and the national averages for illegitimacy and conception before marriage indicate that 5·45 per cent of this age group became pregnant; this suggests that for every three girls who have premarital sexual intercourse, one becomes pregnant. Unfortunately there is very little information on the fecundity of girls under twenty. Anderson (1960) questioned 62 adolescent unmarried mothers and found that over half (58 per cent) claimed that they had conceived after less than four experiences of sexual intercourse. Gebhard (1959) found that 12·6 per cent of the girls under twenty in his sample of American women who had had premarital intercourse became pregnant; that is, for every eight girls with experience of intercourse one became pregnant. So the English girls seem to run a much higher risk of pregnancy.

All illegitimacies and maternities legitimised by marriage involve a father as well as a pregnant girl, so the figures in this section are also applicable to the boys if the girls are having intercourse with boys of the same age. In the sample of younger boys 11 per cent had experienced sexual intercourse and this is more than the combined figures of illegitimacy and conceptions before marriage; 30 per cent of the older boys had experienced intercourse compared with the baseline figure of 5·45 per cent. This suggests that about one in five of the older boys who have premarital sexual intercourse will become a putative father.

The incidence figures for venereal disease do not provide a good check because only a very small proportion of the total teenage population ever get the disease. In section E of chapter 6 we estimated that the chances of a girl aged fifteen to nineteen getting VD were about a thousand to one; in fact one girl in our sample of 939 had been infected. It was estimated that among boys aged fifteen to nineteen only one in over 1,600 became infected by venereal disease; in our sample of 934 two boys had been infected.

The figures for premarital intercourse are always higher for boys than for girls in this research and in every other research on sexual behaviour. In this research the incidence for boys is nearly twice as high, but in the surveys by Kinsey (1948, 1953) five times as many teenage boys claimed to have had sexual intercourse. Kinsey attempted to account for this discrepancy in a number of ways and came to the conclusion that the two main factors were differences in the representativeness of his two samples for men and women, and the probability that the females have covered up some part of their premarital experience. In our sample the girls are as representative as the boys, but the social attitudes to premarital intercourse probably mean that girls tend to under-estimate and boys tend to exaggerate their sexual experience. But this is unlikely to be the only explanation because there are other tendencies at work.

Most people would agree that the male is more predatory and is more likely to seek out and demand sexual conquests. Furthermore it is easier for the boy; the consequences of an unwanted pregnancy do not affect the man physically and do not damage him socially. If the boy is discovered to be having premarital intercourse, he is not often blamed, even by his parents, and his reputation in some quarters is likely to be enhanced. But a girl has to be much more careful of her reputation; indeed we have found that some boys make a clearcut distinction between girls who will permit intercourse and girls who are a prospect for marriage.

Therefore it is not too difficult to explain why more boys than girls have sexual intercourse. It remains true, however, that every act of heterosexual intercourse requires a girl as well as a boy. So we still have to answer the question: If more teenage boys than girls have premarital intercourse, who are their sexual partners?

The first thing to note is that for some of these experienced boys sexual intercourse is a rare occurrence. In fact 15 per cent of the experienced boys did not have intercourse in the year before they were interviewed; this was true of only 7 per cent of the experienced girls so in actual numbers more than four times as many boys (29) than girls (7) did not have sexual intercourse in the last year. Furthermore it has been shown that although nearly twice as many boys are experienced, in fact the girls have intercourse more often (section E of chapter 5). Among the experienced girls 31 per cent had sexual intercourse more than 25 times in the last year, whereas only 14 per cent of the experienced boys had intercourse as often as that.

Nevertheless all the experienced boys averaged about six partners each, whereas the girls averaged only about two partners each. It is unlikely that the extra partners found by the boys are girls of twenty or older. Therefore we must assume that some of the boys'

R

partners were extremely promiscuous teenage girls. This possibility is quite credible for in chapter 5 we found signs that there was a small group of highly promiscuous girls not represented in our sample,[1] and it requires only a very few promiscuous girls to oblige many young men.

E. EVALUATION OF THE RESULTS

The interviewer was required to give his estimate of the truthfulness of the responses immediately after each interview. He was instructed to use the highest rating only when he had absolutely no doubts at all. In fact 6 per cent were rated as very high validity, 76 per cent as high, 26 per cent as fair and 2 per cent were rated low validity. Of course this is a subjective judgement but it should not be disregarded altogether. Every experienced interviewer will remember cases when he comes away from the interview happy and confident that he really got to know the interviewee, and he will also remember other times when he comes away perplexed and depressed with the feeling that he never got through to the other person at all.

It was also clear that in the majority of cases the teenager enjoyed the interview and this is a good indication of the validity. Nearly all (96 per cent) agreed to another interview at a later date. They were also asked if they found the interview interesting and we introduced a midway category to distinguish between people who really were interested and those who were being polite. In reply to this question, 3 per cent said they did not find it interesting, 18 per cent gave what the interviewer judged to be the polite reply and 79 per cent expressed a genuine interest.

The five men who interviewed the boys all produced remarkably similar results, but there were some disparities between the results of the five female interviewers. For example, 11 per cent of all the girls were in stages IV and V; the two interviewers with the highest rate found 13 per cent and the two interviewers with the lowest rate found 8 per cent. It would be a mistake to make too much of this because the interviewers with the highest rates in this respect also happened to interview more older girls and so increased the chances of finding more girls in stages IV and V. However, we were left with the impression that some of our interviewers were better than others at persuading the teenage girls to be truthful about their sex experiences. But it was not a simple division; some interviewers

1. We met some of these very promiscuous girls when we interviewed special problem groups (girls in prison, in care and at VD clinics) outside the main random sample. These results will be published in a later report.

were good with middle-class girls while others found it easier to establish *rapport* with working-class girls, and there were many other factors which affected the success of the interview.

As the reports from the interviewers came in, and as we checked the results, we grew more confident about the validity of the responses from the boys and less certain about the girls' replies. But the comparison with other researches shows that our results are low for boys and high for girls.

Musgrove (1963) has rightly warned researchers about the dangers of transferring American results to England. Most of the differences in the accumulative incidences for boys can probably be explained by different circumstances in different countries. But we do not rule out the possibility that other investigators have been misled by the tendency for boys to brag about their sexual adventures. There is a considerable danger that boys who volunteer to relate their sex histories are more likely to exaggerate; in this research we interviewed many boys who were not volunteers and who had to undergo considerable persuasion before they agreed to to be interviewed. Furthermore the construction of our schedule of questions was specially designed to discourage boasting; the events were not taken in chronological order and we asked for a large amount of corroborative detail.

Table 14.3 showed that premarital sexual intercourse was far from rare among women of all ages, but in the two cases where we were able to get information about teenage sexual intercourse we found that our percentages were higher. We found, as others (Kinsey, 1953; Ehrmann, 1959) have found, that much of this sexual intercourse is with steady boy friends and fiancés. If the incidence of premarital intercourse among females is closely related to the age of marriage, as seems likely, and if girls are tending to marry earlier, then we must expect more premarital intercourse among teenagers. There is also the other possibility that increased sexual intercourse among teenagers has led to more early marriages.

In section D of this chapter we found that our results were always above the rate of illegitimacy and conceptions before marriage, but we were surprised by the high risk of pregnancy that these figures revealed. On the other hand we found that girls who do have intercourse have a higher frequency rate than boys; they rarely use contraceptives and do not require their partner to take precautions; so the three to one chance of becoming pregnant is not unbelievable.

Our main concern has been to get a representative sample and to persuade the teenagers to tell us the truth. On the sampling we claim to have been reasonably successful. As far as the validity is concerned, we have found no external evidence that conflicts with our results, but we must recognise that it is very difficult to confirm that our figures are correct.

15 QUESTIONS OF PUBLIC CONCERN

A. PREMARITAL SEXUAL INTERCOURSE

Some readers, as they approach the end of this report, may be expecting a number of definite conclusions. But the object of this report has been to provide basic factual information, not to formulate an answer to the problem of teenage immorality. In any case we doubt whether there is any one easy solution to this problem. But we hope those who are looking for answers will be able to take into account the significant facts we have been able to unearth.

Our study of inceptive behaviour has shown that girls start before boys, but gradually the boys catch up with the girls until by seventeen there are more boys than girls taking part in these activities. Fifteen to nineteen are momentous years in the sex histories of boys; during this period most of them have moved from stage I to stage III or beyond. These are also important years for the girls and over half will have moved from stage I to stage III, but there is a barrier at stage III for girls which is not apparent for boys. Once he has started, a boy will tend to move quickly from stage to stage; but the fact that a girl is at one stage does not mean that she will soon be moving on to the next.

More teenage boys than girls have experience of sexual intercourse. In our sample 11 per cent of the younger boys and 30 per cent of the older boys have had premarital intercourse; the relevant figure for the younger girls is 6 per cent and for the older girls is 16 per cent. By using the accumulative incidence concept, we estimated that at the age of eighteen 34 per cent of the boys and 17 per cent of the girls are sexually experienced.

Sexual intercourse before fourteen was rare and by sixteen 14 per cent of the boys and 5 per cent of the girls had started. The first experience of sexual intercourse was usually with someone who was already experienced; the first partner was often older and in the case of the girls was quite often an adult. It was usually with a friend and more often than not took place in the parental home of the beginner or the partner. The first experience was often unpremeditated and unplanned, and a majority said they did not enjoy it.

Although more boys than girls have intercourse, when incidence and frequency are taken together we find the total sexual outlet is very similar. Fewer girls have intercourse, but those who are experienced do it more often. The boys have more sexual partners;

the girls prefer a more enduring relationship. Girls are slower to agree to intercourse, but once they have agreed they are more active sexually.

Some of the teenagers still hold attitudes which support the ancient double standard which basically states that premarital intercourse is forbidden for women but not for men. Apart from these attitudes there is another difference between boys and girls. The girl is looking for a romantic relationship while the boy is seeking a sexual relationship. The girl is in search of security, but the boy is in search of adventure. Premarital intercourse is most likely to happen when either one modifies his or her attitude so that it comes closer to the other one's aspirations. Then if the boy gives the impression that he is in love with the girl, she is more likely to agree to intercourse; or if the girl is persuaded that sexual activities are an extension of romantic feelings, intercourse is likely to take place.

Our results have made it clear that premarital sexual relations are a long way from being universal among teenagers as over two-thirds of the boys and three-quarters of the girls in our sample have not engaged in sexual intercourse. On the other hand it is equally apparent that teenage premarital intercourse is not a minority problem confined to a few deviates. It is an activity common enough to be seen as one manifestation of teenage conformity.

B. SEX EDUCATION

This research has shown that by the age of thirteen two-thirds of the boys and three-quarters of the girls know, or think they know, about the facts of life. In fact most of them have obtained this information from their friends and much of it is inaccurate and obscene. Prejudices and misunderstandings about sex would be avoided if children first heard about it from their parents. But this research has shown that this does not happen very often.

Two-thirds of the boys and a quarter of the girls had learnt nothing about sex from their parents. Even those who had discussed sex with their parents had usually first heard about it from another source. The only exception to this was middle-class mothers who were more likely to advise their daughters. Teenagers also reported that parental advice about sex usually concentrated on moral problems, and was unspecific and vague. Furthermore we found that the young people who were most likely to have a serious sex problem were also those who were least likely to go to their parents for help.

In some countries, for example, in one state in Australia, sex education in the schools is disallowed because it is believed that the parents are the proper people to instruct the child. But our results suggest that this is unlikely to work out well. Even when special classes are instituted to help the parents to teach their children about sex, the people who attend these classes are probably the ones who would have talked to their children about sex in any case.

The school teacher is the second most important source of sex knowledge for boys, and the third most important source for girls. The teacher has an important role to play in sex education, especially for working-class children who are less likely to learn from their parents.

At present the adolescents who first learn about sex from teachers are those who find out later than their peers. If sex education had been given earlier, more people would have obtained correct information about sex in the first place. As the situation is at present many of those who receive sex education in school are inattentive because they think they already know all there is to know about sex. If sex education comes too late, they will not listen because their ideas and prejudices about sex have already been formed.

Half the boys and 14 per cent of the girls did not receive any sex education at school. In all types of state schools, including grammar schools, as often as not there was no sex education for the boys. The lack of sex education was exactly where it was most needed; it was the working-class boys who were least likely to learn about sex from their parents and were least likely to receive sex education at school.

In view of all the discussion about sex education in recent years, it was surprising to find so many teenagers who said they were never taught about sex at school. A possible explanation is that the teachers think they are giving sex education but the adolescents do not recognise it as such. There were signs of a lack of frankness in the teaching. Sex education, when it occurred, seemed to concentrate on biological and physiological matters and seemed to be unrelated to human affairs, except when it was wholly concerned with putting across a particular moral point of view, which was often the case with the girls.

Nearly half the boys (47 per cent) and girls (43 per cent) felt they should have been told more about sex at school. The teenagers were dissatisfied with the amount of sex education they received, and with its quality. The difficulties of providing viable education about sex are immense; much of the moral code is based upon religious thinking which the teenagers do not accept and many of the arguments against premarital intercourse, when unsupported by moral exhortations, sound weak to many young people. In addition we have found a strong inclination among a large number of teenagers to reject adult advice of all kinds. But there is also plenty of evidence from this research that teenagers are anxious to be informed about sex and want sex education providing it is given with an assurance which is backed by knowledge and with a proper understanding of their particular problems.

C. ILLEGITIMACY AND VENEREAL DISEASE

It is often said that one of the consequences of premarital intercourse is illegitimacy. This is not strictly true. The birth of illegitimate children is caused by premarital sexual intercourse without adequate precaution against an unwanted pregnancy. In this sample 16 per cent of the boys and 18 per cent of the girls knew nothing about birth control and many of the others had only a slight knowledge of contraceptives.

Among those having sexual intercourse less than half the boys always used contraceptives and a quarter never used them. The girls having sexual intercourse usually left it to the man with the result that the majority neither used contraceptives themselves, nor insisted that their partner used them. Ponting (1963) interviewed a much more promiscuous group of teenagers and she found that only 17 per cent took precautions.

Quite a large group in this sample either did not like contraceptives or could not be bothered with them. The most usual birth-control method was either the sheath or withdrawal, but some of the boys who possessed sheaths had not had intercourse and had bought them as a kind of status symbol.

About half the experienced boys said they were inhibited by the fear that their partner might become pregnant, but about 40 per cent seemed to be unconcerned. More of the girls feared pregnancy, but they did very little about it. Many of the boys said they would marry a girl they had made pregnant, and this is what many of the girls hoped or expected. Others said they would want to keep the child if they became an unmarried mother. Neither adoption nor abortion were favoured by teenage girls, so it can be assumed that most pregnancies will lead to a hasty marriage or an illegitimate child.

There is still a strong feeling that the boy who made the girl pregnant has a duty to marry her, although this pressure is less severe when both of them are young. But Greenland (1958) found that among the 45 teenage unmarried mothers in his group, the putative father was over nineteen in 24 (53 per cent) cases. A study of the Registrar-General's figures since 1938 on rates of illegitimacy and premarital conceptions taken together shows that although the illegitimacy rate has gone up, the percentage of teenage brides who were pregnant on their wedding day has gone down. Therefore the social pressures on the unmarried mother to marry have declined, and this decrease in the rate of premarital conceptions 'regularised' by marriage more than accounts for the increase in illegitimate births.

Our inquiries into the use of birth-control methods among teenagers has shown that many boys are not using contraceptives and most girls who are having intercourse are at risk. This does not seem to be because teenagers have difficulty in obtaining contraceptives, but because social disapproval means that many of their sexual adventures are unpremeditated and therefore adequate precautions have not been taken beforehand; many of the teenagers are aware of the risks, but in these extemporary situations sexual desire may override this awareness of the possible consequences.

The problem of venereal disease among teenagers is not so great as the problem of illegitimacy. Nevertheless there has been an increase in the number of infections in the last few years, although this increase has not been so great in this age group as the rise among other sections of the community. It has been shown by the reports of the British Co-operative Clinical Group (1962, 1963) that the main increases in gonorrhoea have been among immigrants, homosexuals and young adults aged twenty to twenty-five. It is this last group that has given rise to misunderstandings because in the past, annual figures for infections have been grouped into age ranges, starting with fifteen to twenty-four. It should also be remembered that since the end of conscription many cases which were previously treated by the Services' medical units would now come to the civilian clinics.

This does not mean that the risks should be disregarded. Most of the teenagers in our sample had heard about VD, but not many of the experienced ones were worried about the possibility of being infected. Ponting (1963) only found 32 per cent who were afraid of VD and she obtained her information from a group who had visited a clinic at least once.

We found that there was still much ignorance about the venereal diseases and some of the misapprehensions and old wives' tales still persisted. About half the young people in our sample would not be able to recognise the symptoms if they were infected. Books were the best source of correct information although Dalzell-Ward (1960) has shown that some of the books on sex education do not mention the venereal diseases at all. Friends were the biggest source of misinformation and there is still some doubt whether a person who suspected that he was infected would really go to a clinic.

As the venereal diseases are sexually transmitted, the spread of the infection must involve, not two, but at least three people; one or both of the partners in the sexual act must have had intercourse with someone else. Therefore the venereal diseases must be associated with promiscuity.

Figure 5.9 showed the number of partners for all the experienced boys and girls, but a better indication of promiscuity is the number of sexual partners *in the last year* as shown in table 15.1. This shows that 7 per cent of the younger boys and 16 per cent of the older boys had more than one partner, while 2 per cent of the younger boys and 10 per cent of the older boys had only one partner; in addition a not inconsiderable number of boys (2 per cent of the younger and 4 per cent of the older) had no experiences in the last year although they had previously had sexual intercourse. Therefore slightly more than half the experienced boys (about 12 per cent of the total sample) can be said to be promiscuous in the strictest sense of the word.[1]

Table 15.1 *The number of sexual partners in the last year analysed by four age/sex groups*

Number of partners	YB, %	OB, %	YG, %	OG, %
More than one partner	7	16	2	3
One partner only	2	10	4	12
None, but experienced	2	4	0	1
Not experienced	89	70	94	84
TOTAL	100	100	100	100
No. (100%) *	415	395	415	399

* This question was not asked in the same form in London C and so the results from this area have not been included.

1. The Oxford dictionary definition of promiscuity uses the words 'indiscriminate mixture' and therefore it is open to doubt if sexual intercourse with two or three people can be called promiscuity. For those who prefer a wider definition of promiscuity, it is noted that about a quarter of the experienced boys (6 per cent of the whole sample) had four or more partners in the last year.

Table 15.1 shows that the girls have fewer partners than the boys. Less than a quarter of the experienced girls (about 2 per cent of the whole sample) had more than one sexual partner in the last year. In chapter 5 and elsewhere in this report we have noted that the boys have more partners than the girls, but this should not hide the fact that a large number of boys have premarital intercourse with one girl only, often with the girl they intend to marry (section C of chapter 10).

These results suggest that promiscuity, although it exists, is not a prominent feature of teenage sexual behaviour. Consequently the risks of venereal disease are not very great, and this conclusion is supported by the figures. Of course it is true that even the teenager who has had only one previous sexual partner may still infect another person. But the main danger of the venereal diseases is that many teenagers are ignorant about the symptoms, which are not always obvious, and may not go to a clinic if they are infected. Three-quarters of the boys who have sexual intercourse and four out of five of the girls at risk would not know if they had been infected (section D of chapter 8). These people are unlikely to reach diagnosis and treatment.

Only a very few teenagers are restrained from having sexual intercourse by the fear of venereal disease (section D of chapter 7). Those people who use the rise in the VD rate in their campaign against premarital intercourse should note that teenagers are not likely to be deterred by this threat.

On the other hand the fear of pregnancy was often given as the reason for not having sexual intercourse (table 7.3), and indeed the risks of pregnancy are greater than the risks of infection by venereal disease. Adults who comment on teenage sexual activities often bracket illegitimacy and venereal disease together, but the risks of illegitimacy are greater.

D. RESTRAINTS AND CONTROLS

It is not one of the objects of this research to suggest ways in which premarital sexual intercourse can be prevented. But it is hoped that those who are concerned about teenage sexual behaviour will be able to make use of some of the specific facts uncovered by this research. For example, it seems to be common practice to end a criticism of adolescent sexual behaviour by adding that we all know the bad ones are an exception and that most of the youth of this country are a grand clean-living bunch of lads. But this qualification is as wrong as the criticism is inept. For the results of this research show clearly that those who are having sexual intercourse are not a tiny minority. In round figures something over 350,000 boys and girls under the age of twenty have had experience of premarital intercourse.

But although it is not a small minority, it is not a majority, and those who are concerned about this problem might begin by asking why, in view of the great strength of the sexual drive, there are not more teenagers who are sexually experienced. Young men under the age of twenty are at their highest sexual potential and social pressures are by no means all on the side of restraint.

In chapter 7 we found that many of the teenagers gave moral reasons for not going farther, although few gave specific religious reasons. Many appeals to youth either assume Christian values or explicitly state Christian doctrines, but most of the young people we interviewed were not interested in Christianity. It is possible that many young people find their way of living incompatible with the moral teaching of Christianity and the Church's emphasis on sexual morality may make the experienced teenager feel that there is no room for him in the Christian Church.

Despite the social and physiological pressures towards sexual intercourse, many teenagers manage to resist these influences. This research has found several differences between those who do and those who do not have sexual intercourse. These are summarised in chapter 13 and they need not be repeated here except to add that these differences do not reveal serious anti-social tendencies in those teenagers with experience of sexual intercourse. The experienced boys were gregarious and outgoing, even hedonistic, but they were not misfits. Sexual experience among teenage girls is closely associated with a desire for freedom and independence from the family, but they were not debauched.

Nor is there any evidence that premarital sexual intercourse leads to or encourages adulterous relations after marriage. Burgess and Wallin (1953) found that 90 per cent of the women who had had premarital intercourse said that it had strengthened their marital relationship. Most of the young people in this sample disapproved of extramarital relations and this is as true of the experienced teenagers as of the others.

Those who are worried about the extent of premarital sexual intercourse among teenagers must accept that these activities cannot be eliminated altogether in the foreseeable future. Murdock (1949), on the basis of evidence compiled from a worldwide sample of 158 societies, found that premarital intercourse was permitted in 70 per cent of them; in the other societies restraints reinforced by disgrace and punishments were not always effective in preventing young people from engaging in premarital intercourse. The most effective way to prevent teenage sexual activities would be to decrease the opportunities by reintroducing ideas like chaperonage of girls and further segregation of the sexes. Descriptions of a Chinese school (Huang, 1964) and of family life in the Soviet Union (Mace, 1963) make it clear that adolescent immorality can be reduced if not eliminated. But if this is what is required, we shall also have to accept a measure of Communist discipline and a reduction in personal freedom.

Many people will have noticed that this research has found an association between sex experience and lack of parental discipline. There is a danger that some people will seize upon this as if it is the most important finding in the report because it fits in with their preconceived ideas and because it appears to be easy to remedy. But it is not certain that further restrictions will be of value. Bier (1963) in the report of a symposium on adolescents warns about the dangers of 'scrupulosity' – a tendency to make an individual see evil where there is no evil, serious sin where there is no sin and obligation where there is no obligation.

In face of much of the uninformed criticism about teenage sexual activities, it is tempting to spend too much time in pointing out that many of the generalisations are without factual foundation, that there are no signs of moral collapse, that more thought should be given to adult immorality, that many teenage attitudes are refreshing and stimulating, that there are many serious young people with great intellectual curiosity and high aspirations. But these assertions of good sense are not a substitute for factual information.

Indeed a disinterested look at the teenage cult will reveal several facets which are quite depressing and many signs that the least valuable and shabbiest aspects of adult society have been adopted with enthusiasm. The flaws in teenage society have been noted in detail by several writers, particularly Fyvel (1963) and the Hechingers (1964). The particular facet which concerns this research is the pressure towards conformity within the teenage cult and the formation of a teenage mythology. A typical example is teenage fashions which may seem daringly different from adult society, but in reality they are an illustration of strict conformism within the teenage subculture.

Four out of five people in Great Britain now live in urban areas, some of immense size. This urbanism has made possible the growth of teenage subcultures which are often at variance with adult standards. The improved economic position of the teenagers has given them more independence and greater mobility. But for many it has become a confused world as they revolt against an imposed middle-class morality and at the same time lose the assurance of their own working-class environment (Bals, 1962).

Within these urban conditions has grown up the teenage mythology, built up by the press, the advertisers and the special teenage and pop music magazines. This has created an image of how the teenager is supposed to behave. Here is an organised system of behaviour expectations and attitudes, and the young person acts out his role, largely learnt from the teenage group to which he belongs.

The sexual behaviour of young people is influenced by this teenage subculture. In chapter 4 we saw that there is a danger that a teenager may feel he is exceptional because he has not had sexual intercourse. In the same chapter we found that half the boys and two-thirds of the girls did not enjoy their first experience of sexual intercourse, but nearly all of them tried it again fairly soon. Yet at the time of the interview there were still 28 per cent of the experienced boys and 39 per cent of the experienced girls who did not always enjoy it.

In chapter 5 we envisaged a situation in which the boy and girl engaged in sexual intercourse although neither of them wanted to do this. In chapter 10 we found that many teenagers felt their friends were having more sex than they were and in chapter 13 we noted that the most enthusiastic advocates of teenage conformity were the sexually experienced boys and girls.

In chapter 12 we found that the sexually experienced were the ones who had the least respect for adult standards. Consequently the time that these people spend with adults is cut to a minimum and there is no interaction between the adult and teenage worlds. The young people no longer have what the Americans call 'corrective feedback' from adults, and youth becomes, not 'an ephemeral privilege' as Cocteau thought it ought to be, but 'a separate hardy race setting itself up in opposition to the decaying race of the old'.

Yet it is obvious that this teenage subculture has been created by the adult world, not by the young people themselves. For example, the sexually experienced went to the cinema more often than the others and therefore could see that sexual satisfaction is all important in most films, and premarital sex is acceptable in many. The teenagers with the most sexual experience were also those with the most money to spend and therefore the quarry for the very active salesmen of the teenage commercial market. Incidentally the only group of teenagers that sets out to resist the blandishments of the marketeers are the Beats, and they come in for an extra measure of social hostility.

The adult world, unlike the Beats, cannot contract out. It is our responsibility for it is our society that has created the modern teenager. No matter what measures are taken to restrict or control or change or influence the activities of our young people, it is certain that in the immediate future a not inconsiderable number of teenagers will engage in premarital sexual intercourse. These sexually experienced teenagers are every bit as much our responsibility as the others. Whatever the long-term answer may be, there is an urgent short-term task, and that is to make youthful sex activities less harmful. This may be done by increasing the amount of knowledge and enlightenment on sexual matters, by introducing more and better sex education in the widest sense, and by providing individual counselling which on some occasions will mean making available methods of birth control to those who need them. Above all it is vital that future programmes of advice, help and restraint should be based, less on unsubstantiated impressions, and more on the demonstrable facts. It is hoped that this research has gone some way towards providing this necessary factual information.

PART V
APPENDICES

Appendix 1

PREPARATION

A. THE FACE-TO-FACE INTERVIEW

The object of the research was to obtain facts, and in particular to report on the extent of sexual experience in the fifteen to nineteen age group and, if possible, to identify any factors that seemed to be associated with sexual experience. Consequently this research did not start out with any hypothesis beyond the simple assumption that some teenagers are sexually experienced and some are not, and that there may be a difference between those who are experienced, and those who are not.

The ideal situation would be for the research team to administer some psychological test which had no apparent association with sexual behaviour, and this test would reveal the extent of sexual experience in each person. Not surprisingly no such test exists, and although there are numerous personality tests from which to choose, none of them, individually or collectively, produce results which give any indication of sexual experience.

In the present state of knowledge in the social sciences, the information could be collected in only two ways:

(a) the face-to-face interview;
(b) the self-administered written questionnaire.

The relative advantages of either method have often been tested and discussed (Ellis, 1948). The disadvantages of both methods are magnified when the questions refer to sexual behaviour.

The great advantage of the self-administered questionnaire is that it is possible to obtain very large numbers. For example a 1 per cent sample of the age group studied in this research would require answers from 35,000 people. Obviously it would have been prohibitively expensive to have an hour-long interview with so many people, but it might have been possible to post off that number of questionnaires. But there would be a large number of refusals and the people who did answer might be a very biased sample. In fact, it is possible to over-estimate the value of large numbers and there is a tendency to make researches seem more important than they really are by obtaining results from hundreds of similar subjects.

The disadvantages of the questionnaire outweigh the chance it gives to obtain a large sample. Difficulties with wording are a constant source of trouble in questionnaires.[1] Individuals often answer a question in different terms and at another level from that in the mind of the person who constructed the questionnaire. In the interview the research worker is able to persist until he has got the relevant answer.

In a research into sexual behaviour the actual language to be used is a big problem. In a written questionnaire it would be difficult to avoid using long words with Latin roots; it would certainly be necessary to avoid putting vernacular words into print. But in the interview situation a careful use of the vernacular often helps to make clear the meaning of a question.

Many people who can answer verbally are unable to put their thoughts down on paper. The written questionnaire would exclude a large number of people because they cannot read fluently and are not literate enough to answer the detailed questions.

It is possible to build up a friendly relationship in the early part of the interview so that by the time the questions on sex are reached, the teenager feels that he has a sympathetic and impartial listener. Sometimes the reassurances of the interviewer are better than the questionnaire as a guarantee of anonymity. The interviewer also has the opportunity to overcome an unwillingness to answer a particular question, an important advantage in researches of this kind. In an interview there is also a better chance of knowing when the teenager is covering up or avoiding the issue.

There is also the danger that the questionnaire will be filled in with others looking on, and it is obvious that this will affect the answers given and is almost sure to make them invalid. In this research there were 234 questions on an interview schedule of 16 pages. This would be a very daunting sight for a teenager if he were asked to spend time filling in a form of this length. But in the hands of an interviewer it sometimes took less than an hour. This was because not all the questions applied to all the adolescents. For example, it seemed important to ask the teenager several questions about the circumstances of and his reactions to the first experience of sexual intercourse. If a girl of fifteen had no such experience, then obviously none of these questions would be asked. But in a written questionaire they would all have to be listed, and it is not difficult to imagine what some parents would say if they happened to see such a questionnaire.

In order to get over the embarrassment of talking to a stranger

1. In one written questionnaire given to girls the question, 'Are you a virgin?' brought the reply, 'Not yet.'

about sex, it was suggested that the questions should be recorded and the teenager left alone to record the answers. But this has the same inflexibility as the questionnaire and thus the same disadvantages, such as difficulties with vocabulary, dissimilar experiences, no chance to clear up misunderstandings, no opportunity to probe on a question, nor to gauge the extent of embarrassment or cover-up in an answer.

Group interviews would not allow for individual variation and inevitably the stronger personalities would set the pace. Such a discussion might well be very informative and instructive for the less forward members of the group, but as a method of obtaining information about individuals it is not very useful.

Sexual activities are surrounded by strong social conventions and privacy is essential. The written questionnaire presents too great a temptation for the teenagers to mislead, understate or exaggerate. Providing careful training is given to the interviewers, and the schedule of questions is elaborately tested, the interview situation is still the best method of obtaining information about sexual behaviour.

B. THE PILOT RESEARCH

During the exploratory stage visits were made to a well-known jazz club where we expected to find sexually experienced teenagers, to a suburban youth club to find the more conforming type of adolescent, to schools so that we could interview younger boys and girls, to a Day Continuation College for a cross section of teenagers educated at secondary modern schools and to university students (some of whom were social scientists) so that we could obtain an articulate and detailed reaction to the research team's methods and techniques.

After each interview the teenager was asked to criticise the schedule of questions. Sometimes an interviewee would show quite clearly that he had not understood the questions even when he made no comment. After a series of interviews those who had volunteered were persuaded to meet together as a group with the research team. This group was then encouraged to criticise the questions on the schedule and tape-recordings of these group discussions revealed extra information on the right approach and the best wording to use. Here are a few examples of the kind of remarks made during these discussions:

Boy: 'Nearly everything you've said we don't use the same word for.'

Boy about masturbation: 'It's all right to ask but change the word.'

Boy about having the interview in a church hall: 'You couldn't *say* anything there.'

Girl about the interview: 'I would have felt funny at home.'

Boy on not wanting to be interviewed in a consulting room: 'I'd think the doctor was going to examine me.'

Boy: 'You want to get us where we're not interested in anything' (i.e. not in a youth club where they could be doing something else).

Boy about interviewer calling at his home: 'If you send us a letter first with the proper paper . . .'

Experience gained during the exploratory stage revealed that many of the questions on sexual behaviour would have to be restricted or altered for the younger age group. We decided to abandon our original intention of interviewing adolescents of thirteen and fourteen because the state of physical maturity is very variable at that age and in addition there would be difficulties in vocabulary and a high rate of refusal from parents. It was also clear that the leisure activities and sexual behaviour of married teenagers would be so different that comparisons with the unmarried adolescents would be meaningless. Accordingly it was decided to concentrate on unmarried adolescents between fifteen and nineteen.

Few of the researches undertaken in this country are able to spend so much time in the exploratory stage of the work. It would be satisfying to say that all possible individual reactions were anticipated and allowed for in the schedule of questions. But this was not the case. People do not fit into the preconceived ideas of researchers and teenagers do not fall nicely into groups or patterns of behaviour. After nearly every interview there were discussions and queries and modifications. Even so, the basic task of the exploratory period was achieved, and a schedule of questions was devised so that the information about teenage sexual behaviour was collected in a systematic and consistent manner.

Appendix 2

THE QUESTIONS

A. THE FIRST DRAFT

The basic purpose of the investigation was to establish the incidence of sexual activity among young people. With this aim went a hypothesis that certain types of sexual activity were concomitant with certain social and psychological variables. These two factors shaped the schedule of questions to be used at each interview. To cover social variables a large net of questions was constructed which attempted to tap all aspects of the teenager's background and leisure activities, and especially those activities where opportunities or facilities for sexual experience appeared to be a possibility. Thus reading habits were not included, but questions were asked about going to parties.

Although the questions were first compiled in sections, they were not placed in the schedule section by section. The sequence of questions was decided by a number of considerations. It was important to keep up the interest of the adolescent so the dull questions had to be kept apart; one question had to follow another without too sudden a jump from one subject to the next; sometimes it was necessary to insert waste questions in order to lead up logically and smoothly to an important question. The fact that the questions were not asked in chronological order meant that it was much more difficult for a teenager to mislead or act a fictitious role, because inconsistencies would become apparent when the questioner returned to the same subject later in the interview.

Three different drafts of the interview schedule were tested during the exploratory period before the final list of questions was standardised for the random sample. Modifications were required because the questions did not elicit the information they were designed to obtain, because some of the words were not universally understood, and because the sequence of questions appeared to interrupt the flow of the interview. Inevitably verbal responses vary in a survey covering all educational levels. Standardised questions do not always bring standardised answers, for the same question can mean different things to different people. Yet some sort of standardisation is necessary if statistical analysis is to be used. The difficulty is to find words and phrases that are both exact and understood.

For example, a number of adolescents thought that the term 'birth control' meant controlling the delivery of a baby at birth. Some of the younger adolescents had not heard about venereal disease. When one of the grammar school boys was asked what he knew about VD he replied: 'Nothing, unless you mean vapour density.' One of the early questions in the first draft was: 'Do you think contraceptives are 100 per cent reliable?' It was hoped that this would indicate a difference in attitude between the experienced and inexperienced boys. Unfortunately the word 'contraceptive' was not always understood, and so when the answer was 'I don't know', as was usually the case, it was not clear if the answer referred to the reliability of contraceptives, or merely meant that the question had not been understood.

The object was to cover the total social and sexual experience of each adolescent besides getting basic classifying information. If this were to be achieved in a time that would not bore or fatigue the interviewee, a certain amount of speed was essential. Hence a majority of the questions were pre-coded but interviewers were instructed to write the answers in full alongside the question whenever there was any doubt about the correct code to mark. Even so, 14 open-ended questions remained, and in 18 more cases the interviewers were instructed to write in full the actual answers given. There were also more than 130 operational instructions and definitions to add to the precision of the standardised questions.

B. QUESTIONS ON SEX

The design of the schedule was planned so that comparatively impersonal information was obtained in the first part of the interview. It commenced with questions on age, place of birth, father's occupation, type of education, size of family, work and many questions on leisure interests. All questions which attempted to find out the extent of a leisure activity were asked in two ways. For example, they were first asked: 'How often do you go to the cinema?' Then they were asked: 'When did you last go?' The latter question usually gave a better record of the actual frequency of an activity (Prais and Houthakker, 1955). In this part of the interview it was possible to build up a good relationship with the teenager, especially as many of them enjoyed the chance to talk about their spare-time activities. In this way the interviewee acquired sufficient confidence to answer questions about his sexual behaviour.

Sexual behaviour was treated in the schedule as though each individual progressed through certain stages of development. This was a reasonable assumption that was reinforced during the exploratory period. If an interviewee denied a certain activity, it had to be assumed that he had not passed through the later stages of sexual experience. In this way we avoided putting unnecessary questions about sexual behaviour to inexperienced boys and girls. This sifting approach helped particularly in the interviews with immature adolescents as it was imperative that inessential sex questions should not be asked, in case we were accused of 'putting ideas into their heads'. We had constantly to bear in mind that we might offend or shock some of the interviewees, or (more probably) their parents, if we asked questions about sexual behaviour which extended beyond their experience.

The actual form of the sex questions assumed that the interviewee had engaged in the relevant activity. So the question was phrased: 'When did you first . . . ?' This was better than: 'Have you ever . . . ?' This placed the onus of denial on the interviewee. It also helped to assure the young person that the interviewer would not be surprised or shocked if he had had such an experience. Many boys and girls said this approach helped them considerably because this assumption about their experience made them feel less embarrassed; they did not have to admit something but just give a date.

At the end of the interview the teenager had to be assessed on nine items, including appearance, clothes, response, behaviour and truthfulness. The latter was a subjective estimate by the interviewer of the validity of the young person's answers. Each interviewer also wrote a descriptive account of the interview situation. They were asked to comment on anything that had a direct bearing on the interview. For example, the interviewee might have been forced to attend the interview by his parent, or there may have been interruptions while the mother brought in coffee. Quite often the young people would continue to talk freely after the interview and much valuable information was obtained in this way.

Although the pre-coded answers listed after nearly all the questions were necessary for statistical analysis, it was realised that the qualitative aspect was also important. For this reason the questions and pre-coded categories were printed on the left half of the page, leaving space opposite each question for the interviewer to note down the comments, queries and remarks of the teenagers.

C. SUBJECT HEADINGS

As there are plans for a follow-up to this research using the same set of questions, the Research Committee decided that the complete schedule of questions should not be included with this report. The schedule has 261 different items of which 234 were direct questions. These were distributed throughout the schedule under the following headings:

Subject	No. of questions asked
Classifying questions	8
Education	10
Type of school	
Attainment	
Work	10
Number of jobs	
Contentment	
Earnings	
Family	35
Conditions in the home	
Parent occupations	
Parental relations	
Restrictions	
Religion	
Leisure activities	46
Youth clubs	
Sports	
Dancing	
Cinema	
Smoking	
Drinking	
Parties	
Social relations	15
Group composition	
Girl friends	
Boy friends	
Sexual relations	64
Commencement	
Frequency	
Extent	
Partners	

Subject	No. of questions asked
Sex knowledge	30
Source	
Education	
VD	
Birth control	
Marriage	10
Attitudes	
Expectations	
Delinquency	6
Trouble with police	
Court appearances	
Admitted misconduct	

D. INFERENTIAL ASSESSMENTS

Sometimes it is not possible to devise one question that will give an accurate picture of a young person's behaviour. In such cases it is necessary to use a whole battery of questions, but for the purpose of analysis these groups of questions have to be converted into a quantitative form which can be used statistically.

Ideally this can be done by allocating a score for a particular answer to each of the questions in the battery, and then plotting the resulting summation on a rating scale. But this method often gives the appearance of a mathematical neatness that is rarely justified. In any case we wanted to leave room for the subjective judgements of the interviewers. Although each question was worded with as great an emphasis as possible on objectivity, it was hoped that the 'all-round' picture of the adolescent gained at the end of the interview would add to the material obtained from the direct questions.

After each interview the research worker was required to make inferential assessments under ten headings. In practice this requirement meant that the adolescent had to be given a ranking position on ten scales. For the sake of clarity these are called rating scales in chapter 13, but the word 'scale' probably gives the appearance of a degree of accuracy that is not justified in this case. For example, the interviewer was required to assess the degree of 'intensity of family influence' and to place the teenager in one of these six categories:

1. Hardly ever goes out. All activities with family.
2. Spends most of time at home, but not always with family.

3. Member of other groups, but most often with family.
4. Spends some time at home, but active social life outside.
5. Usually out of home.
6. Living away from home.

These were known as 'anchor definitions'. It was unlikely that a teenager would fit exactly into one of these categories, but it was possible to learn enough about each teenager so as to feel that he was 'anchored' to one of these definitions.

The interviewers were instructed to read over the teenagers' answers to the questions relevant to the assessment under consideration. In the case of the 'intensity of family influence', they had to review the answers to 16 relevant questions.

After they had considered the answers to these questions, the interviewers took into account any other extra information obtained during the interview, and from this overall impression made their assessment.

Although these inferential assessments are not free from subjective bias, they have been used successfully by Robb (1954), Westwood (1960) and others as a convenient method of summarising a range of questions on similar subjects.

Appendix 3

THE ATTITUDE INVENTORY

A. THE ASSESSMENT OF PERSONALITY

Although it was decided that the information about sexual behaviour could only be obtained by direct questions at a face-to-face interview, it was hoped that an objective picture of the personality of each individual could be obtained by some other method. Ideally what was required was a personality test:

(a) which was suitable for the age range fifteen to nineteen;
(b) which had been standardised for use in this country;
(c) which had gained a large measure of acceptance; and
(d) which could be easily administered and take less than twenty minutes.

Several pencil-and-paper tests for the assessment of personality have been constructed by clinical and social psychologists both here and in America. Most of these require the subject to indicate his agreement or disagreement with a number of statements which could be related to himself. The aim of the test is usually to give the subjects a score on a number of personality factors or traits. These factors tend to have names derived from the particular theory of personality which the test constructor supports. The total score is designed to give a 'profile' of the subject's personality.

A typical example of such a test is Cattel's High School Personality Inventory which gives an American high-school child a score on sixteen personality factors ranging from 'tough–sensitive' to 'dull–bright'. These tests can be criticised on a number of grounds but the most serious disadvantage from the point of view of this research was that they have been standardised largely in the United States. In many cases the language and subject matter of some of the test items require modification for use with an English sample and at the time when this research started, no norms for English teenagers were available for any of the established tests.[1]

One of the well-standardised English tests is the Maudsley Personality Inventory (Eysenck, 1954), but it was decided not to

1. The results of Dr Warburton's work on the Cattel 16 P.F. test at Manchester University were not available at that time.

use this because it has been primarily developed as a clinical instrument. One of the two factors it measures is 'neuroticism', and this would not be expected to reveal very interesting results in the context of this research.

It was planned to give the test immediately after the interview which took over an hour on its own. Therefore it was imperative that the test should not be of such a length as to tax the patience of the adolescents.[1] Most of the teenagers had much better things to do than stay in to help out our interviewers. There was a very good chance that if the total time exceeded an hour and a half, the deterioration in response would seriously affect the results. Accordingly it was decided that any pencil-and-paper test must not exceed twenty minutes.

For these reasons it was decided not to use a personality test but to limit our assessment of personality to a study of the adolescent's attitude on a number of topics. This served a dual purpose. It made it possible to obtain the responses of the teenagers on single items and therefore provided useful information on individual attitudes (chapter 7). At the same time the tendency of certain attitudes to lie in particular directions could be revealed by the use of factor analysis (chapter 12). Both sides of this study of attitudes can be usefully related to the material obtained from the personal interviews.

Answers to most of the simpler attitude questions could be obtained more efficiently by using the inventory, thus making it possible to shorten the already long interview. In other cases the questions on the interview schedule were complementary to the attitude inventory. More important still, it was expected that correlations between the results of the factor analysis and sexual experience would show a relationship between aspects of personality and sexual behaviour.

Therefore with some reluctance it was decided not to use any of the existing tests and to design a new social attitude inventory consisting of fifty opinion statements relating to a large number of topics. Each of these topics was one in which teenagers could be expected to have a strong interest and they were asked to indicate their agreement or disagreement with each statement.

1. This ruled out many of the best-known American tests such as the Minnesota Multiphasic Personality Inventory which requires ninety minutes to administer in its complete form.

B. THE CONSTRUCTION OF THE INVENTORY

The first draft of the social attitude inventory was tested in London C. At the end of each interview the teenager was asked to give his opinions about these statements. He was encouraged to ask questions and make comments, and the interviewer made a note of all cases where there was some doubt about the meaning of the statement. Analyses were made of the responses throughout this period and a study was made of inventories which contained responses which were inconsistent to see if this was because the statements had not been understood. As the statements were being continually modified during the interviews in London C, none of the inventories filled in by adolescents from this area are included in the results. The final draft of the inventory was not completed until the research team had moved on to the second area (South A).

Several other sources were used before the final draft of the inventory was completed. The aim was to produce a list of statements covering the important areas in a teenager's life, such as attitudes to the family and its restraints, other teenagers, marriage, the moral code, sex, crime, etc. For some months the research unit had employed a press-cutting agency to send them all the newspaper clippings about teenagers, including the oft-expressed opinions of adults about young people. In a short time a large number of press cuttings was collected. This included quotations from adults of varying sympathies and outlooks about teenagers and their behaviour. There were also other quotations from teenagers themselves, about each other and how they behave or should behave. Other press cuttings were from parents about their teenage children. Still others were statements from the representatives of official bodies. A content analysis was made of this large collection and the most frequent items were rewritten as a series of attitude statements.

In addition other statements were listed from the questionnaire circulated by the BMA Committee on the problem of venereal disease, from Eysenck's Social Attitude Inventory (Eysenck, 1954), and from an earlier personality test (Terman and Miles, 1936) which contained a number of statements about teenagers.

After further testing and discussion this list was eventually reduced to fifty statements. Items were rejected because they were too topical for a research extending over three years, because the idea or vocabulary would have been clear only to middle-class teenagers, and because the statements might have caused embarrassment or resentment.

This attitude inventory was used in six of the seven areas. The time it took the adolescent to complete the inventory varied considerably, but the average time was less than ten minutes. Most of the teenagers found it interesting and only a very few regarded it as an imposition. In all 780 boys and 761 girls completed the inventory.

C. FACTOR ANALYSIS

In order to make the fifty statements on the attitude inventory more manageable, a factor analysis was made of the responses. This method of analysis was developed primarily through the work of Spearman and later Burt, Thurstone and Thompson to explain the intercorrelations between psychological tests of ability (Holzinger and Harman, 1941). Since then its application has extended over a much wider field of psychological interest and it has proved particularly valuable in the study of social attitudes (Eysenck, 1954). It permits the explanation of the correlations between a large number of attitude statements in terms of a much smaller number of fundamental attitude components. This is done by factor analysing the intercorrelations between the scores on the statements (Osgood, 1957). Responses to each of the statements in our attitude inventory were scored as follows: strongly agree = 1; agree on the whole = 2; can't decide = 3; disagree on the whole = 4; strongly disagree = 5.

A factor analysis takes place in two stages. The primary aim is first to reduce the number of variables (statements) to a smaller number of uncorrelated components or factors. Having discovered these factors, the loading[1] of each factor on each variable is calculated. At this stage it is often difficult to interpret adequately the various factors and in order to facilitate this, the next step is to rotate them. Rotation to oblique simple structure (Thurstone, 1949) has the effect of maximising the weightings of a factor on some variables and minimising the loading of the same factor on others. Thus the factor can be identified and labelled in terms of the statements which have the highest loadings on it.

When factors are rotated to oblique simple structure they are themselves correlated. The matrix of correlation between the factors can itself be factor analysed and a smaller number of 'second order' factors is produced. This process can be repeated until no higher-order factors can be extracted, i.e. until the matrix consists of two or three factors only.

1. This is a measure of the association between the factor and the statement, but in the method employed here it is not identical with the correlation coefficient between these two variables (Cattel, 1962).

Having extracted all the factors, a 'factor score' can be calculated for each individual on each factor. This score can be produced in standard form, with a mean value of 0 for each factor and a unit variance. The individual scores on any factor will be negative or positive, with 68 per cent falling between $+1$ and -1; 95 per cent between $+2$ and -2; and 99·7 per cent between $+3$ and -3. Factor score is a measure of the extent to which the individual shows the factor in the attitudes he expresses. A high negative or high positive score makes his or her opinions predictable on the statements with high loadings. A positive score means agreement on statements with a negative loading on the factor and disagreement on statements with a positive loading. A negative score means disagreement on statements with a negative loading on the factor and agreement on statements with a positive loading. For simplicity the scores are always referred to in a positive sense in chapter 12. Thus a high positive score will be referred to as a high score and a high negative score will be referred to as a low score.

The actual method used was developed by Hendrickson and White (1964). Product moment correlations were calculated between the scores on each pair of statements. Thus a fifty-fifty correlation matrix was produced for each sex. The matrix was analysed by the principle component method. For the boys fifteen first-order factors were discovered (latent roots >1) and sixteen first-order factors were discovered for the girls. The first-order factors were rotated to oblique simple structure using the Promax method developed by Hendrickson and White for the IBM 7090 Computer and the loadings of the factors on each statement were calculated. The process was repeated on the correlation matrixes of the first-order factors to produce five second-order factors for the boys and six second-order factors for the girls. These were also rotated to oblique simple structure. Finally two third-order factors were produced for the boys and three for the girls. No further factors could be extracted from the matrix. Loadings were obtained for each statement on each factor and standard scores for each individual were also calculated.

T

Appendix 4

THE SAMPLE

A. LONDON C

In order to obtain a random sample of any section of the population, it is necessary to have a complete list from which to extract the names. The most usual method is to use the National Polling Register, but this list is of no value to a research studying people under the age of twenty-one. Various alternatives were considered, but the most complete list seemed to be the record of National Health patients kept by the local Executive Councils. This list covers 97·5 per cent of the population throughout the full age range (Gray and Cartwright, 1953), and it was thought that the percentage would be even higher for young people. The Clerk of the London Executive Council agreed to cooperate and a sample was drawn, as follows:

1. The Executive Council supplied a list of all the doctors in the area. Doctors whose practices were on the borders of the borough were excluded because it was expected that a large number of their patients would be resident in neighbouring boroughs.
2. From this list the Research Unit selected 20 doctors by random sampling.
3. The staff of the Executive Council then studied the cards of all the patients of these 20 doctors. They listed: (a) the name, (b) the address, (c) the date of birth, for all patients who were born between 1943 and 1946 inclusive, but excluding those who were foreign-born.
4. This produced a list of 2,478 teenagers from which a stratified sample was drawn by the Research Unit.[1]

It was decided to stratify this sampling frame so as to produce approximately equal numbers in four age/sex groups:

> Girls born 1943–44.
> Girls born 1945–46.
> Boys born 1943–44.
> Boys born 1945–46.

1. The name of the patient was not linked with the doctor in the list sent to the Research Unit.

A sampling fraction of one in 20 was chosen so as to make sure that every teenager on the list had an equal chance of being drawn. In fact a very large number of names had to be drawn because the rate of non-response was very high (43 per cent). Altogether 148 people were lost because the Executive Council lists were not up to date.

Moved out of area   45
Not traced   74
Other errors in the list   29

     148

It became clear that the list included people who had left the area several years ago and not just those who had moved recently. There were also many other inaccuracies in the list. For example:

Emigrated to Eire 11 years ago.
Interviewee was Turkish; moved after being in this country only nine months.
The house was demolished.
Family had moved 16 years ago.
Interviewee was born 1953 (not 1943 as on the list).
Interviewee had been adopted at the age of 18 months, 14 years ago.
Never heard of at this address.

In addition 53 other young people refused to be interviewed and 13 were married and therefore not eligible for the sample. In order to get 249 interviews the research team had to call on 463 people. In fact they had to make many more calls than this as it was necessary to call on most people several times before an appointment could be made. The number of calls for this area alone probably exceeds a thousand.

The research team had to spend a lot of time attempting to find people who in fact had left the area (incidentally this provided an excellent checking system for the Executive Council and helped them to bring their list up to date). Despite the disadvantages it was a workable list from which further samples could have been drawn and it was intended to use this method in the other areas. Unfortunately the Ministry of Health was unable to give the necessary authority to the Executive Councils in the other areas and therefore the London Executive Council were not asked to supply any more lists of teenagers.

London C was the only case where the teenagers have been sampled from the whole borough. In other cases, as the following sections will show, each area consists of a number of wards which add up to rather less than a complete borough. In theory every British-born teenager living in London C had the chance of being drawn into our sample. It is estimated that the total number of unmarried teenagers aged fifteen to nineteen in the area was 11,953. Of these it is estimated that 15 per cent, or 1,753, were foreign-born, and therefore not eligible for this sample. In fact 249 valid interviews were completed in London C and so one in every 41 teenagers was represented in our sample.

B. SOUTH A AND B

Although a list of adolescents living in these areas had already been extracted by the staff of the local Executive Council, it was not possible to get Ministry of Health approval to use it. So another method of sampling had to be devised.

It so happened that a record of all children between the ages of five to fifteen living in this borough were kept in a series of books at the School Attendance Office. Lists were kept up to date by periodic visits to each house by the School Attendance Officers. If a family had moved the records were amended. If a child had left school then his or her name was lightly crossed off the list but it was still legible. Ten months before the research team obtained this list, the staff had stopped keeping it up to date, following a visit from a management consultant. Therefore the research was able to make use of a reasonably accurate list of the teenagers. The two disadvantages were:

1. The list was almost a year out of date, so any adolescent moving to the area during the last ten months would not be recorded.
2. An adolescent over fifteen would not be recorded if he moved into the area after he had left school.

As two samples were required, one representing the middle-class section of the town and the other representing the working-class section, it was decided to use the index of jurors (J-index) as an indication of social class. This is an index which gives the percentage of electors who are jurors on the electoral register of each ward. It has been shown (Gray, Corlett and Jones, 1951) that if an electoral ward has a high index of jurors, then a larger proportion of the electors will be in class I and II of the Registrar-General's scale of social class. Similarly a low index of jurors indicates a high representation of social classes IV and V.

The J-index ratings were obtained for each of the electoral wards in the town. The four electoral wards having the highest J-index ratings were chosen for the middle-class sampling frame (South A). The working-class sampling frame (South B) was derived from the five wards having the lowest ratings on the J-index. The School Attendance Office listed the name and address of all the children born between 1943 and 1947 in each of these wards. Thus the sample of teenagers was drawn from a sampling frame of 2,384 in South A and 3,510 in South B.

The lists of names provided by the Attendance Officer were checked against the registers of three schools in the town. Of 300 names which were checked, a 6 per cent error in the lists was recorded. In 4 per cent of the cases this was due to clerical errors and in 2 per cent of the cases the School Attendance Officer was unable to account for the errors.

Both the samples were stratified into four age/sex groups as in London C. The interviewing started at the end of 1962 and continued into 1963: as from 1 January 1963 the younger age groups were made up of teenagers born 1946–47, and the older age groups were made up of those born 1944–45, in order to maintain constant ages within the groups.

The sampling fraction used in both samples was one in 20. Altogether 551 interviews were completed. The wastage caused by inadequacies in the sampling frame consisted of:

> 66 living away from home.
> 134 families had moved out of the area.
> 6 uninterviewable (E.S.N., deaf, etc.).
> 26 married.

In addition there were 109 adolescents who refused to be interviewed, and a further nine refused to answer the questions about sex behaviour.

The estimated number of unmarried teenagers aged fifteen to nineteen in the four selected wards of South A is 2,270. Of these, 273 were interviewed, so one in every eight teenagers in South A was represented in our sample.

The estimated number of unmarried teenagers aged fifteen to nineteen in the five selected wards of South B is 3,350. Of these 278 were interviewed, so one in every 12 teenagers in South B was represented in our sample.

C. NORTH A AND B

For the other areas a third method of sampling was devised. A market research agency was employed to locate all the teenagers living in selected areas. As before two sampling areas were required for the northern teenagers – one with a large middle-class population (North A) and the other with a predominantly working-class population (North B). Using the J-index as a guide two wards were chosen for the middle-class sample and three wards for the working-class sample.

This time the first stage of the sampling was by streets. It was calculated that to find approximately 1,000 teenagers as a sampling frame for each area, one in every two streets in these wards would have to be covered. The agency was instructed to send people to call at every house in the selected streets. The agency's caller was told to inquire at each house whether there were any teenagers normally resident at that address. Only teenagers born in Great Britain between 1944 and 1947 were listed. The christian name, surname and date of birth for each teenager was noted by the agency caller. Adolescents at boarding schools as well as students or lodgers living at the house were included.

The agency's representative was to call three times at each house making at least one call in the evening in an attempt to get this information. A note was to be taken of each address where it was impossible to get the information either through refusals on the part of the householder or through inability to get a reply.

In North A 5,939 households were visited and 995 (16·7 per cent) teenagers were found; 102 (1·7 per cent) refused information, and in 230 (3·9 per cent) cases no contact was made with any resident in the household.

In North B 5,880 households were visited and 963 (16·3 per cent) teenagers were found; 48 (0·9 per cent) refused, and 142 (2·4 per cent) were not contacted.

A sampling fraction of one in two was used and the sample was stratified into four age/sex groups as in the other areas.

In the middle-class sample (North A) 259 interviews were completed; 29 refused; four were no contacts; two were uninterviewable; 10 were away from home; one had moved and four had married.

It was estimated that there were 2,470 unmarried teenagers aged fifteen to nineteen in North A. Altogether 259 interviews were completed in this area, so one in every nine teenagers was represented in our sample.

In the working-class sample 262 teenagers were interviewed; 45 refused; 18 were impossible to contact in the time available; two refused to answer questions about sex; six were away from home; three had moved; five were married and three were uninterviewable.

It was estimated that 2,540 unmarried teenagers aged fifteen to nineteen lived in North B. Altogether 262 interviews were completed in this area, so one in every 10 teenagers was represented in our sample.

D. LONDON A AND B

The London B sample was found in the same way as the northern samples and the same market research agency was employed. The five electoral wards with the lowest J-index ratings were chosen in a south London borough.

Every other street in these five electoral wards was listed, 6,030 households were visited and 1,023 (16·9 per cent) teenagers were found. There were 26 (0·43 per cent) refusals, and in 227 (3·7 per cent) cases no contact was made with a resident of the household.

Using a fraction of one in two, the sample was stratified into four age/sex groups as before. In this area 262 teenagers were interviewed, 53 would not agree to an interview, two refused to answer questions on sexual behaviour, two were uninterviewable, 10 were away from home, 15 had moved and 16 were married.

It is estimated that there are 2,196 unmarried teenagers aged fifteen to nineteen in London B. Of these, 262 were interviewed, so one in every eight teenagers in this area was represented in our sample.

The same method was used for London A, but the work was carried out by a different market research agency. The same brief and similar instructions were given to this agency.

The four wards with the highest J-index ratings were chosen in a London residential borough. The agency was required to list the name, address and date of birth of all the teenagers living in every other street in these four wards.

Unfortunately this agency failed to provide details of the number of households who had refused to supply the required information. Furthermore the list of 552 teenagers contained many who were foreign-born, or too old or too young; indeed only 460 were eligible for the sample. Because of these inaccuracies the research team called at every house in ten of the streets which had already been covered by the agency. The research team located 65 teenagers where the agency had found 60. Therefore there may be an error of about 8 per cent in this sampling frame.

The full list of 460 teenagers was used to stratify into the four age/sex groups. This resulted in 290 interviews, 39 refusals, two who were uninterviewable, 24 away from home, 37 who had moved, and nine who were married.

It was estimated that there were 1,067 unmarried teenagers aged fifteen to nineteen in London A. Altogether 290 young people were interviewed, so nearly one in every three teenagers in this area was represented in our sample.

E. EVALUATION OF THE SAMPLING

All three of the sampling methods used had their disadvantages. The Executive Council was able to provide the best ready-made list for a particular area. Although teenagers are alleged to be the healthiest segment of the population, the results of this research suggest that they made frequent visits to their doctors. We found that 79 per cent of our sample had visited their doctor within the last twelve months.

It is reasonable to assume that any adolescent who still lives with his family in the home where he was born would be registered with a doctor in nearly all cases. In fact it is probable that the Executive Council's lists contain most of the teenagers in a particular area. The trouble is that they contain a lot more besides. The first section of this appendix makes it clear that these lists contain the names of many people who have left the district years ago. It is obvious that the machinery devised to keep the Executive Council lists up to date is faulty.[1] An incidental but important by-product of this sampling method was that the Executive Council lists have been checked and brought up to date by the research team in those areas where the interviewing took place.

The success of the samples in South A and B was due to a lucky chance. Although it might have been possible to get lists from School Attendance Officers in other areas, the staff do not keep these lists up to date after a child has left school. So the accuracy of the list decreases with the age of the teenager over fifteen, and the list of nineteen-year-old teenagers would have been four years out of date.

But the lists used in South A and B were kept up to date, even if the child had left school, right up to one year before the research team visited the town. It is not clear why this was done, and it was

---

1. With the result that doctors have a large number of non-existent patients on their lists.

because no satisfactory explanation for this work could be given to a visiting management consultant that this extra work was stopped.

In theory at least the research was working from a sampling frame that was only about 2 per cent inaccurate, although spot checks revealed inaccuracies up to 8 per cent. In many ways this was the least satisfactory sample, and so it is interesting to see how similar the results are to those in other areas where different sampling methods were used (chapter 3).

The third sampling method was the best from the administrative point of view. It can be arranged that the agency makes the calls and compiles the list just a week or so before the interviewing starts. So the list will be completely up to date and transients will be included even if it is not their permanent address.

But there are disadvantages. People do not like callers on the doorstep who are compiling lists and many are tempted to mislead and deny. Whatever the reason for the list, they suspect that it will lead to further trouble (and, in a sense, their suspicions were justified in this case). Another disadvantage is that the attitude and image of the agency caller may prejudice the chance of obtaining an interview or bias the response. But the biggest disadvantage of all is the cost of compiling such a list. It cost £780 to get the list of teenagers in North A and B where 521 interviews were completed. So it cost just under thirty shillings to find each person and this is before the interview began. When one adds to this the wages of the interviewers, together with overheads and analysis costs, it can be seen that this is a very expensive way of conducting a survey.

Expense can be saved by restricting the size of the area. But this can be the cause of another disadvantage, for if teenagers living near to one another are interviewed, before long word has gone round the neighbourhood about the research and this can lead to prepared and biased answers or to refusals.

Whatever the merits and demerits of the three methods, it is remarkable that very similar results were obtained from three lists compiled in completely different ways. There is little doubt that the use of random samples was worth the extra time and cost. This is the only research on sexual behaviour that is based on large random samples. Although Kinsey (1948) had a large sample, it was not randomly collected and it has been criticised because it relied too heavily on volunteers – the implication being that people who volunteer to talk about their sex lives are not typical. In the areas where our research team worked every teenager had an equal chance of being contacted for an interview. This can only serve to give added confidence in the veracity of the results.

Appendix 5

FIELD WORK

A. DESCRIPTION OF THE AREAS

London C. This was a large and densely populated metropolitan borough. It was mainly residential but there was some commerce and light industry. It had a large immigrant population which tended to be concentrated in certain areas. London C was well supplied with cinemas, pubs and cafés, and a large park for football and other games. But many of the principal attractions for teenagers lay outside the borough, and the West End with its dance halls, coffee bars and jazz clubs was easily accessible.

There were several slum areas in the borough and other parts had a rundown and seedy appearance. But London C had a large number of teenagers whose fathers were skilled manual workers and this sample came somewhere in between the three A (middle-class) samples and the three B (working-class) samples. It can be said to represent the social class that used to be known as artisans.

South A. South A and B were selected wards in a city in the south of England. There were exceptional sports facilities in this town as well as an ice-rink, bowling alley, stadium and dance hall. All of these were well patronised by the teenagers.

South A comprised the four electoral wards with the highest ratings on the index of jurors. This area was largely middle-class in character although there were exceptions. For example, one ward was a wealthy residential area north of and on the outskirts of the town and contained some of the most expensive housing in the area; but on the eastern side there was a large prewar housing estate which was working-class in character.

South B. This area comprised the five electoral wards with the lowest J-index rating and were predominantly working-class in character. Two of the wards contained large housing estates on the outskirts of the town, and the other three wards were the poorer districts in the centre of the city.

North A. This comprised some of the wealthiest middle-class areas of a northern industrial city. There were many new housing estates and a fine shopping centre, although other parts of the town consisted of condemned slum properties, some of them still occupied. For teenagers entertainments were much the same as in other places:

bowling, many cinemas, an ice-rink, two large dance halls, a number of coffee bars and a large park. Several of the pubs and clubs (of the northern variety) provided entertainment but these were not very popular with teenagers. The exception to this were the few which held jazz concerts. Two wards were selected for North A because of their residential middle-class character and this was confirmed by their high J-index.

North B. Some of the poorer districts of the same northern industrial city were used for North B. Three wards with low J-index ratings were selected. In two of these wards much of the housing was nineteenth-century back-to-back terracing; large areas of these wards were being cleared for redevelopment, and the third ward consisted of a prewar housing estate. There were no central focal points in any of these wards and most teenagers went to the city centre for their entertainment.

London A. This was one of the wealthiest residential areas in London, and contained some of the best-known houses and blocks of luxury flats. With the exception of a small area where there were council flats, the children who lived in London A were usually sent away to boarding school and in consequence they had very little social life in this area.

The older teenagers, including the few who had gone to school in London, tended to appear in two sets; on one hand there was the wealthy débutante and fast sports-car set who went to the West End for most of their entertainment; on the other hand there was a bohemian-beat set who were more likely to congregate in the bars and coffee houses of a nearby borough.

London B. The northern part of this borough was mainly commercial and industrial while the southern part was residential. The J-index rating for the whole borough is low, and the sample of teenagers was taken from the five wards with the lowest J-index ratings. Though not one of the poorest boroughs, it was a traditionally working-class area with a relatively stable population. There were minority groups of Greeks, Maltese and West Indians, but these were not of any significant size.

A large number of teenagers lived, worked and spent their spare time in the borough, in spite of its proximity to the centre of London. Others took advantage of the entertainment facilities of the West End and used the coffee bars and dance halls there. Two of the neighbouring boroughs had dance halls which attracted a number of them. The borough was well supplied with cinemas, pubs, cafés and youth clubs, but was short of open spaces. Partly because of this, many teenagers spent their summer weekends in the countryside which was quite easy to reach by bus or motor-bike.

B. MAKING THE APPOINTMENT

Grouping. Word soon gets around about a research of this kind. There was a danger that one teenager would tell his friends about the questions and some of these friends would also be on our sample. This would mean that some of our subjects had foreknowledge of the questions which would alter their response; it might also mean that some of them would be tempted to refuse to be interviewed if they were forewarned about the questions. Obviously it was better to get in and out of a district as quickly as possible, interviewing all the teenagers on our list within a few days, and then moving on to the next district.

Therefore all the teenagers in each sample were grouped into small districts of only a few streets and all the interviewers worked in this district at the same time. Each interviewer was given the names and addresses of a batch of teenagers on whom he had to call. The result of every call, call-back and interview was recorded on a progress sheet.

The introductory letter. Each teenager received the following letter before the interviewer called:

'I am writing to you on behalf of the Research Unit of the Central Council for Health Education. We are carrying out a nation-wide research project on the interests and attitudes of young people in this country.

'This work is now in progress and is being financed by the Nuffield Foundation. Of course we cannot meet every young person between the ages of fifteen and nineteen, so we are taking what is called a random sample. This means that names are drawn quite by chance from lists of young people in various areas. You have been chosen in this way from a list of all young people who live in your district.

'In the next few days I shall be calling on you to arrange a convenient time for an interview which will take about an hour. As I am only interested in your own views and opinions, I should prefer to see you on your own either in your home or at our local office. If you would prefer to have the talk at home, perhaps you will discuss with your parents what would be a suitable time.

'Many teenagers all over the country have helped us in this way and many more are being contacted. I am sure you will find it interesting and I look forward to meeting you in the near future.'

This first step was important because it was the young person's first contact with the research and the impression made by the letter was likely to be decisive in determining whether or not he would agree to an interview. It was signed personally by the interviewer and posted so that it arrived the day before the call. This gave him very little time to write back asking our interviewer not to call and the letter was still in his mind at the time of the call.

The value of the letter was that it obviously came from an organisation conducting a serious research. The underlying assumption was that the teenager would take part and it attempted to explain why he had been chosen. The letter was addressed to the teenager, not to his parents. This personal approach to the young person himself was very valuable. Our aim was to make him realise that we considered his views to be important. But the letter does suggest that arrangements for the interview should be discussed with his parents and in most cases the parents had read the letter before the interviewer had called at the house. A few parents resented this method, but in effect they always had the chance to prevent the interview from taking place, and indeed did so on several occasions. The interviewers were instructed to obtain the permission of the parents except when the teenager was living away from home.

The doorstep. The interviewer called at the teenager's home and if he was able to speak to the person concerned, he assumed their co-operation and simply said that he had called round to arrange a suitable time and place for the interview. The appointment was made as easy as possible for the teenager to fulfil. He was given the choice of having the interview at home or in a nearby office, and it was part of the interviewer's job to make himself available at any time and day suggested by the teenager.

If the interview was to be at home, care was taken to ensure that a room would be available where there would be no disturbance or interruptions. After fixing an appointment the interviewer filled in a card stating time, date and place for the interview, and handed it to the teenager. He also recorded these details on his progress sheet.

At no time was the possibility of refusing suggested to the teenager, which meant that if he could not be persuaded to fix an appointment, the onus was upon him to say he would not co-operate. For some teenagers, in the situation of a doorstep discussion, such a statement is difficult to make and so sometimes the result would be either a half-fixed interview or a postponement of the decision until a later date. This usually led on to a succession of further calls before an interview or a refusal was obtained. Obviously there is a limit to the amount of pressure that can be put upon someone to agree to an interview. But as the interviewer plainly and patiently showed that he was prepared to fit in with any suggested time and place, it was difficult for the teenager to put him off because he was too busy or because he had no free time in the immediate future.

Quite often a parent would want to know more about the research before allowing his child to take part, and other parents raised objections to all types of research on principle. If the teenager was out, the interviewer was instructed to call back to the house until he got the interview, or until it became clear that he would not get it.

C. THE LOCATION OF THE INTERVIEW

The local offices. Part of the policy of making it as easy as possible for the teenager to attend for an interview was to provide an office within easy reach of his home. In each town a central office was set up for the administration of the research, which could also be used for interviewing, both during the day and in the evening. It was important that this office should be easy to find and should be at some central point in the town, with easy access by public transport from any part of the neighbourhood. Besides this central office other rooms were made available which were within easy walking distance of that particular sampling area. Finding suitable rooms presented a serious problem in some areas, as landlords were not interested in short leases. It was also important that the approach to the rooms should not be disconcerting in any way; teenage girls cannot be expected to walk down badly lit streets on their way to an interview. In some areas the Educational Departments allowed us to use some of their rooms, and small rooms in Church Halls and offices were also used. As a rule the teenager was only free in the evening, but rooms had to be available during the day for those who preferred to be interviewed on their days off, and for schoolchildren during the holidays.

Home interviews. Appointments were usually made for the interview to take place in an office rather than in the home unless there was any indication that the appointment might not be kept. This was because interviews in the home were sometimes subject to interruptions and disturbances which made it difficult to obtain the right atmosphere of privacy. When noises and conversation from other members of the family in another room were clearly audible, it was obviously difficult to persuade the teenager to talk freely.

Girls appeared to be more relaxed and confident in their own home whereas boys seemed more at ease in the office.

In some homes there are enough rooms so that privacy can be obtained without disturbing other members of the family, and interviews in these homes were very successful; the teenager felt at ease in his own home surroundings and the interviewer's approach was helped by this chance to observe the home background of the young person. But in a crowded home it was often better to get the teenager away; sometimes a family which had been turned out of the room with the television showed signs of impatience, or the boy friend of the girl being interviewed arrived to take her out, or the mother came in with the tea and stayed for a chat. But in an interview of this kind privacy was essential and if it could not be assured, the discussion was terminated and arrangements were made to continue the interview away from the home on another day.

Failed appointments. Fixing interviews in the office had one major drawback; there was no guarantee that the teenager would turn up. Broken appointments were due to a variety of reasons. Sometimes it was through a misunderstanding. A few teenagers expected to find a committee of people waiting to meet them. Sometimes the prospect became so forbidding or uninteresting that the teenager changed his mind once he was away from the interviewer's persuasive influence. One girl got the idea that she would be undressed to see if she had VD. Conversations with others who had been interviewed might have deterred a few teenagers.

The usual reason for failed appointments was lack of interest in the first place. In these cases the teenager agreed to an appointment simply to get rid of the interviewer and had no intention of turning up at the appointed time.

Of course this was very disheartening for the interviewer who had to arrive at the agreed time and wait to no avail. But it was important that no trace of annoyance was shown when the interviewer called back to inquire gently why the appointment had not been kept, and to make another one. Such persistence often impressed the teenager and in many cases it was possible to get an interview although the teenager had been apathetic at first. There were altogether 118 cases when the tact and determination of the interviewer resulted in a successful interview although the teenager had failed to keep the first appointment.

D. SUPERVISION

Call-backs. Each day the interviewers were required to report their progress to the main office. Unlike market research agencies which usually have a maximum number of calls (often three), this research worked on the basis of a minimum number of six calls. The call-backs were then discontinued only if there seemed to be no hope of getting the interview.

Quite often there were a series of calls and broken appointments extending sometimes over a period of several weeks. If three broken appointments had occurred, then the supervisor might decide to terminate the calls. Decisions of this kind were taken on the basis of all the information the interviewer was able to give about the teenager. In general the interviewer was advised to keep on trying until it had become obvious that the chances of getting the interview were virtually nil. It is estimated that over 4,450 calls were made during the course of this research; that is an average of 2·4 calls per interview.

Checking. The most important part of the supervision was going over the completed schedule soon after the interview had occurred. Every schedule was handed in to the supervisor who checked each question to see that it had been correctly coded. This was done on the basis of information recorded in the right-hand margin by the interviewer and also logical consistency throughout the whole schedule.

The value of this close supervision was that it took place soon after the interview when the replies and the circumstances were still fresh in the mind of the interviewer. Thus it was possible to go into detail about the correct coding of each question and discuss the circumstances in a way that would have been impossible if the editing had been left until a later date.

Appendix 6

THE INTERVIEWERS

A. SELECTION

Ten interviewers were used during the course of the research. Three were full-time members of the research team and seven were employed specifically for interviewing. All of them had some experience of working with young people and all of them were young graduates with an average age of twenty-five. Although most of them had previous experience of interviewing, they were not chosen for this reason. The interviewing techniques needed for this research were rather different from those used in case-work where the emphasis is placed on diagnosis and therapy. The calm collection of emotionally charged information required a detached and straightforward manner with no hint that any act was untoward or any attitude was displeasing.

The interviewer's job required four main qualities; a pleasing appearance; determination; a methodical way of working; and the ability to establish and maintain rapport.

A pleasing appearance was essential because the interviewer had only a few minutes on the doorstep to persuade the parent or the adolescent to agree to an interview. First impressions are very important in this kind of situation. Clothes, accent, manner and appearance were just as important as the short introductory talk given by the interviewer on the doorstep.

Determination and persistence were necessary, as many teenagers were apathetic and showed no interest in the research, while others appeared to be interested but failed to keep appointments. The interviewers also had to learn to put up with remarks from some parents who were rude or aggressive. They had to make repeated calls on cold wet nights at houses where they could not expect to be welcome.

Methodical and accurate recording was essential because it was necessary to get a large amount of information on to the schedule in a standardised form so that it could be read by other people and used statistically.

Rapport and a natural capacity for making social contact was the most important requirement of all. It was essential that the interviewer quickly established a friendly relationship so that the young person soon felt at ease and well-disposed towards the idea of answering the questions.

B. TRAINING

Each interviewer was given a two weeks course of intensive training before he was sent out into the field. This consisted of a detailed background briefing, a series of trial interviews, sessions listening to recordings of their own and other interviews, and practice of the whole routine on subjects not in the sample.

The long exploratory stage meant that many new techniques could be passed on to the interviewers. Many hours were spent on getting to know the schedule of questions almost by heart. Familiarity with the wording and order of the questions was essential so that (1) the interviewer could look at the adolescent when talking, (2) the interview could continue at a good speed without awkward pauses and (3) the interviewer could give his full attention to maintaining rapport and recording the answers.

The first trial interview was carried out with one of the research team taking the role of the interviewee. In each trial interview the member of the research team would play a different role – from very inexperienced sexually to very experienced. This was made more realistic by using a schedule filled in from an actual interview during the exploratory stage. Afterwards it was possible to check the new interviewer's record with the other schedule. The research team had already been interviewing for six months before the training of the additional interviewers had started and so they were able to warn the interviewers of recurring difficulties and suggest how to deal with them.

During the exploratory period some tape-recordings were made of actual interviews with teenagers. These were played over to the new interviewers as a group and they were required to record the answers on a schedule. Afterwards the schedules were compared and differences were discussed and resolved, so that a standardised form of documentation evolved. These tape-recorded interviews were particularly valuable for teaching the interviewer to hear more than what is being said; for making him alert to what is not being said; for preparing him to deal with evasions and omissions.

Tape-recordings were also made of the trial interviews so that the interviewers could then listen to their own voices. This helped the new interviewers to correct wrong inflections and emphasis in the way they asked some of the questions. Special care was taken to avoid the hushed voice or apologetic tone when asking questions on sexual behaviour.

No amount of simulated interviews could really substitute for conversations with adolescents, and so the interviewers went along with the research team to a youth club outside the sample areas and tried to persuade the boys and girls to be interviewed. This was excellent experience, and probably a more difficult situation than the one they would have to face on the doorstep of a home where at least a formal letter of introduction had paved the way. They were also given some practice at using the exact fieldwork procedure. A letter was sent to an adolescent not in the sample informing him that a particular interviewer would be calling to arrange an interview. The interviewer called in the evening with a member of the research team who observed his manner on the doorstep, his introductory remarks and his powers of persuasion with parent, adolescent or both. The interviewer was required to carry out all the administrative details that would be used in the field, including the explanation to others on the doorstep, recording the number of calls made on his progress sheets and, if there had been a refusal, writing up the reasons for this. Thus each interviewer was able to obtain practice before interviewing the teenagers in the sample.

C. THE INTERVIEW

The first essential was to insist that only the teenager should be present during the interview. Taietz (1962) has shown that the individual tends to modify his answers when other members of the family are present. It was necessary to convince each teenager that the information was strictly confidential and his name was not put on any part of the schedule. Experience gained during the exploratory stage convinced us that our five male interviewers should interview all the boys, and our five female interviewers should interview all the girls. Benney, Reisman and Star (1956) reported that the least inhibited answers to questions on sex were obtained when respondent and interviewer were young and of the same sex.

The interviewer had to make sure that the younger boy or girl felt at ease. There was a tendency for these interviews to be serious and formal, developing into a relationship similar to schoolmaster and pupil. If the interviewer received an answer like: 'No sir, not me,' he could be sure that he had failed. With the older interviewees more stress had to be laid on the precautions taken to keep the interview anonymous, and to make it easy for them to talk about their sexual adventures.

Interviewers were encouraged to ask the questions fairly rapidly. As well as avoiding fatigue and deterioration in response, quick spontaneous answers gave less opportunity for cover up or untrue replies. If a teenager gave an answer that was inconsistent or obviously false, care was taken to give him the chance to make a correction without implying that the interviewer knew he was lying. On a few occasions the teenager offered to go back over the questions and give a second, more truthful version of his sex behaviour.

When asking questions about sex the interviewer never apologised for asking these questions but implied by his manner that such things could be talked about quite freely without embarrassment. No attempt was made to avoid vernacular words by using long Latin substitutes, and the teenager's behaviour, however unusual, was accepted without comment.

Although a standardised form of question was used in all cases, the interviewer was allowed to press for further information if the answer was unclear or unsatisfactory. In a few cases the use of probes was forbidden, and in other cases the probe was a standardised phrase. But in most cases additional elaboration was encouraged. All the interviewers were issued with a manual so that queries and unusual circumstances arising out of the answers to the questions could be interpreted consistently.

One of the advantages of the interview over the questionnaire is that valuable information can be obtained if the interviewee is persuaded to add more than the simple answer to the question. The interviewers were also instructed not to force an answer into an unsuitable category. Results and tables may look neater without 'other' and 'don't know' categories, but in this case they would give a false picture. As we were reporting on all types of teenagers, we had to accept that even our long list of pre-coded answers would not fit every case.

The time when the teenager was doing the attitude inventory provided a useful ten minutes for the interviewer to go over the schedule and check the whole record; then queries or inconsistencies could be settled before the interview was brought to a close. In most cases the teenager was relaxed and eager to talk by the end of the interview, and they were encouraged to add further comments and observations. Finally all of them were asked if they would agree to another interview at a later date. More than 95 per cent of the boys and 97 per cent of the girls willingly agreed and it is felt that this indicates that the full cooperation of the teenagers was obtained in most cases.

Inevitably in a research of this kind the standard of the interview varied from excellent to poor. Not surprisingly some teenagers were not interested in social research of any kind, and others felt that the subject of this research was too personal a matter to discuss with strangers. Some parents were suspicious, others rude. Our interviewers had to contend with apathy and lethargy. Sometimes an evening was set aside for a particular interview only to find that the teenager failed to keep the appointment. Most of the work had to be done in the evenings as it was part of the job for the interviewer to make himself available at the time when it best suited the young person concerned.

Against this, the majority were friendly and cooperative, happy to talk about themselves and to take the interviewer completely into their confidence. Most of them did not hesitate to answer the interviewer's questions earnestly and truthfully, even when the questions were inquiring about the intimate details of their sexual behaviour. Indeed many of them found it a relief to be able to talk about these things to a sympathetic stranger.

Appendix 7

REFUSALS AND NON-RESPONSE

A. ALL TYPES OF NON-RESPONSE

In every area introductory letters were sent out to the teenagers until a minimum of 60 in each age/sex group had been interviewed. In order to get 1,873 interviews it was necessary to send out 2,828 letters. This gives a total non-response rate of 34 per cent. Table A7.1 shows the seven types of non-response in each of the seven areas.

Table A7.1 shows that most of the total non-response is the result of inadequacies in the sampling frame. This is the case with most social researches although they often do not give the relevant figures. Ideally every single address in the list from which the sample is to be drawn should have an interviewable teenager living there at the time when the introductory letter arrived at that address. In practice this could only occur if the interview was to be carried out immediately after the name and address was listed. By the time the letters are actually sent, there is bound to be a loss of potential interviews because the teenagers move, marry or leave home in between being listed and receiving the letters. At its best (North A) more than 95 per cent of the teenagers received the introductory letter; at its worst (in London C) over a quarter never received the letter asking for an interview. This loss is out of the control of the research team and is a reflection of the sampling frame which may be incomplete, inaccurate or out of date.

The very high non-response rate in London C is largely the result of inadequacies in the London Executive Council's National Health lists. The 119 teenagers who had moved or could not be traced had probably ceased to be patients of the local doctors some time ago. We know that some of them had not lived in the borough for several years.

The extent to which the different sampling frames were out of date in other areas is shown in table A7.2. The first column shows the total non-response rate by subtracting the number of completed interviews from the number of letters sent. This shows that the School Attendance lists used in South A and B were slightly more up to date than the National Health lists used in London C, and that the agency lists used in the other areas were the best of all. This fact is even more strikingly demonstrated in the second column of

Table A7.1 *Total non-response in the seven areas*

Area	Letters sent N	Completed interviews Z	Refused R	No contact C	Refused sex questions S	Uninterviewable U	Away A	Moved M	Married W
South A	442	273	48	6	3	3	30	68	11
South B	473	278	61	8	6	3	36	66	15
North A	309	259	29	4	0	2	10	1	4
North B	344	262	45	18	2	3	6	3	5
London A	423	290	39	22	0	2	24	37	9
London B	369	262	53	9	2	2	10	15	16
London C	468	249	53	0	5	7	22	119	13
TOTAL	2,828	1,873	328	67	18	22	138	309	73

Letters sent $N = Z + R + C + S + U + A + M + W$

Letters sent (N) is the total number of letters sent out to teenagers.

Completed interviews (Z) refers to the number of interviews completed and used in the analysis.

Refused (R) is the number of teenagers who refused to be interviewed.

No contact (C) describes those cases where it was not possible to fix an interview in the time available. There was always reasonably good evidence that an interview would have been possible if the research team had not had to move on to another area.

Refused sex questions (S) refers to the interviews where the teenager refused to answer all the questions about his sexual experience. It also includes a few cases where interruptions from the parents made the validity of the replies suspect. All these cases were excluded from the analysis.

Uninterviewable (U) refers to all teenagers in the sample whose last secondary school had been a special one for the education of the physically or mentally handicapped or the educationally subnormal. In these cases interviews were not attempted except for a few cases where the adolescent was anxious to take part and it would have been invidious to refuse. These few cases were not included in the analysis.

Away (A) describes those teenagers who were living away from their family homes during the period the research team was interviewing in that area. Interviews were occasionally conducted with teenagers living away from home if they returned for a short period and it was possible to see them.

Moved (M) gives the number of teenagers whose families had moved out of the sampling area at the time when the introductory letter was sent to them. If the move had been to another address in the sampling area, then the teenager was sent another letter and interviewed.

Married (W) refers to those teenagers who were married at the time the introductory letter was sent to them.

this table in which the *refusals, refused sex questions* and *no contact* figures have also been eliminated from the non-response figures.

The figures in table A7.1 suggest that early marriage appears to be less common in the North than in the South. The marriage rates are always lower in the A (middle-class) areas; there were 24 married teenagers in the three A areas compared with 36 in the three B areas. This reflects the tendency towards early marriages in working-class areas.

Table A7.2 *Rate of non-response and refusals in the seven areas*

Area	Total non-response rate	Non-response excluding R, S and C
	$$\frac{N - Z}{N} \times 100$$	$$\frac{N - (Z + R + S + C)}{N} \times 100$$
	%	%
South A	40	28
South B	41	25
North A	16	5
North B	23	5
London A	31	16
London B	29	12
London C	46	34
All areas	34	29

The number of teenagers who refused to answer sex questions (S) in each area is small and fairly constant. The slight variations appear to reflect almost exactly the variations in refusal rate between the areas. The absence of the S category in two areas (London A and North A) reflects the part that social class plays in refusal situations (see the next section). Middle-class teenagers appear to find questioning on sexual matters more acceptable than their working-class contemporaries.

The variation in the C (no contact) rates between the areas is mainly a reflection of the different administrative procedures adopted and the time available to complete each section of the research. The two extremes are London C where none were placed in the C category, and London A and North B with 22 and 18 no contacts respectively. Interviewing continued in London C until the required numbers were obtained in each age/sex group. In the other areas time limits had to be fixed. The research in North B and London A was carried out in the summer when many teenagers were on holiday. If they returned while the research team was still working in the area, it was usually possible to interview them. But some of them, especially the students and those who had just left school, took on holiday work in other towns or went abroad for several weeks. Technically they were not living away from home, but they did not return before we were forced to move on to the next area. The numbers lost through no contact in the other areas are much smaller and of little significance.

B. DIFFERENCES IN THE REFUSAL RATE

The *R* category (refusals) is the major part of the non-response which is not due to errors in the sampling frame, but is the direct result of methods used in the fieldwork. The most profitable way of studying this is to calculate the percentage of possible interviews which turned out to be refusals. This relates directly to the completed interviews independently of the other categories of non-response. Table A7.3 shows the refusal rates in the different areas.

Table A7.3 *The refusal rate in the seven areas*

Area	Interviews	Refusals	Percentage
South A	273	48	15%
South B	278	61	18%
North A	259	29	10%
North B	262	45	15%
London A	290	39	12%
London B	262	53	17%
London C	249	53	18%
TOTAL	1,873	328	15%

This table shows that there is some variation in the refusal rate in the seven areas. In all three towns the number of refusals are lower in the A areas than in the B areas. The A refusal rate was 13 per cent compared with the B refusal rate of 17 per cent. This suggests that middle-class teenagers and their parents show more sympathy towards the aims of social research. Even when they felt disinclined to cooperate, they were more likely to listen to the arguments put forward by the interviewers. Their working-class contemporaries were more likely to stand impassively on the doorstep repeating the same phrase ('I'm not interested'), leaving the interviewers little chance to use their powers of persuasion.

The refusal rates were higher in South A and B than elsewhere.

This was the result of the large amount of publicity given to teenage sexual behaviour while the research team was in these areas. Most of the outcry in the national and local papers was unfavourably disposed towards the teenagers and therefore it is not surprising that some of them were reluctant to cooperate with the Central Council for Health Education. Another increase in the number of refusals was caused by the announcement of a large increase in the VD figures of that area which led to the supposition that our interviewers were social workers looking for the source of the infection.

Another difficulty was caused by the British Medical Association's Committee on Venereal Disease and Young People, first when it was announced that a famous pop singer had been asked to give evidence before the Committee, and then the subsequent publicity given to the various versions of what that singer had said to the Committee. This episode tended to create difficulties for all researches into teenage behaviour. Later the Teenage Guild, a market research agency, announced that the BMA Committee had asked them to investigate adolescent sex behaviour by sending out a postal questionnaire. Then the Teenage Guild reported that the results were even more disturbing than had been feared. No details were released but obviously this discouraged some young people from cooperating with this research. As each of these episodes got wide coverage in the popular press, so our refusal rate went up and only came down again as each incident was forgotten.

The lowest refusal rates were in North A and B; this came as no surprise to the interviewers who all remarked on the different reception they received in this area. There seemed to be a greater degree of genuine hospitality towards visitors in the North and a greater willingness to cooperate when requested to take part in research. At that time people in the North were less aware of the activities of the market research agencies; consequently they did not suspect we were working for a commercial organisation and they rather appreciated the novelty of being asked to help. It is also said that there is a more favourable response to public authority in the North, and if this is true, they might have felt obliged to help the research.

C. TYPES OF REFUSAL

The detailed history of every refusal, including those received by letter, was recorded by the interviewer. This history covered each call that was made, included impressions about the teenager's home and also recorded as much detail as possible about the reasons for refusing. Tables A7.4 to A7.8 are constructed from content analyses made of these records.

Table A7.4 *The number of refusals from teenagers and parents*

	Boys		Girls		Total	
	No.	%	No.	%	No.	%
Teenager	129	83	127	74	256	78
Parent	27	17	45	26	72	22
TOTAL	156	100	172	100	328	100

In tables A7.5–6 we have classified the type of refusal into five categories as follows:

Face to face. A refusal received directly from the teenager or parent.

Letter or telephone. Refusal received by letter or telephone and no further contact made with the teenager. When a refusal was received by letter it was usual to make at least one visit and sometimes the teenager could be persuaded to take part after all. If it was clear from the tone of the letter that further contact with the teenager would be fruitless, then the letter was accepted as final.

Teenager seen, message left. Sometimes after fixing an appointment or agreeing to call back, the interviewer was avoided on subsequent visits and another member of the household refused on the adolescent's behalf.

Teenager not seen, message left. More often the teenager was never seen and the parent or someone else refused on his behalf. In some cases this may really be a parent refusal, but when the interviewer was told that the decision had come from the teenager, the refusal was placed in this category. These were rarely accepted initially, but if it became clear that there was no hope of seeing the teenager, then no further calls were made.

Miscellaneous. Refusals received from other sources than parents, and those cases where the teenager repeatedly cancelled the appointment or failed to keep it three or more times were put in this category.

Table A7.5 *Types of refusals by teenagers*

Type	Boys		Girls		Total	
	No.	%	No.	%	No.	%
Face to face	56	43	56	44	112	44
Letter/phone	10	8	18	14	28	11
Teenager not seen, message left	39	30	31	25	70	27
Teenager seen, message left	19	15	18	14	37	15
Miscellaneous	5	4	4	3	9	3
TOTAL	129	100	127	100	256	100

Table A7.6 *Type of refusals by parents*

Type	Boys		Girls		Total	
	No.	%	No.	%	No.	%
Face to face	21	78	38	84	59	82
Letter/phone	6	22	4	9	10	14
Miscellaneous	—	—	3	7	3	4
TOTAL	27	100	45	100	72	100

There appears to be a close similarity between the types of refusal received from boys and those from girls. Parental refusals, however, reveal a difference between the sexes. Table A7.4 shows that 26 per cent of girls' refusals came from their parents, whereas 17 per cent of the boys' refusals came from their parents. This reveals the more protective attitude of the girls' parents who take on the responsibility of refusing for their daughters, whereas the boys' parents do not concern themselves to the same extent.

D. REASONS FOR REFUSING

Our interviewers did their best to find out why the teenager would not agree to an interview. This was not an easy task and in over a quarter (29 per cent) of the cases the teenager would give no reason, and 22 per cent of the parents who refused to allow their children to be interviewed would not give a reason. But from a content analysis of the written descriptions of each refusal, we have classified the reason for refusing into eight categories. In tables A7.7 and A7.8 the reasons for refusing given by teenagers and parents have been kept separate.

Table A7.7 *Reasons given for refusing by teenagers*

	Boys		Girls		Total	
	No.	%	No.	%	No.	%
Not interested	32	25	31	24	63	25
No time	22	17	13	10	35	14
Heard about (sex)	9	7	18	14	27	10
Heard about (other)	11	8	11	9	22	8
Resent intrusion	11	9	6	5	17	7
Other reasons	8	6	10	8	18	7
No reason given	36	28	38	30	74	29
TOTAL	129	100	127	100	256	100

The most usual reason for refusing was lack of interest. If a teenager asked how he stood to gain from offering his cooperation, it was difficult to give an answer that he would view with satisfaction. Appeals to altruism did not carry much weight with some teenagers. Many of the boys and girls were occupied most nights of the week and there really was no good reason why they should agree to an interview. Considering what little inducement we had to offer, and the many counter-attractions in the life of the teenager, it is very much to their credit that less than 3 per cent of all the people we asked said they were not interested.

As well as those who said they were not interested, there were those who said they had no time. This was a more common reason among the boys than among the girls. The interviewers made themselves available at any time of the day or evening, and so it can be said that if the adolescents had really been interested, they could have found the time. We made it difficult for the teenagers to make this a valid excuse, but there were times when we had to accept this as the reason for not agreeing to an interview. This was also a reason given by some parents who felt they ought to protect their sons from outside distractions.

Table A7.8 *Reasons given for refusing by parents*

	Boys		Girls		Total	
	No.	%	No.	%	No.	%
Resent intrusion	7	26	12	27	19	27
Heard about (sex)	3	11	8	18	11	15
Heard about (other)	2	7	8	18	10	14
No time	4	15	1	2	5	7
Too shy	—	—	3	7	3	4
Other reasons	5	19	3	6	8	11
No reason given	6	22	10	22	16	22
TOTAL	27	100	45	100	72	100

Some people refused because they had heard about the research from other people. Sometimes they knew someone else who had been interviewed; at other times it was a garbled version of the research arising from other sources. We divided those who specifically mentioned that they had heard the interview contained questions about sex, and those who had heard about other aspects of the research.

The girls were more likely than the boys to refuse because they had heard about the interviews; 23 per cent of the girls and 15 per cent of the boys refused for this reason; the parents of the girls were also likely to refuse for this reason.

Some parents refused to allow their children to cooperate because they resented the intrusion into their private affairs. These were the most difficult refusals to deal with, for these people consider all social researches to be an incursion into their personal liberty and sometimes they were rude and unpleasant to the interviewers. Not many of the teenagers resented the intrusion, although there were a few who felt that increased knowledge about teenage activities would do more harm than good.

The younger age group were more likely to refuse than the older ones; 53 per cent of the boys' refusals were from the younger boys, and 59 per cent of the girls' refusals were from the younger girls. Thus the largest group of refusals were among the younger girls (101 people), then the younger boys (83 people), then the older boys (73 people) and the older girls (71 people).

E. THE REFUSAL FORM

Whenever a refusal was recorded, the teenager was sent a refusal form and a reply-paid envelope. The form was headed by the following two paragraphs:

'Although I respect any reason you may have for not taking part in this research, it would be of great help to me if you could answer the questions at the end of this letter. It will only take a minute.

'As you have been selected from a random sample, no one else can act as a substitute for you. Consequently I need to know a little about the people who feel they cannot help, just so as to be sure that we are not leaving out a particular group of people.'

There followed a small number of questions which were taken from the interview schedule. They were on subjects which were unlikely to cause any annoyance to the teenager and were also easy and quick to answer by ticks in the appropriate place. They covered school, job, clubs, dances, sport, church and siblings and provided enough information to give a reasonable description of the people who had refused to cooperate.

Table A7.9 *The number of refusal forms returned*

	Boys	Girls	Total
Number of refusals	156	172	328
Number of forms returned	78	84	162
Percentage returned	50%	49%	49%

This form was designed to give some information which could be compared directly with the answers obtained from those teenagers who had been interviewed. Table A7.9 shows the number of forms that were returned. Approximately half the refusing teenagers were prepared to fill in the form and answer 16 questions about themselves. In addition four other girls returned an uncompleted form with a note repeating their refusals. The remaining 162 did not use the reply-paid envelope.

The difference in the response between boys and girls does not appear to follow any particular pattern. In two areas, the girls appear to have been less cooperative than the boys. In the other areas more girls than boys returned the form. But the overall response from each area was constant, and was never lower than 41 per cent. Thus some information was obtained from 49 per cent of the girls and 50 per cent of the boys. This left 88 girls and 78 boys who refused to give any information at all about themselves. These represent only 7·5 per cent of the teenagers who were asked to agree to an interview.

Thus it will be seen that we obtained some information about many of the people who refused. The influence of these refusals and the results obtained from analysing the returned refusal forms are discussed in chapter 14.

REFERENCES

ABRAMS, MARK (1961) *Teenage Consumer Spending in 1959*. London, London Press Exchange.

ACHILLES, P. S. (1923) *The Effectiveness of Certain Social Hygiene Literature*. New York, American Social Hygiene Association.

ANDERSON, E. W., KENNA, J. C. and HAMILTON, M. W. (1960) 'A study of extra marital conception in adolescence.' *Psychiatrica et Neurologia* **139**, 313–62.

BALS, CHRISTEL (1962) *Halbstarke unter Sich*. Koln, Kiepenheuer & Witsch.

BARTLETT, M. S. (1962) 'Factor Analysis as a Statistician Sees It,' in *Essays on Probability and Statistics*. London, Methuen.

BENNEY, M., REISMAN, D. and STAR, S. A. (1956) 'Age and Sex in the Interviewer.' *Am. J. of Soc.* **62**, 143–52.

BERNSTEIN, B. (1961) 'Social Structure, Language and Learning.' *Educ. Res.* **3**:3, 163–76.

BIER, WILLIAM C., ed. (1963) *The Adolescent: His Search for Understanding*. New York, Fordham University Press.

BOTT, E. J. (1957) *Family and Social Network*. London, Tavistock Publications.

BROMLEY, D. D. and BRITTEN, F. H. (1938) *Youth and Sex. A Study of 1300 College Students*. New York, Harper.

BURGESS, E. W. and WALLIN, P. (1953) *Engagement and Marriage*. Chicago, Lippincott.

CARSTAIRS, G. M. (1963) *This Island Now*. London, Hogarth.

CATTEL, R. B. (1962) 'The basis of recognition and interpretation of factors,' *Educ. and Psychol. Measurement*. **22**:4, 667–97.

CHESSER, EUSTACE (1956) *The Sexual, Marital and Family Relationships of the English Woman*. London, Hutchinson.

CHRISTENSEN, H. T. and CARPENTER, G. R. (1962) 'Value behaviour discrepancies regarding pre-marital coitus in three western cultures,' *Amer. Sociol. Rev.* **27**, 66–74.

CLINARD, M. B. (1958) 'Areas for research in deviant behaviour.' *Sociol. and Social Res.* **42**:6, 415–19.

COCHRAN, W. G., MOSTELLER, F. and TUKEY, J. W. (1953) 'Statistical problems of the Kinsey Report.' *J. of the Amer. Stat. Ass.* **48**, 673–716.

COCHRAN, W. G., MOSTELLER, F. and TUKEY, J. W. (954) 'Principles of sampling.' *J. Amer. Stat. Ass.* **49**, 13–35.

COHEN, A. K. (1955) *Delinquent Boys: The Culture of the Gang.* Glencoe, Free Press.

COMFORT, ALEX. (1963) *Sex in Society.* London, Duckworth.

DALZELL–WARD, A. J. (1960) 'Venereal diseases and the teenager—health education aspects.' *Roy. Soc. Hlth. J.* 80, 419–23.

DAVIS, K. B. (1929) *Factors in the Sex Life of Twenty-Two Hundred Women.* New York, Harper.

DESCHIN, CELIA S. (1961) *Teenagers and Venereal Disease: A Sociological Study.* New York, U.S. Department of Health Education and Welfare, Public Health Service.

DICKINSON, R. L. and BEAM, L. (1931) *A Thousand Marriages.* Baltimore, Williams & Wilkins.

DOUGLAS, J. W. B. (1964) *The Home and the School.* London, MacGibbon & Kee.

EHRMANN, W. W. (1959) *Premarital Dating Behaviour,* New York, Henry Holt.

ELLIS, ALBERT (1948) 'Questionnaire versus interview methods in the study of human love relationships.' *Amer. Sociol. Rev.* 13, 61–5.

EXNER, M. J. (1915) *Problems and Principles of Sex Instruction. A Study of 948 College Men.* New York, Association Press.

EYSENCK, H. J. (1953) *The Structure of Human Personality,* London, Methuen.

EYSENCK, H. J. (1954) *The Psychology of Politics.* London, Routledge & Kegan Paul.

EYSENCK, H. J., ed. (1960) *Experiments in Personality,* London, Routledge & Kegan Paul.

FINESTONE, HAROLD (1957) 'Narcotics and criminality.' *Law and Contemporary problems.* 22, 69–85.

FINGER, F. W. (1947) 'Sex beliefs and practices among male college students.' *J. Abnorm. & Soc. Psychol.* 42, 57–67.

FISHER, R. A. and YATES, F. (1963) *Statistical Table (6th edn.).* Edinburgh, Oliver and Boyd.

FYVEL, T. R. (1963) *The Insecure Offenders.* London, Penguin.

GARDNER, G. E. (1944) 'Sex behaviour of adolescents in wartime.' *Ann. Amer. Acad. Pol. Sci.* 236, 60–6.

GEBHARD, P., POMEROY, W., MARTIN C., and CHRISTENSEN, C. (1959) *Pregnancy, Birth and Abortion.* London, Heinemann.

GLUECK, S. and GLUECK, E. (1952) *Delinquents in the Making.* New York, Harper.

GRAY, P. G. and CARTWRIGHT, ANN (1953) 'Choosing and changing doctors.' *The Lancet.* 265, 1308–9.

GRAY, P. G., CORLETT, T. and JONES, P. (1951) *The Proportion of Jurors as an Index of the Economic Status of a District.* Methodology Series, No. M42, The Social Survey, London, Central Office of Information.

GREENE, GAEL (1964) *Sex and the College Girl*. New York, S. J. R. Saunders.

GREENLAND, CYRIL (1958) 'Putative fathers.' *The Medical Officer*, **99**, 281–6.

HAMILTON, G. V. (1929) *A Research in Marriage*. New York, Boni.

HECHINGER, GRACE and HECHINGER, FRED (1964) *Teenage Tyranny*. London, Duckworth.

HENDRICKSON, A. E. and WHITE, P. O. (1964) 'Promax: a quick method for rotation to oblique simple structure.' *Brit. J. Stat. Psychol.* **17**, 65–70.

HENDRICKSON, A. E. and WHITE, P. O. 'A Method for the Rotation of Higher Order Factors.' Unpublished.

HIMELHOCHE, JEROME and FAVA, SYLVIA, eds. (1955) *Sexual Behaviour in American Society*. New York, Norton.

HOHMAN, L. B. and SCHAFFNER, B. (1947) 'The sex lives of unmarried men.' *Amer. J. Sociol.* **52**, 501–7.

HOLLINGSHEAD, A. DE B. and REDLICH, F. C. (1958). *Social Class and Mental Illness*. New York, Wiley.

HOLZINGER, K. J. and HARMAN, H. H. (1941) *Factor Analysis*. Chicago. University of Chicago Press.

HUANG, W. (1964) 'Adolescent problem solved.' *Times Educational Supplement*, **2556**, 1342–3.

HUGHES, W. L. (1926) 'Sex experiences of boyhood.' *J. Soc. Hyg.* **12**, 262–73.

JEPHCOTT, A. P., SEEAR, N. and SMITH, J. (1962) *Married Women Working*. London, Allen & Unwin.

KANIN, E. J. and HOWARD, D. H. (1958) 'Post marital consequences of premarital sex adjustments.' *Amer. Soc. Rev.* **23**, 556–62.

KERR, ANTHONY (1964) *Youth of Europe*. Cambridge, Bowes and Bowes.

KINSEY, A. C., POMEROY, W. B. and MARTIN, C. E. (1948) *Sexual Behaviour in the Human Male*. Philadelphia, Saunders.

KINSEY, A. C., POMEROY, W. B., MARTIN, C. E. and GEBHARD, P. H. (1953) *Sexual Behaviour in the Human Female*. Philadelphia, Saunders.

KIRKENDALL, L. A. (1961) *Premarital Intercourse and Interpersonal Relationships*. New York, Julian Press.

KNONHAUSEN, PHYLLIS and KNONHAUSEN, EBERHARD (1960) *Sex Histories of American College Men*. New York, Ballantine.

LANDIS, C. *et al.* (1940) *Sex In Development*. New York, Hoeber.

LANDIS, C. and BOLLES, M. M. (1942) *Personality and Sexuality of the Physically Handicapped Woman*. New York, Hoeber.

LANDIS, JUDSON, T. and LANDIS, MARY G. (1953) *Building a Successful Marriage*. New York, Prentice-Hall.

LAWLEY, D. N. and MAXWELL, A. E. (1963) *Factor Analysis as a Statistical Method*. London, Butterworths.

LEE, J. A. H. (1963) 'Motor-cycle accidents to male teenagers.' *Proc. Roy. Soc. Med.* **56**, 365–7.

LOLLI, GIORGIO (1961) *Social Drinking: The Effects of Alcohol.* New York, Collier Books.

MACE, DAVID and MACE, VERA. (1963) *The Soviet Family.* New York, Doubleday.

MERRILL, L. (1918) 'A summary of findings in a study of sexualism among a group of one hundred delinquent boys.' *J. Juv. Res.* **3**, 255–67.

MOSER, C. A. (1958) *Survey Methods in Social Investigation.* London, Heinemann.

MOSER, C. A. and SCOTT, WOLF (1961) *British Towns: a Statistical Study of their Social and Economic Differences.* Edinburgh, Oliver & Boyd.

MURDOCK, GEORGE P. (1949) *Social Structure.* New York, Macmillan.

MUSGROVE, FRANK (1963) 'Inter-generation attitudes.' *Brit. J. of Soc. Clin. Psychol.* **2**, 209–23.

MYERS, J. K. and ROBERTS, B. H. (1959) *Family and Class Dynamics in Mental Illness.* New York, Wiley.

MYRDAL, A. and KLEIN, V. (1956) *Women's Two Roles: Home and Work.* London, Routledge & Kegan Paul.

NEWSON, J. and NEWSON, E. (1963) *Infant Care in an Urban Community.* London, Allen & Unwin.

OSGOOD, C. E., SUCI, G. J. and TANNENBAUM, P. H. (1957) *The Measurement of Meaning,* Urbana, University of Illinois Press.

PEARL, RAYMOND (1925) *The Biology of Population Growth.* New York, Knopf.

PECK, M. W. and WELLS, F. L. (1923) 'On the psycho-sexuality of college graduate men.' *Ment. Hyg.* **7**, 697–714.

PETERSON, K. M. 'Early sex information and its influence on later sex concepts. Unpublished thesis (1938) in library of the College of Education, University of Colorado.

PONTING, L. I. (1963) 'The social aspects of venereal disease among young people in Leeds and London.' *Brit. J. Ven. Dis.* **39**, 273–7.

PRAIS, S. J. and HOUTHAKKER, H. S. (1955) *The Analysis of Family Budgets.* Cambridge, Cambridge University Press.

RAMSEY, G. V. (1943) 'The sexual development of boys.' *Amer. J. Psychol.* **56**, 217–33.

RAMSEY, G. V. (1943) 'The sex information of younger boys.' *Amer. J. Orthopsychiat.* **13**, 347–52, 1943.

RECKLESS, W. C. (1961) *The Crime Problem.* New York, Appleton-Century.

REISS, IRA L. (1960) *Premarital Sexual Standards in America.* Glencoe, Free Press.

ROBB, JAMES (1954) *Working Class Anti Semite.* London, Tavistock Publications.

ROSS, R. T. (1950) 'Measures of the sex behaviour of college males compared with Kinsey's results.' *J. Abnorm. & Soc. Psychol.* 45, 753–5.

SCHOFIELD, MICHAEL (1964) 'The sociological contribution to health education.' *Health Education Journal* 22, 44–8.

SCHOFIELD, MICHAEL (1965) *Sociological Aspects of Homosexuality.* London, Longmans.

SLATER, E. and WOODSIDE, M. (1951) *Patterns of Marriage.* London, Cassell.

SPINLEY, B. M. (1953) *The Deprived and the Privileged.* London, Routledge & Kegan Paul.

STRAKOSCH, F. M. (1934) *Factors in the Sex Life of Seven Hundred Psychopathic Women.* New York, State Hospitals Press.

TAIETZ, PHILIP, (1962) Conflicting Group Norms and the 'Third' Person in the Interview. *Am. J. of Soc.* 68, 97–104.

TANNER, J. M. (1961) *Education and Physical Growth.* London, University of London Press.

TANNER, J. M. (1962) *Growth at Adolescence.* Oxford, Blackwell.

TAYLOR, W. S. (1933) 'A critique of sublimation in males: a study of forty superior single men.' *Genetic Psychol. Monogr.* 13, No. 1.

TERMAN, L. M. and MILES, C. C. (1936). *Sex and Personality,* New York, McGraw-Hill.

TERMAN, L. M. (1938) *Psychological Factors in Marital Happiness.* New York, McGraw-Hill.

THOMSON, G. H. (1939) *The Factorial Analysis of Human Ability.* Boston, Houghton Mifflin.

THURSTONE, L. L. (1949) *Multiple Factor Analysis.* Chicago, University of Chicago Press.

WEST, DONALD. (1963) *The Habitual Prisoner.* London, Macmillan.

WESTWOOD, GORDON. (1960) *A Minority: A Report on the Life of the Male Homosexual in Great Britain.* London, Longmans.

WHYTE, W. F. (1943) *Street Corner Society.* Chicago, University of Chicago Press.

WILKINS, L. T. (1955) *The Adolescent in Britain.* London, Central Office of Information.

WIMPERIS, V. (1960) *The Unmarried Mother and her Child.* London, Allen & Unwin.

Reports

15–18: *A Report of the Central Advisory Council for Education* (Crowther Report). (1959) London, HMSO.

The Youth Service in England and Wales (Albemarle Report). (1960) London, HMSO.

British Co-operative Clinical Group (1962). *Brit. J. Ven. Dis.* 38, 1–18.

British Co-operative Clinical Group. (1963) *Brit. J. Ven. Dis.* **39**, 1–18.
The Registrar General's Statistical Review of England and Wales for the Year 1961. (1963) London, HMSO.
Criminal Statistics. (1963) London, HMSO.
Half our future: a Report of the Central Advisory Council for Education (Newsom Report) (1963) London, HMSO.
Venereal Disease and Young People. (1964) London, British Medical Association.
The Annual Report of the Chief Medical Officer of the Ministry of Health for the year 1963. (1964) London, HMSO.

INDEX

313

WOLFGRAM LIBRARY, WIDENER COLLEGE
CHESTER, PA.

S10662